INDIANA
GLENCOE
MATH

AUTHORS
Carter • Cuevas • Day • Malloy
Kersaint • Reynosa • Silbey • Vielhaber

Mc
Graw
Hill
Education

connectED.mcgraw-hill.com

STEM McGraw-Hill is committed to providing instructional materials in Science, Technology, Engineering, and Mathematics (STEM) that give all students a solid foundation, one that prepares them for college and careers in the 21st century.

Send all inquiries to:
McGraw-Hill Education
8787 Orion Place
Columbus, OH 43240

ISBN: 978-0-07-672132-0 (*Volume 1*)
MHID: 0-07-672132-9

Printed in the United States of America.

4 5 6 7 8 9 LMN 22 21 20 19 18 17

CONTENTS IN BRIEF

Units

Indiana Glencoe Math is organized into units based on groups of related standards. The Standards for Process Standards are embedded throughout the course.

Everything you need,

anytime, anywhere.

With ConnectED, you have instant access to all of your study materials—anytime, anywhere. From homework materials to study guides—it's all in one place and just a click away. ConnectED even allows you to collaborate with your classmates and use mobile apps to make studying easy.

Resources built for you—available 24/7:

- Your eBook available wherever you are

- Personal Tutors and Self-Check Quizzes to help your learning

- An Online Calendar with all of your due dates

- eFlashcard App to make studying easy

- A message center to stay in touch

Go Mobile!

Visit mheonline.com/apps to get entertainment, instruction, and education on the go with ConnectED Mobile and our other apps available for your device.

Go Online!

connectED.mcgraw-hill.com

Vocab

Learn about new vocabulary words.

Watch

Watch animations and videos.

Tutor

See and hear a teacher explain how to solve problems.

Tools

Explore concepts with virtual manipulatives.

Sketchpad

Discover concepts using The Geometer's Sketchpad®.

Check

Check your progress.

eHelp

Get targeted homework help.

Worksheets

Access practice worksheets.

UNIT 1 Ratios and Proportional Relationships

UNIT PROJECT PREVIEW
page 2

Chapter 1
Ratios and Proportional Reasoning

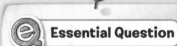

Essential Question

HOW can you show that two objects are proportional?

Real World
p. 45

Chapter 2
Percents

Essential Question

HOW can percent help you understand situations involving money?

Real World
p. 121

UNIT PROJECT 183

Become a Travel Expert

UNIT 2 The Number System

UNIT PROJECT PREVIEW
page 185

Chapter 3
Integers

 Essential Question

WHAT happens when you add, subtract, multiply, and divide integers?

Real World
p. 233

Chapter 4
Rational Numbers

Real World
p. 319

@ **Essential Question**

WHAT happens when you add, subtract, multiply, and divide fractions?

UNIT PROJECT

Explore the Ocean Depths

UNIT 3 Expressions and Equations

UNIT PROJECT PREVIEW
page 344

Chapter 5
Expressions

Essential Question

HOW can you use numbers and symbols to represent mathematical ideas?

p. 387

x

Chapter 6
Equations and Inequalities

Real World
p. 437

Essential Question

WHAT does it mean to say two quantities are equal?

UNIT PROJECT 527

Stand Up and Be Counted!

UNIT 4 Geometry

UNIT PROJECT PREVIEW
page 530

Chapter 7
Geometric Figures

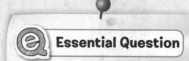

Essential Question

HOW does geometry help us describe real-world objects?

Real World
p. 535

Chapter 8
Measure Figures

Essential Question

HOW do measurements help you describe real-world objects?

Real World
p. 623

UNIT PROJECT 703

Turn Over a New Leaf

UNIT 5 Statistics and Probability

UNIT PROJECT PREVIEW
page 706

Chapter 9 Probability

Essential Question

HOW can you predict the outcome of future events?

Real World
p. 733

Chapter 10
Statistics

Essential Question

HOW do you know which type of graph to use when displaying data?

UNIT PROJECT 853

Math Genes

Indiana Glencoe Math, Grade 7

Indiana Glencoe Math, Course 2, focuses on four critical areas: (1) developing understanding of and applying proportional relationships; (2) operations with rational numbers and working with expressions and linear equations; (3) solving problems involving scale drawings, geometric constructions, and surface area, and volume; and (4) drawing inferences about populations.

Unit Overview

Ratios and Proportional Relationships

- Analyze proportional relationships and use them to solve real-world and mathematical problems.

The Number System

- Apply and extend previous understandings of operations with fractions to add, subtract, multiply, and divide rational numbers.

Expressions and Equations

- Use properties of operations to generate equivalent expressions.
- Solve real-life and mathematical problems using numerical and algebraic expressions and equations.

Geometry

- Draw, construct and describe geometrical figures and describe the relationships between them.
- Solve real-life and mathematical problems involving angle measure, area, surface area, and volume.

Statistics and Probability

- Use random sampling to draw inferences about a population.
- Draw informal comparative inferences about two populations.
- Investigate chance processes and develop, use, and evaluate probability models.

PS Process Standards

1 Make sense of problems and persevere in solving them.
2 Reason abstractly and quantitatively.
3 Construct viable arguments and critique the reasoning of others.
4 Model with mathematics.
5 Use appropriate tools strategically.
6 Attend to precision.
7 Look for and make use of structure.
8 Look for and express regularity in repeated reasoning.

Track Your Progress

These pages list the key ideas that you should be able to understand by the end of the year. You will rate how much you know about each one. Don't worry if you have no clue **before** you learn about them. Watch how your knowledge grows as the year progresses!

☹ I have no clue.   😐 I've heard of it.   😊 I know it!

	Before			After		
NUMBER SENSE	☹	😐	😊	☹	😐	😊
7.NS.1 Find the prime factorization of whole numbers and write the results using exponents.						
7.NS.2 Understand the inverse relationship between squaring and finding the square root of a perfect square integer. Find square roots of perfect square integers.						
7.NS.3 Know there are rational and irrational numbers. Identify, compare, and order rational and common irrational numbers ($\sqrt{2}$, $\sqrt{3}$, $\sqrt{5}$, Π) and plot them on a number line.						

COMPUTATION	☹	😐	😊	☹	😐	😊
7.C.1: Understand $p + q$ as the number located a distance $|q|$ from p, in the positive or negative direction, depending on whether q is positive or negative. Show that a number and its opposite have a sum of 0 (are additive inverses). Interpret sums of rational numbers by describing real-world contexts.						
7.C.2: Understand subtraction of rational numbers as adding the additive inverse, $p - q = p + (-q)$. Show that the distance between two rational numbers on the number line is the absolute value of their difference, and apply this principle in real-world contexts.						
7.C.3: Understand that multiplication is extended from fractions to rational numbers by requiring that operations continue to satisfy the properties of operations, particularly the distributive property, leading to products such as $(-1)(-1) = 1$ and the rules for multiplying signed numbers.						
7.C.4: Understand that integers can be divided, provided that the divisor is not zero, and that every quotient of integers (with non-zero divisor) is a rational number. Understand that if p and q are integers, then $-(p/q) = (-p)/q = p/(-q)$.						
7.C.5: Compute unit rates associated with ratios of fractions, including ratios of lengths, areas and other quantities measured in like or different units.						
7.C.6: Use proportional relationships to solve ratio and percent problems with multiple operations, such as the following: simple interest, tax, markups, markdowns, gratuities, commissions, fees, conversions within and across measurement systems, percent increase and decrease, and percent error.						
7.C.7: Compute with rational numbers fluently using a standard algorithmic approach.						
7.C.8: Solve real-world problems with rational numbers by using one or two operations.						

ALGEBRA AND FUNCTIONS	Before			After		
	☹	😐	😊	☹	😐	😊
7.AF.1: Apply the properties of operations (e.g., identity, inverse, commutative, associative, distributive properties) to create equivalent linear expressions, including situations that involve factoring (e.g., given $2x - 10$, create an equivalent expression $2(x - 5)$). Justify each step in the process.						
7.AF.2: Solve equations of the form $px + q = r$ and $p(x + q) = r$ fluently, where p, q, and r are specific rational numbers. Represent real-world problems using equations of these forms and solve such problems.						
7.AF.3: Solve inequalities of the form $px + q$ (> or ≥) r or $px + q$ (< or ≤) r, where p, q, and r are specific rational numbers. Represent real-world problems using inequalities of these forms and solve such problems. Graph the solution set of the inequality and interpret it in the context of the problem.						
7.AF.4: Define slope as vertical change for each unit of horizontal change and recognize that a constant rate of change or constant slope describes a linear function. Identify and describe situations with constant or varying rates of change.						
7.AF.5: Graph a line given its slope and a point on the line. Find the slope of a line given its graph.						
7.AF.6: Decide whether two quantities are in a proportional relationship (e.g., by testing for equivalent ratios in a table or graphing on a coordinate plane and observing whether the graph is a straight line through the origin).						
7.AF.7: Identify the unit rate or constant of proportionality in tables, graphs, equations, and verbal descriptions of proportional relationships.						
7.AF.8: Explain what the coordinates of a point on the graph of a proportional relationship mean in terms of the situation, with special attention to the points (0, 0) and (1, r), where r is the unit rate.						
7.AF.9: Identify real-world and other mathematical situations that involve proportional relationships. Write equations and draw graphs to represent proportional relationships and recognize that these situations are described by a linear function in the form $y = mx$, where the unit rate, m, is the slope of the line.						

	Before			After		
GEOMETRY AND MEASUREMENT	☹	😐	🙂	☹	😐	🙂
7.GM.1: Draw triangles (freehand, with ruler and protractor, and using technology) with given conditions from three measures of angles or sides, and notice when the conditions determine a unique triangle, more than one triangle, or no triangle.						
7.GM.2: Identify and describe similarity relationships of polygons including the angle-angle criterion for similar triangles, and solve problems involving similarity.						
7.GM.3: Solve real-world and other mathematical problems involving scale drawings of geometric figures, including computing actual lengths and areas from a scale drawing. Create a scale drawing by using proportional reasoning.						
7.GM.4: Solve real-world and other mathematical problems that involve vertical, adjacent, complementary, and supplementary angles.						
7.GM.5: Understand the formulas for area and circumference of a circle and use them to solve real-world and other mathematical problems; give an informal derivation of the relationship between circumference and area of a circle.						
7.GM.6: Solve real-world and other mathematical problems involving volume of cylinders and three-dimensional objects composed of right rectangular prisms.						
7.GM.7: Construct nets for right rectangular prisms and cylinders and use the nets to compute the surface area; apply this technique to solve real-world and other mathematical problems.						

DATA ANALYSIS AND STATISTICS	Before			After		
	☹	😐	🙂	☹	😐	🙂
7.DSP.1: Understand that statistics can be used to gain information about a population by examining a sample of the population and generalizations about a population from a sample are valid only if the sample is representative of that population. Understand that random sampling tends to produce representative samples and support valid inferences.						
7.DSP.2: Use data from a random sample to draw inferences about a population. Generate multiple samples (or simulated samples) of the same size to gauge the variation in estimates or predictions.						
7.DSP.3: Find, use, and interpret measures of center (mean and median) and measures of spread (range, interquartile range, and mean bsolute deviation) for numerical data from random samples to draw comparative inferences about two populations.						
7.DSP.4: Make observations about the degree of visual overlap of two numerical data distributions represented in line plots or box plots. Describe how data, particularly outliers, added to a data set may affect the mean and/or median.						
7.DSP.5: Understand that the probability of a chance event is a number between 0 and 1 that expresses the likelihood of the event occurring. Understand that a probability near 0 indicates an unlikely event, a probability around 1/2 indicates an event that is neither unlikely nor likely, and a probability near 1 indicates a likely event. Understand that a probability of 1 indicates an event certain to occur and a probability of 0 indicates an event impossible to occur.						
7.DSP.6: Approximate the probability of a chance event by collecting data on the chance process that produces it and observing its relative frequency from a large sample.						
7.DSP.7: Develop probability models that include the sample space and probabilities of outcomes to represent simple events with equally likely outcomes. Predict the approximate relative frequency of the event based on the model. Compare probabilities from the model to observed frequencies; evaluate the level of agreement and explain possible sources of discrepancy.						

Process Standards Handbook

Essential Question

WHAT processes help me explore and explain mathematics?

PS Process Standards

The Process Standards will help you become a successful problem solver and to use math effectively in your daily life.

What You'll Learn

PS Throughout this handbook, you will learn about each of these Process Standards and how they are integrated in the chapters and lessons of this book.

1. **Focus on Process Standard**
   Persevere with Problems

2. **Focus on Process Standard**
   Reason Abstractly and Quantitatively

3. **Focus on Process Standard**
   Construct an Argument

4. **Focus on Process Standard**
   Model with Mathematics

5. **Focus on Process Standard**
   Use Math Tools

6. **Focus on Process Standard**
   Attend to Precision

7. **Focus on Process Standard**
   Make Use of Structure

8. **Focus on Process Standard**
   Use Repeated Reasoning

Place a checkmark below the face that expresses how much you know about each Process Standard. Then explain in your own words what it means to you.

☹ I have no clue.   😐 I've heard of it.   😊 I know it!

Process Standards

Process Standard	☹	😐	😊	What it Means to Me
1				
2				
3				
4				
5				
6				
7				
8				

Persevere with Problems

What does it mean to persevere in solving problems?

PS **Process Standard 1**

Make sense of problems and persevere in solving them.

Look up the word "persevere" in a dictionary. You might see "be persistent" or "follow something through to the end." When you persevere in solving math problems, you don't always stop at the first answer you get. You check if your solution is accurate, if it answers the problem, and if it makes sense!

Jared wants to paint his room. The dimensions of the room are 12 feet by 15 feet, and the walls are 9 feet tall. There are two windows, each with dimensions 6 feet by 5 feet. There are two doors, each with dimensions 30 inches by 6 feet. If a gallon of paint covers about 350 square feet, how many gallons of paint will he need to put two coats of paint on the wall?

1. **Understand** That's a lot of information! Go back and read the problem again. This time, circle the information given and underline what you are trying to find.

2. **Plan** Before you do ANY calculations, make a plan to solve the problem. List the steps you need to take.

_____

_____

_____

3. **Solve** Apply your plan to solve the problem.

   Jared will need ⬚ gallons of paint.

4. **Check** Is your solution accurate? Does it make sense? Explain.

_____

_____

_____

5. Did you feel like giving up at any point while solving the problem? Explain.

_____

_____

It's Your Turn!

Solve each problem by using the four-step problem-solving model.

6. There are about 48,000 farms in Nebraska using approximately 45 million acres of land. This farmland covers about $\frac{9}{10}$ of the state. About how many acres are not made up of farmland?

   Understand (Circle) the information you know and <u>underline</u> what you are trying to determine. Is there any information you will not use?

   _____

   Plan What strategy will you use to solve this problem?

   _____

   Solve Solve the problem. What is the solution?

   _____

   Check Does your answer make sense? Can you solve the problem another way to check your work?

   _____

7. You and a friend went to the movies. You bought a student ticket and a drink. You split the cost of popcorn and a candy. You have $4.75 left. How much did you take with you? Show your steps below. Check your solution.

Student	$9	Popcorn	$6.50
Adult	$12	Candy	$5
Senior	$10	Drink	$4.50

   _____

   _____

   _____

Ⓕ ind it in Your Book!

PS Persevere with Problems

Look in Chapter 1. Provide an example of where Process Standard 1 is used. Explain why your example represents this process.

_____

_____

_____

_____

Reason Abstractly and Quantitatively

I need to double this recipe. How much flour do I need?

Suppose you want to double the ingredients from the recipe below. If you write an expression or an equation to figure out what you need, you are reasoning quantitatively. When you simplify the expression or solve the equation algebraically, you are reasoning abstractly.

PS Process Standard 2

Reason abstractly and quantitatively.

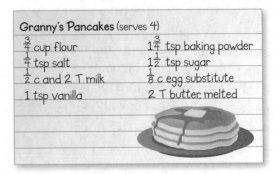

Granny's Pancakes (serves 4)

$\frac{3}{4}$ cup flour $1\frac{3}{4}$ tsp baking powder
$\frac{1}{4}$ tsp salt $1\frac{1}{2}$ tsp sugar
$\frac{1}{2}$ c and 2 T milk $\frac{1}{8}$ c egg substitute
1 tsp vanilla   2 T butter, melted

1. What skill(s) will you use to see how much of each ingredient you would use if you were to double the recipe?

_____

2. You planned for eight people to come for a pancake breakfast, but just found out that 10 people are coming! The recipe serves 4. Defne a variable and write an expression to determine the amount of each ingredient to serve 10 people. _____

_____

3. Use the expression from Exercise 2 to complete the recipe card so that it serves 10 people. Is it appropriate to round any of the ingredients? Explain.

_____

Granny's Pancakes (serves 10)

☐ cup flour   ☐ tsp baking powder

☐ tsp salt   ☐ tsp sugar

☐ c and ☐ T milk   ☐ egg substitute

☐ tsp vanilla   ☐ T butter, melted

Reason abstractly or quantitatively to find a solution.

4. The graph shows the percent of people in different age groups that recently attended an amusement park. A total of 1.045 million people attended. How many of them were less than 25 years of age?

_____

_____

5. Cave exploration or spelunking is a very popular activity. Your family signs up for tours at a state park. On one of the tours, your brother is lowered 160 feet below the surface by rope. Then he continues another 70 feet below the surface to a room. You take the tree top tour where you climb to an adventure course that is 60 feet above ground. What is the difference between the elevations?

_____

_____

6. You and your family are traveling to a football game. You and your mother leave at 8:00 A.M. Your dad needs to wait for your sister to get home from dance practice, so he leaves at 9:30 A.M. If your mother drives at an average rate of 50 miles per hour, and your dad drives at an average rate of 65 miles per hour, when will he pass her? Suppose the game is 205 miles away. Who will get there first?

_____

_____

Find it in Your Book!

PS Reason Abstractly

Look in Chapter 1. Provide an example of where Process Standard 2 is used. Explain why your example represents this process.

_____

_____

_____

Construct an Argument

Have you ever questioned something that someone else said?

If your friend told you that his dog could run 45 miles per hour, would you believe him? What would your friend need to do to justify his comment? You might want to see the dog run and use a stopwatch to time him. In math, we often need to justify our conclusions as well. We can use *inductive* or *deductive* reasoning.

1. Use the Internet or another source to look up the meanings of the terms *inductive reasoning* and *deductive reasoning*. Write the meanings in your own words.

   _____

   _____

   _____

2. Label each example below as either using inductive or deductive reasoning.

   _____ Reasoning

   Every dog that Elijah met has fleas, so he believes that all dogs have fleas.

   _____ Reasoning

   Equilateral triangles have 3 congruent sides. Elena has a triangle with 3 congruent sides, so she has an equilateral triangle.

Throughout this text, you may be asked to evaluate an argument that someone else made. If you determine that the argument is false, you may be asked to provide a counterexample. A *counterexample* is just one example that shows a statement is not true.

3. Determine if the following statement is true. If it is not true, provide a counterexample:

   All prime numbers are odd.

   _____

Complete each step in the solution shown. Use the Properties of Equality (Addition, Subtraction, Multiplication, or Division).

4. $a - 15 = 36$ Write the equation.

$\underline{+\ 15 = +\ 15}$

$a = 51$ Simplify.

5. $5p = 35$ Write the equation.

$\dfrac{5p}{5} = \dfrac{35}{5}$

$p = 7$ Simplify.

For each of the following statements, determine if the statement is *true* or *false*. If false, provide a counterexample.

6. All four-legged pieces of furniture are tables.

_____

7. All rectangles have 4 right angles.

_____

8. The population of Pennsylvania is about 4% of the total population of the United States. Daniel claims that since the population of the United States is about 312 million, the population of Pennsylvania must be around 17.5 million. Is his claim reasonable? Explain.

_____

_____

_____

Find it in Your Book!

PS **Construct an Argument**

Look in Chapter 1. Provide an example of where Process Standard 3 is used. Explain why your example represents this process.

Model with Mathematics

Are you a visual person or do you prefer to use words?

You might prefer to use diagrams or drawings when explaining ideas. Or you might prefer to use words. In math, we also use different ways to model the same idea. We can use words, graphs, tables, numbers, symbols, or diagrams.

1. Suppose you are selling T-shirts as a fundraiser for Key Club. The club makes a $6.30 profit for every T-shirt sold. Complete each model shown.

Words	Numbers	
_____ per T-shirt	**Profit ($)**	**Number of shirts**
	6.30	1
	12.60	
	18.90	
Symbols	**Graph**	
Let p = profit t = number of T-shirts sold $p =$ ☐ t		

All of these model the same relationship between profit and number of T-shirts sold, just in different ways.

2. Which relationship would you prefer to use to determine the profit if 100 T-shirts were sold? Explain.

_____

_____

_____

It's Your Turn!

Use the models shown to solve each problem.

3. A waterpark cycles about 24,000 gallons per minute through the local river.

   a. **Tables** Complete the table to show the number of gallons used in 1, 2, 3, 4, and 5 minutes.

   b. **Graph** Graph the ordered pairs on the coordinate plane.

Time, x (minutes)	Gallons, y (thousand gallons)

   c. **Symbols** Write an equation to show the number of gallons of water y used in x minutes.

   _____

4. Kitra is creating a treasure hunt for the school carnival. The scale on the map is 0.5 inch = 0.25 mile.

Map Length m (in.)	Distance d (mi)

   a. **Tables** Complete the table to determine the actual distance for 0.5, 1, 1.5, 2, and 2.5 inches on the map.

   b. **Symbols** Write an equation to determine the actual distance d for m inches on the map. _____

Find it in Your Book!

PS **Model with Mathematics**

Look in Chapter 6. Provide an example of where Process Standard 4 is used. Explain why your example represents this process.

_____

_____

_____

_____

Use Math Tools

Which tools would you use to finish this piece of artwork?

You might need paints, a brush, or maybe charcoal or colored pencils. You might also need some art training! So, let's investigate how to choose and use the proper tools and strategies to solve math problems.

> **PS Process Standard 5**
>
> Use appropriate tools strategically.

1. Math tools are objects like paper and pencil, calculators, algebra tiles, and rulers. List three more math tools that are helpful in solving problems.

Math Tools

_____

_____

_____

2. Some math strategies are estimation, drawing a diagram, and using mental math. List three more math strategies that are helpful in solving problems.

Math Strategies

_____

_____

_____

3. Describe a situation in which you would use a protractor.

_____

_____

It's Your Turn!

List the tools or strategies you would use to solve each problem.
Then solve the problem.

4. You need to make a scale model of your room for your art class. The scale is
$\frac{3}{4}$ inch represents 1 foot. What are the dimensions of your model?

_____

_____

5. Your family wants to go to a Green Bay
Packers football game. About how much
would it cost a family of four to go to a
game, park, buy 2 programs, and each
have a soda and a hot dog?

_____

_____

_____

Green Bay Packers Football	
Average Ticket Price	$78.84
Parking	$40.00
Soda	$4.25
Hot Dog	$5.50
Program	$6

6. Your dance group spent $679.35 on props, hall space,
and programs for a recital. The ticket prices for the
recital are shown in the table. If you sold a total of
46 adult tickets and 59 student tickets, how much
did the group make after paying for the supplies?

Recital Tickets
Adult $15.00
Student $8.00

_____

_____

Find it in Your Book!

PS Use Math Tools

Look in Chapter 1. Provide an example
of where Process Standard 5 is used.
Explain why your example represents
this process.

Attend to Precision

What does it mean to communicate precisely?

Communicating precisely is not just about giving the right answer. It also includes using terms, units, symbols, ideas, and procedures appropriately when discussing or solving problems.

Marlon drives his scooter to soccer practice every day. Each week, his scooter uses a quarter of a tank of gas. The practice field is 3 miles from his house and the gas tank holds 2.4 gallons of gas. He wants to find the unit rate per gallon of gas. Pair up with a classmate to discuss and answer the following.

1. In your own words, write the definitions for *ratio, equivalent ratio, bar diagram,* and *unit rate.*

2. How do the words from Exercise 1 relate to the problem?

3. Discuss with your partner the steps you will use to solve this problem. Summarize your discussion, and then solve the problem.

4. What units of measure will describe the unit rate per gallon of gas?

5. What is the unit rate per gallon for Marlon's scooter?

Solve each problem.

The state of Colorado is shaped like a rectangle as shown in the map. The rate $\frac{1 \text{ cm}}{100 \text{ km}}$ can be used to find actual distances.

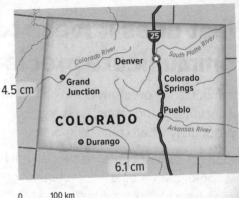

6. Use equivalent rates to find the actual distance x.

   a. $\frac{4.5 \text{ cm}}{x}$ b. $\frac{6.1 \text{ cm}}{x}$

   _____   _____

7. What is the perimeter of the state on the map? the actual perimeter?

   _____

8. Claire is in charge of the 7th grade picnic and needs to order the food for the 90 students attending. She surveys a sample population of 18 students. Ten students chose hamburgers, 7 chose hot dogs, and 1 chose a veggie burger.

   a. Make a conjecture about how many students at the picnic will choose each type of food.

   _____

   _____

   b. Discuss with a partner if these numbers are exact or estimates. Then determine what problems Claire may have by using those numbers.

   _____

   _____

   _____

Find it in Your Book!

PS **Attend to Precision**

Look in Chapter 1. Provide an example of where Process Standard 6 is used. Explain why your example represents this process.

_____

_____

_____

_____

Make Use of Structure

What is structure in mathematics?

Finding and making use of structure is important when solving problems. There is structure in writing and solving an equation or finding a pattern. We rely on being able to identify and use structure to sometimes find easier ways to solve problems.

At the Atlas Arcade, you can select a lunch combo from their new menu. First choose the type of sandwich. Then choose from a list of sides and a cookie.

Sandwich	Sides	Cookie
Chicken	Salad	Chocolate chip
Veggie	French fries	Oatmeal
Meatball	Onion rings	Raisin
	Soup	

1. Create a tree diagram or organized list that shows all of the possibilities for a veggie sandwich.

2. How many possible outcomes are there for a veggie sandwich?

   _____

3. How many total possibilities for all three types of sandwiches?

   _____

4. Can you think of another way to find the total number of outcomes?

   _____

   _____

5. Find a classmate that used a different method than you did and discuss the advantages and disadvantages of each method. Summarize your discussion.

   _____

   _____

   _____

It's Your Turn!

Describe the method you would use to solve each of the following.
Then solve.

6. Haney's scores on his science tests were 76%, 93%, 87%, 91%, and 83%. Haney wants a 90% test average for the term. If all tests are weighted the same, is it possible for him to get a 90% test average if there is only one more test? Explain.

_____

_____

_____

7. You need to make a model of your bedroom for your art class. The scale is $\frac{3}{4}$-inch = 1 foot. What are the dimensions of your model?

_____

_____

_____

8. A rectangle has a length of 4 centimeters and a width of 3 centimeters. The length and width are each multiplied by a factor of 3. Is the ratio $\dfrac{\text{area of new rectangle}}{\text{area of original rectangle}}$ equivalent to the ratio $\dfrac{\text{side length of new rectangle}}{\text{side length of original rectangle}}$? If not, explain how they are related.

_____

_____

_____

Find it in Your Book!

PS **Make Use of Structure**

Look in Chapter 1. Provide an example of where Process Standard 7 is used. Explain why your example represents this process.

_____

_____

_____

_____

Use Repeated Reasoning

How can repeated reasoning help me in math?

Sometimes, if you find repeated reasoning or patterns in mathematics, you can actually create shortcuts that help you in calculations.

1. Complete the table by choosing a set of three consecutive numbers. Then compare the product of the two outer numbers to the middle number squared. The first one is started for you.

Consecutive Numbers	Product of Two Outer Numbers	Middle Number Squared
4, 5, 6	$4 \times 6 =$	$5 \times 5 =$

2. What is the relationship between the product of the two outer numbers and the middle number squared?

_____

_____

3. Suppose you want to find 22×24. Write an expression using the middle number that can help you find the product.

_____

4. Use this reasoning to astound your family and friends by using mental math to find 49×51!

_____

$49 \times 51 = \dots$

5. Do you think this process works for three digit numbers? How can you test your conjecture?

_____

_____

_____

Solve.

6. Valerie is creating a treasure hunt for the school carnival. The scale on the map is 0.5 inch = 0.25 mile.

   a. **Table** Complete the table to determine the actual distance for 0.5 inch, 1 inch, 1.5 inches, 2 inches, and 2.5 inches on the map.

   b. **Symbols** Write an equation to find the actual distance d for m inches on the map.

   _____

Map Length (in.) m	Distance (mi) d

A famous number pattern is Pascal's Triangle shown below. Use Pascal's Triangle to complete Exercises 7 and 8.

7. Complete the triangle below. What relationship exists among the numbers in each row compared to the numbers in the previous row?

   _____

   _____

8. Determine the sum of the numbers in each row. Analyze the relationship between the sum of the numbers in each row compared to the sum of the numbers in the previous row.

   _____

   _____

   _____

Find it in Your Book!

PS **Use Repeated Reasoning**

Look in Chapter 5. Provide an example of where Process Standard 8 is used. Explain why your example represents this process.

_____

_____

_____

_____

Use the Process Standards

Solve.

The courtyard at Eastmoor Middle School is shaped like a rectangle that is 40.3 feet long. The width of the courtyard is 14.6 feet less than the length.

a. Draw and label a diagram of the school courtyard. What is the perimeter of the courtyard? _____

b. Student council wants to plant 14 trees so they are equally spaced around the courtyard. Draw a diagram showing where the trees should be planted. About how far apart are the trees? _____

Determine which Process Standards you used to determine the solution. Shade the circles that apply.

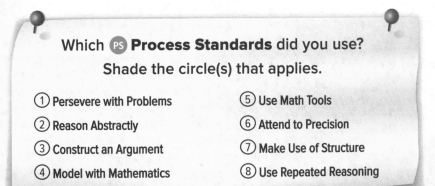

Which **PS** **Process Standards** did you use?
Shade the circle(s) that applies.

① Persevere with Problems   ⑤ Use Math Tools

② Reason Abstractly   ⑥ Attend to Precision

③ Construct an Argument   ⑦ Make Use of Structure

④ Model with Mathematics   ⑧ Use Repeated Reasoning

Reflect

 Answering the Essential Question

Use what you learned about the Process Standards to complete the graphic organizer. Write two different practices that you use for each category. Then describe how each practice helps you explore and explain mathematics.

Explore

Practice

Practice

Essential Question

WHAT processes help me explore and explain mathematics?

Practice

Practice

Explain

Answer the Essential Question. WHAT processes help me explore and explain mathematics?

_____

_____

_____

_____

UNIT 1

Ratios and Proportional Relationships

Essential Question

HOW can you use mathematics to describe change and model real-world situations?

Chapter 1

Ratios and Proportional Reasoning

Proportional relationships can be used to solve real-world problems. In this chapter, you will determine whether the relationship between two quantities is proportional. Then you will use proportions to solve multi-step problems.

Chapter 2

Percents

Proportional relationships can be used to solve percent problems. In this chapter, you will find percent of increase and decrease and use percents to solve problems involving sales tax, tips, markups and discounts, and simple interest.

Watch

Become a Travel Expert Traveling to a new place can be very exciting. Whether you are traveling a few states away or going overseas, you will surely experience and learn something new.

When you plan a trip, one thing you should definitely consider is the amount of money the trip will cost. Carefully planning the budget for a trip will ensure that you have enough money and it might help you save a few bucks as well. At the end of Chapter 2, you'll complete a project about the many costs involved with travel.

Choose a city in the United States. Complete the table by estimating the cost of different parts of a one-week family vacation to your city.

My Trip to _____	
Item	**Cost ($)**
Round Trip Plane Ticket	
Hotel	
Rental Car	
Food	
Attractions	

Chapter 1
Ratios and Proportional Reasoning

 ## Essential Question

HOW can you show that two objects are proportional?

 Indiana Academic Standards
7.C.5, 7.C.6, 7.AF.4, 7.AF.5, 7.AF.6, 7.AF.7, 7.AF.8, 7.AF.9

PS Process Standards
1, 2, 3, 4, 5, 6

Math in the Real World

Airplanes used for commercial flights travel at a speed of about 550 miles per hour.

Suppose an airplane travels 265 miles in one-half hour. Draw an arrow on the speedometer below to represent the speed of the airplane in miles per hour.

FOLDABLES
Study Organizer

 Cut out the Foldable on page FL3 of this book.

 Place your Foldable on page 92.

 Use the Foldable throughout this chapter as you learn about proportional reasoning.

Vocabulary

complex fraction	direct variation	rate of change
constant of proportionality	equivalent ratios	slope
constant rate of change	nonproportional	unit rate
constant of variation	proportion	unit ratio
coordinate plane	proportional	*x*-axis
cross products	ordered pair	*x*-coordinate
dimensional analysis	origin	*y*-axis
	quadrants	*y*-coordinate
	rate	

Review Vocabulary

Functions A function is a relationship that assigns exactly one output value for each input value. The function rule is the operation performed on the input. Perform each indicated operation on the input 10. Then write each output in the organizer.

Input	**Rule**	**Output**
10	Add 2.	
	Subtract 3.	
	Multiply by 4.	
	Divide by 5.	

What Do You Already Know?

Read each statement. Decide whether you agree (A) or disagree (D). Place a checkmark in the appropriate column and then justify your reasoning.

Ratios and Proportional Reasoning			
Statement	A	D	Why?
A rate is a ratio that compares two quantities with different units.			
A relationship between two quantities is proportional.			
The cross products of the proportion $\frac{a}{b} = \frac{c}{d}$ are ac and bd.			
A linear relationship has a constant rate of change.			
Slope can be expressed as $\frac{rise}{run}$.			
The graph of a direct variation always passes through the origin.			

When Will You Use This?

Here are a few examples of how rates are used in the real world.

Activity 1 Professional race car drivers race in qualifying runs to compete for a good starting position. Do you think that they could predict their actual race time based on qualifying times? Explain your reasoning.

_____

_____

Activity 2 Go online at **connectED.mcgraw-hill.com** to read the graphic novel **The Go-Kart Race**. How long did it take Seth to complete 12 laps? How long is each lap?

Seth and Hannah in

The Go-Kart Race

That's ok. We can estimate the rest of the times based on your times so far.

Are You Ready?

Try the Quick Check below.
Or, take the Online Readiness Quiz.

Quick Review

Example 1

Write the ratio of wins to losses as a fraction in simplest form.

wins ┈┈▶ $\frac{10}{12} = \frac{5}{6}$
losses ┈┈▶

Madison Mavericks Team Statistics	
Wins	10
Losses	12
Ties	8

The ratio of wins to losses is $\frac{5}{6}$.

Example 2

Determine whether the ratios 250 miles in 4 hours and 500 miles in 8 hours are equivalent.

Compare the ratios by writing them in simplest form.

250 miles : 4 hours = $\frac{250}{4}$ or $\frac{125}{2}$

500 miles : 8 hours = $\frac{500}{8}$ or $\frac{125}{2}$

The ratios are equivalent because they simplify to the same fraction.

Quick Check

Ratios Write each ratio as a fraction in simplest form.

1. adults : students _____

2. students : buses _____

3. buses : people _____

Seventh-Grade Field Trip	
Students	180
Adults	24
Buses	4

Equivalent Ratios Determine whether the ratios are equivalent. Explain.

4. 20 nails for every 5 shingles
   12 nails for every 3 shingles
   _____
   _____

5. 12 out of 20 doctors agree
   15 out of 30 doctors agree
   _____
   _____

How Did You Do?

Which problems did you answer correctly in the Quick Check?
Shade those exercise numbers below.

(1) (2) (3) (4) (5)

Inquiry Lab
Unit Rates

 Inquiry HOW can you use a bar diagram to solve a real-world problem involving ratios?

Indiana Academic Standards
7.AF.6, 7.AF.7

PS **Process Standards**
1, 3, 4

When Jeremy gets his allowance, he agrees to save part of it. His savings and expenses are in the ratio 7:5. If his daily allowance is $3, find how much he saves each day.

Hands-On Activity

You can use a bar diagram to represent the ratio 7:5.

Step 1 Complete the bar diagram below by writing *savings, expenses,* and *$3* in the correct boxes.

Total amount = ☐
(Daily Allowance)

Step 2 Let *x* represent each part of a bar. Write and solve an equation to find the amount of money each bar represents.

$7x + \boxed{}x = 3$ Write the equation.

$12x = 3$ There are 12 parts in all.

$\dfrac{12x}{12} = \dfrac{3}{12}$ Division Property of Equality

$x = \dfrac{\boxed{}}{\boxed{}}$ or 0.25   Simplify.

Step 3 Determine the amount Jeremy saves each day. Since each part of the bar represents $0.25, Jeremy's savings are represented by

$7 \times \$\boxed{}$ or $1.75.

So, Jeremy saves $\boxed{}$ each day.

Investigate

Work with a partner to answer the following question.

1. The ratio of the number of boys to the number of girls on the swim team is 4:2. If there are 24 athletes on the swim team, how many more boys than girls are there? Use a bar diagram to solve. _____

Total athletes = [ ]

Analyze and Reflect

Work with a partner to answer the following question.

2. **PS Reason Inductively** Suppose the swim team has 24 athletes, but the ratio of boys to girls on the swim team is 3:5. How would the bar diagram change? _____

_____

Create

3. **PS Model with Mathematics** Write a real-world problem that could be represented by the bar diagram shown below. Then solve your problem.

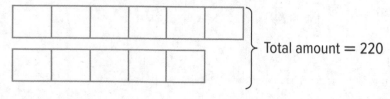

Total amount = 220

_____

_____

_____

4. **Inquiry** HOW can you use a bar diagram to solve a real-world problem involving ratios?

_____

_____

Rates

 Real-World Link Watch ▶

Pulse Rate You can take a person's pulse by placing your middle and index finger on the underside of their wrist. Choose a partner and take their pulse for two minutes.

1. Record the results in the diagram below.

beats

minutes

 Essential Question

HOW can you show that two objects are proportional?

 Vocab **Vocabulary**

rate
unit rate

🟡 **Indiana Academic Standards**
7.AF.6, 7.AF.7

PS **Process Standards**
1, 3, 4, 5

2. Use the results from Exercise 1 to complete the bar diagram and determine the number of beats per minute for your partner.

Beats in 2 minutes =

| Number of beats in 1 minute. | Number of beats in 1 minute. |

beats ---+--- beats

So, your partner's heart beats ☐ times per minute.

3. Use the results from Exercise 1 to determine the number of beats for $\frac{1}{2}$ minute for your partner.

Which PS Process Standards did you use?
Shade the circle(s) that applies.

① Persevere with Problems
② Reason Abstractly
③ Construct an Argument
④ Model with Mathematics

⑤ Use Math Tools
⑥ Attend to Precision
⑦ Make Use of Structure
⑧ Use Repeated Reasoning

Find a Unit Rate

A ratio that compares two quantities with different kinds of units is called a **rate**. When you found each other's pulse, you were actually finding the heart *rate*.

$$\frac{160 \text{ beats}}{2 \text{ minutes}}$$

The units *beats* and *minutes* are different.

When a rate is simplified so that it has a denominator of 1 unit, it is called a **unit rate**.

$$\frac{80 \text{ beats}}{1 \text{ minute}}$$

The denominator is 1 unit.

The table below shows some common unit rates.

Rate	Unit Rate	Abbreviation	Name
$\frac{\text{number of miles}}{1 \text{ hour}}$	miles per hour	mi/h or mph	average speed
$\frac{\text{number of miles}}{1 \text{ gallon}}$	miles per gallon	mi/gal or mpg	gas mileage
$\frac{\text{number of dollars}}{1 \text{ pound}}$	price per pound	dollars/lb	unit price

Example

Tutor

1. Adrienne biked **24 miles in 4 hours**. If she biked at a constant speed, how many miles did she ride in one hour?

$$24 \text{ miles in 4 hours} = \frac{24 \text{ mi}}{4 \text{ h}}$$ Write the rate as a fraction.

$$= \frac{24 \text{ mi} \div 4}{4 \text{ h} \div 4}$$ Divide the numerator and the denominator by 4.

$$= \frac{6 \text{ mi}}{1 \text{ h}}$$ Simplify.

Adrienne biked 6 miles in one hour.

Got it? Do these problems to find out.

Find each unit rate. Round to the nearest hundredth if necessary.

    a. $300 for 6 hours

    b. 220 miles on 8 gallons

STOP and Reflect

Circle the unit rate below that represents 18 cans for $6.

$\frac{9 \text{ cans}}{\$3}$ $\frac{3 \text{ cans}}{\$1}$ $\frac{4 \text{ cans}}{\$1}$

Show your work.

a. _____

b. _____

Example

2. Find the unit price if it costs $2 for eight juice boxes.

$2 for eight boxes $= \dfrac{\$2}{8 \text{ boxes}}$ Write the rate as a fraction.

$= \dfrac{\$2 \div 8}{8 \text{ boxes} \div 8}$ Divide the numerator and the denominator by 8.

$= \dfrac{\$0.25}{1 \text{ box}}$ Simplify.

The unit price is $0.25 per juice box.

Got it? Do this problem to find out.

c. Find the unit price if a 4-pack of mixed fruit sells for $2.12.

Show your work.

c. _____

Example

3. The prices of 3 different bags of dog food are given in the table. Which size bag has the lowest price per pound rounded to the nearest cent?

Dog Food Prices	
Bag Size (lb)	**Price ($)**
40	49.00
20	23.44
8	9.88

- 40-pound bag
  $49.00 \div 40$ pounds $\approx \$1.23$ per pound

- 20-pound bag
  $23.44 \div 20$ pounds $\approx \$1.17$ per pound

- 8-pound bag
  $9.88 \div 8$ pounds $\approx \$1.24$ per pound

The 20-pound bag sells for the lowest price per pound.

Alternative Method

One 40-lb bag is equivalent to two 20-lb bags or five 8-lb bags. The cost for one 40-lb bag is $49, the cost for two 20-lb bags is about $2 × $23 or $46, and the cost for five 8-lb bags is about 5 × $10 or $50. So, the 20-lb bag has the lowest price per pound.

Got it? Do this problem to find out.

d. Tito wants to buy some peanut butter to donate to the local food pantry. Tito wants to buy as much peanut butter as possible. Which brand should he buy?

Peanut Butter Sales	
Brand	**Sale Price**
Nutty	12 ounces for $2.19
Grandma's	18 ounces for $2.79
Bee's	28 ounces for $4.69
Save-A-Lot	40 ounces for $6.60

d. _____

Example

4. Lexi painted 2 faces in 8 minutes at the Crafts Fair. At this rate, how many faces can she paint in 40 minutes?

Method 1 Draw a Bar Diagram

It takes 4 minutes to paint one face. In 40 minutes, Lexi can paint 40 ÷ 4 or 10 faces.

Method 2 Find a Unit Rate

2 faces in 8 minutes = $\dfrac{2 \text{ faces} \div 8}{8 \text{ min} \div 8} = \dfrac{0.25 \text{ face}}{1 \text{ min}}$ Find the unit rate.

Multiply the unit rate by 40 minutes.

$\dfrac{0.25 \text{ face}}{1 \text{ min}} \cdot 40 \text{ min} = 10 \text{ faces}$ Divide out the common units.

Using either method, Lexi can paint 10 faces in 40 minutes.

Guided Practice

 Check

1. CD Express offers 4 CDs for $60. Music Place offers 6 CDs for $75. Which store offers the better buy? (Examples 1–3)

_____

2. After 3.5 hours, Pasha had traveled 217 miles. If she travels at a constant speed, how far will she have traveled after 4 hours? (Example 4) _____

 Show your work.

3. Write 5 pounds for $2.49 as a unit rate. Round to the nearest hundredth. (Example 2)

_____

4. **Building on the Essential Question** Use an example to describe how a *rate* is a measure of one quantity per unit of another quantity.

_____

Rate Yourself!

Are you ready to move on? Shade the section that applies.

YES   ?   NO

For more help, go online to access a Personal Tutor.

Tutor

Independent Practice

Go online for Step-by-Step Solutions   eHelp

Find each unit rate. Round to the nearest hundredth if necessary.
(Examples 1 and 2)

1. 360 miles in 6 hours _____

2. 6,840 customers in 45 days _____

Show your work.

 3. 45.5 meters in 13 seconds _____

4. $7.40 for 5 pounds _____

5. Estimate the unit rate if 12 pairs of socks sell for $5.79. (Examples 1 and 2)

_____

6. **PS Justify Conclusions** The results of a swim meet are shown. Who swam the fastest? Explain your reasoning. (Example 3)

_____

Name	Event	Time (s)
Tawni	50-m Freestyle	40.8
Pepita	100-m Butterfly	60.2
Susana	200-m Medley	112.4

7. Ben can type 153 words in 3 minutes. At this rate, how many words can he type in 10 minutes? (Example 4)

8. Kenji buys 3 yards of fabric for $7.47. Then he realizes that he needs 2 more yards. How much will the extra fabric cost? (Example 4)

9. The record for the Boston Marathon's wheelchair division is 1 hour, 18 minutes, and 27 seconds.

a. The Boston Marathon is 26.2 miles long. What was the average speed of the record winner of the wheelchair division?

Round to the nearest hundredth. _____

b. At this rate, about how long would it take this competitor to complete a 30-mile race? _____

10. At Tire Depot, a pair of new tires sells for $216. The manager's special advertises the same tires selling at a rate of $380 for 4 tires. How much do you save per tire if you purchase the manager's special? _____

H.O.T. Problems Higher Order Thinking

11. (PS) **Use Math Tools** Find examples of grocery item prices in a newspaper, on television, or on the Internet. Compare unit prices of two different brands of the same item. Explain which item is the better buy.

_____

_____

12. (PS) **Find the Error** Seth is trying to find the unit price for a package of blank compact discs on sale at 10 for $5.49. Find his mistake and correct it.

_____

_____

_____

10 ÷ $5.49
$1.82 each

(PS) **Persevere with Problems** Determine whether each statement is *sometimes, always,* or *never* true. Give an example or a counterexample.

13. A ratio is a rate.

_____

_____

_____

14. A rate is a ratio.

_____

_____

_____

15. (PS) **Justify Conclusions** A 96-ounce container of orange juice costs $4.80. At what price should a 128-ounce container be sold in order for the unit rate for both containers to be the same? Explain your reasoning.

_____

_____

_____

Extra Practice

Find each unit rate. Round to the nearest hundredth if necessary.

16. 150 people for 5 classes

30 people per class

$$\frac{150 \text{ people} \div 5}{5 \text{ classes} \div 5} = \frac{30 \text{ people}}{1 \text{ class}}$$

30 people per class

Homework Help ➡

17. 815 Calories in 4 servings

203.75 Calories per serving

$$\frac{815 \text{ Calories} \div 4}{4 \text{ servings} \div 4} = \frac{203.75 \text{ Calories}}{1 \text{ serving}}$$

203.75 Calories per serving

18. $1.12 for 8.2 ounces

_____

19. 144 miles on 4.5 gallons

_____

20. (PS) **Justify Conclusions** A grocery store sells a 6-pack of bottled water for $3.79, a 9-pack for $4.50, and a 12-pack for $6.89. Which package costs the least per bottle? Explain your reasoning.

_____

_____

21. (PS) **Justify Conclusions** Dalila earns $108.75 for working 15 hours as a holiday helper wrapping gifts. At this rate, how much money will she earn if she works 18 hours the next week? Explain.

_____

_____

22. (PS) **Use Math Tools** Use the graph that shows the average number of heartbeats for an active adult brown bear and a hibernating brown bear.

a. What does the point (2, 120) represent on the graph?

_____

_____

b. What does the ratio of the *y*-coordinate to the *x*-coordinate for each pair of points on the graph represent?

_____

_____

c. Use the graph to find the bear's average heart rate when it is active and when it is hibernating.

_____

_____

23. The table shows the number of hours a group of friends worked doing various jobs and the amount each earned. Select the correct hourly rate to complete the table. Then place a checkmark in the row for the person who had the greatest hourly rate.

$6.25	$7.90
$6.75	$8.00
$7.25	$8.70

	Hours Worked	Amount Earned ($)	Earnings per hour ($)	Greatest Hourly Rate?
Caleb	5	36.25		
Jeremy	7.5	65.25		
Maria	4.25	34.00		
Rosa	8	54.00		

24. Mrs. Ross needs to buy dish soap. There are four different sized containers. Sort the brands from least to greatest unit price. Round each unit price to the nearest thousandth.

Dish Soap Prices	
Brand	**Price**
Lots of Suds	$0.98 for 8 ounces
Bright Wash	$1.29 for 12 ounces
Spotless Soap	$3.14 for 30 ounces
Lemon Bright	$3.50 for 32 ounces

	Brand	Unit Price (per ounce)
Least		
Greatest		

Which brand is the best buy? [ ]

Spiral Review

Solve. Write in simplest form.

25. $\dfrac{1}{2} \times \dfrac{4}{7} = \dfrac{\square}{\square}$

26. $\dfrac{2}{3} \times \dfrac{1}{6} = \dfrac{\square}{\square}$

27. $\dfrac{1}{4} \div \dfrac{3}{8} = \dfrac{\square}{\square}$

Complex Fractions and Unit Rates

 Real-World Link

Speed Skating Dana is skating laps to train for a speed skating competition. She can skate 1 lap in 40 seconds.

1. Write a ratio in simplest form comparing Dana's time to her number of laps.

Dana's time (s) ┄┄➤ ☐
Number of Laps ┄┄➤ ☐

2. Suppose Dana skates for 20 seconds. How many laps will she skate?

3. Write the ratio of Dana's time from Exercise 2 to her number of laps.

Dana's time ┄┄➤ ☐
                    ☐
Number of Laps ┄┄➤ ☐

4. How could you simplify the ratio you wrote in Exercise 3?

 Essential Question

HOW can you show that two objects are proportional?

Vocab **Vocabulary**

complex fraction

 Indiana Academic Standards
7.C.5

PS **Process Standards**
1, 3, 4, 6

Which PS Process Standards did you use?
Shade the circle(s) that applies.

① Persevere with Problems   ⑤ Use Math Tools

② Reason Abstractly   ⑥ Attend to Precision

③ Construct an Argument   ⑦ Make Use of Structure

④ Model with Mathematics   ⑧ Use Repeated Reasoning

Simplify a Complex Fraction

Fractions like $\dfrac{20}{\frac{1}{2}}$ are called complex fractions. **Complex fractions** are fractions with a numerator, denominator, or both that are also fractions. Complex fractions are simplified when both the numerator and denominator are integers.

 Examples

---

1. Simplify $\dfrac{\frac{1}{4}}{2}$.

Recall that a fraction can also be written as a division problem.

$$\dfrac{\frac{1}{4}}{2} = \frac{1}{4} \div 2 \qquad \text{Write the complex fraction as a division problem.}$$

$$= \frac{1}{4} \times \frac{1}{2} \qquad \text{Multiply by the reciprocal of 2, which is } \frac{1}{2}.$$

$$= \frac{1}{8} \qquad \text{Simplify.}$$

So, $\dfrac{\frac{1}{4}}{2}$ is equal to $\dfrac{1}{8}$.

. . . .

2. Simplify $\dfrac{1}{\frac{1}{2}}$.

Write the fraction as a division problem.

$$\dfrac{1}{\frac{1}{2}} = 1 \div \frac{1}{2} \qquad \text{Write the complex fraction as a division problem.}$$

$$= \frac{1}{1} \times \frac{2}{1} \qquad \text{Multiply by the reciprocal of } \frac{1}{2}, \text{ which is } \frac{2}{1}.$$

$$= \frac{2}{1} \text{ or } 2 \qquad \text{Simplify.}$$

So, $\dfrac{1}{\frac{1}{2}}$ is equal to 2.

> **Divide Fractions**
>
> To divide by a whole number, first write it as a fraction with a denominator of 1. Then multiply by the reciprocal.
>
> So, $\dfrac{\frac{1}{4}}{2}$ can be written as $\dfrac{1}{4} \div \dfrac{2}{1}$.

Show your work.

a. _____

b. _____

c. _____

d. _____

Got it? Do these problems to find out.

a. $\dfrac{2}{\frac{2}{3}}$

b. $\dfrac{6}{\frac{1}{3}}$

c. $\dfrac{\frac{2}{3}}{7}$

d. $\dfrac{\frac{2}{4}}{2}$

Find Unit Rates

When the fractions of a complex fractions represent different units, you can find the unit rate.

  Examples

3. Josiah can jog $1\frac{1}{3}$ miles in $\frac{1}{4}$ hour. Find his average speed in miles per hour.

Write a rate that compares the number of miles to hours.

$\dfrac{1\frac{1}{3}\text{ mi}}{\frac{1}{4}\text{ h}} = 1\frac{1}{3} \div \frac{1}{4}$ — Write the complex fraction as a division problem.

$= \dfrac{4}{3} \div \dfrac{1}{4}$ — Write the mixed number as an improper fraction.

$= \dfrac{4}{3} \times \dfrac{4}{1}$ — Multiply by the reciprocal of $\frac{1}{4}$, which is $\frac{4}{1}$.

$= \dfrac{16}{3}$ or $5\frac{1}{3}$ — Simplify.

So, Josiah jogs at an average speed of $5\frac{1}{3}$ miles per hour.

4. Tia is painting her house. She paints $34\frac{1}{2}$ square feet in $\frac{3}{4}$ hour.

At this rate, how many square feet can she paint each hour?

Write a ratio that compares the number of square feet to hours.

$\dfrac{34\frac{1}{2}\text{ ft}^2}{\frac{3}{4}\text{ h}} = 34\frac{1}{2} \div \frac{3}{4}$ — Write the complex fraction as a division problem.

$= \dfrac{69}{2} \div \dfrac{3}{4}$ — Write the mixed number as an improper fraction.

$= \dfrac{69}{2} \times \dfrac{4}{3}$ — Multiply by the reciprocal of $\frac{3}{4}$, which is $\frac{4}{3}$.

$= \dfrac{276}{6}$ or 46 — Simplify.

So, Tia can paint 46 square feet per hour.

Got it? Do these problems to find out.

e. Mr. Ito is spreading mulch in his yard. He spreads $4\frac{2}{3}$ square yards in 2 hours. How many square yards can he mulch per hour?

f. Aubrey can walk $4\frac{1}{2}$ miles in $1\frac{1}{2}$ hours. Find her average speed in miles per hour.

e. _____

f. _____

5. On Javier's soccer team, about $33\frac{1}{3}$% of the players have scored a goal. Write $33\frac{1}{3}$% as a fraction in simplest form.

$$33\frac{1}{3}\% = \frac{33\frac{1}{3}}{100}$$ Definition of percent

$$= 33\frac{1}{3} \div 100$$ Write the complex fraction as a division problem.

$$= \frac{100}{3} \div 100$$ Write $33\frac{1}{3}$ as an improper fraction.

$$= \frac{\overset{1}{\cancel{100}}}{3} \times \frac{1}{\cancel{100}}$$ Multiply by the reciprocal of 100, which is $\frac{1}{100}$.

$$= \frac{1}{3}$$ Simplify.

So, about $\frac{1}{3}$ of Javier's team has scored a goal.

Guided Practice

Check ✓

Simplify. (Examples 1 and 2)

1. $\dfrac{18}{\frac{3}{4}} =$ _____

2. $\dfrac{\frac{3}{6}}{4} =$ _____

3. $\dfrac{\frac{1}{3}}{\frac{1}{4}} =$ _____

Show your work.

4. Pep Club members are making spirit buttons. They make 490 spirit buttons in $3\frac{1}{2}$ hours. Find the number of buttons the Pep Club makes per hour. (Examples 3 and 4) _____

5. A county sales tax is $6\frac{2}{3}$%. Write the percent as a fraction in simplest form. (Example 5) _____

6. **Building on the Essential Question** What is a complex fraction? _____

_____

_____

Rate Yourself!

How confident are you about simplifying complex fractions? Check the box that applies.

For more help, go online to access a Personal Tutor.

Tutor

Independent Practice

Go online for Step-by-Step Solutions

Simplify. (Examples 1 and 2)

1. $\dfrac{\frac{1}{2}}{3} =$ _____

2. $\dfrac{\frac{2}{3}}{11} =$ _____

3. $\dfrac{\frac{8}{9}}{6} =$ _____

4. $\dfrac{\frac{2}{5}}{9} =$ _____

5. $\dfrac{\frac{4}{5}}{10} =$ _____

6. $\dfrac{\frac{1}{4}}{\frac{7}{10}} =$ _____

7. Mary is making pillows for her Life Skills class. She bought $2\frac{1}{2}$ yards of fabric. Her total cost was \$15. What was the cost per yard? (Examples 3 and 4)

_____

8. Doug entered a canoe race. He rowed $3\frac{1}{2}$ miles in $\frac{1}{2}$ hour. What is his average speed in miles per hour? (Examples 3 and 4)

_____

9. Monica reads $7\frac{1}{2}$ pages of a mystery book in 9 minutes. What is her average reading rate in pages per minute? (Examples 3 and 4) _____

Write each percent as a fraction in simplest form. (Example 5)

10. $56\frac{1}{4}\% =$ _____

11. $15\frac{3}{5}\% =$ _____

12. $13\frac{1}{3}\% =$ _____

13. A bank is offering home loans at an interest rate of $5\frac{1}{2}\%$. Write the percent as a fraction in simplest form. (Example 5) _____

14. **PS Be Precise** Karl measured the wingspan of the butterfly and the moth shown below. How many times larger is the moth than the butterfly?

$3\frac{1}{4}$ in.

Black Swallowtail Butterfly

$3\frac{1}{2}$ in.

Hummingbird Moth

 H.O.T. Problems Higher Order Thinking

15. **PS Construct an Argument** Explain how complex fractions can be used to solve problems involving ratios. _____

_____

16. **PS Reason Inductively** Write three different complex fractions that simplify to $\frac{1}{4}$.

_____

17. **PS Persevere with Problems** Use mental math to find the value of $\frac{15}{124} \cdot \frac{230}{30} \div \frac{230}{124}$.

_____

18. **PS Justify Conclusions** The value of a mutual fund increased by $3\frac{1}{8}$%. Write $3\frac{1}{8}$% as a fraction in simplest form. Justify your answer.

_____

_____

19. **PS Persevere with Problems** The distance around the tire of a motorized scooter is 21.98 inches. The tires make one revolution every $\frac{1}{10}$ second. Find the speed of the scooter in miles per hour. Round to the nearest tenth. (*Hint:* The speed of an object spinning in a circle is equal to the distance around the circle divided by the time it takes to complete one revolution.)

_____

_____

Extra Practice

Simplify.

20. $\dfrac{1}{\frac{1}{4}} = 4$

$\dfrac{1}{\frac{1}{4}} = 1 \div \frac{1}{4}$

$= \frac{1}{1} \times \frac{4}{1}$

Homework Help ➡

$= \frac{4}{1}$ or 4

21. $\dfrac{\frac{12}{5}}{\frac{3}{5}} =$ _____

22. $\dfrac{\frac{9}{10}}{9} =$ _____

23. $\dfrac{\frac{1}{2}}{\frac{1}{4}} =$ _____

24. $\dfrac{\frac{1}{12}}{\frac{5}{6}} =$ _____

25. $\dfrac{\frac{5}{6}}{\frac{5}{9}} =$ _____

26. Mrs. Frasier is making costumes for the school play. Each costume requires 0.75 yard of fabric. She bought 6 yards of fabric. How many costumes can Mrs. Frasier make?

_____

27. A lawn company advertises that they can spread 7,500 square feet of grass seed in $2\frac{1}{2}$ hours. Find the number of square feet of grass seed that can be spread per hour.

_____

Write each percent as a fraction in simplest form.

28. $2\frac{2}{5}\% =$ _____

29. $7\frac{3}{4}\% =$ _____

30. $8\frac{1}{3}\% =$ _____

31. **PS Justify Conclusions** The value of a certain stock increased by $1\frac{1}{4}\%$.

Explain how to write $1\frac{1}{4}\%$ as a fraction in simplest form. _____

_____

_____

32. Debra bought $3\frac{1}{4}$ yards of fabric at a remnant sale for $13. Determine if each of the following remnant deals have the same unit price as Debra's deal. Select yes or no.

a. $4\frac{2}{3}$ yards for $16 ☐ Yes ☐ No

b. $2\frac{3}{4}$ yards for $11 ☐ Yes ☐ No

c. $6\frac{1}{2}$ yards for $26 ☐ Yes ☐ No

33. The table shows the distances traveled by 4 cyclists. Sort the speeds of the riders, in miles per hour, from slowest to fastest.

	Rider	Speed (mph)
Slowest		
Fastest		

Bicycle Rides		
Rider	Distance	Time
Elena	$20\frac{1}{2}$ mi	$2\frac{1}{4}$ h
Julio	$12\frac{1}{4}$ mi	$1\frac{1}{2}$ h
Kevin	$20\frac{2}{3}$ mi	$1\frac{2}{3}$ h
Lorena	$33\frac{1}{4}$ mi	$2\frac{1}{3}$ h

Which rider had the fastest rate of speed? ☐

Spiral Review

Fill in each box with the equivalent customary measurement.

34. 2 feet = ☐ inches

35. 5 tons = ☐ pounds

36. 8 gallons = ☐ quarts

Fill in each box with the equivalent metric measurement.

37. 1 meter = ☐ centimeters

38. 1 liter = ☐ milliliters

39. 1 kilogram = ☐ grams

Convert Unit Rates

 Real-World Link

Animals Squirrels, chipmunks, and rabbits are capable of running at fast speeds. The table shows the top running speeds of these animals.

Animal	Speed (mph)
Squirrel	10
Chipmunk	15
Cottontail Rabbit	30

 Essential Question

HOW can you show that two objects are proportional?

Vocab **Vocabulary**

unit ratio
dimensional analysis

🎓 **Indiana Academic Standards**
7.C.6, 7.AF.6

PS **Process Standards**
1, 3, 4, 5

1. How many feet are in 1 mile? 10 miles?

   1 mile = _____ feet

   10 miles = _____ feet

2. How many seconds are in 1 minute? 1 hour?

   1 minute = _____ seconds

   1 hour = _____ seconds

3. How could you determine the number of feet per second a squirrel can run?

   _____

   _____

4. Complete the following statement. Round to the nearest tenth. 10 miles per hour ≈ [   ] feet per second

FINISH

Which PS Process Standards did you use?
Shade the circle(s) that applies.

① Persevere with Problems

② Reason Abstractly

③ Construct an Argument

④ Model with Mathematics

⑤ Use Math Tools

⑥ Attend to Precision

⑦ Make Use of Structure

⑧ Use Repeated Reasoning

Convert Rates

The relationships among some commonly used customary and metric units of measure are shown in the tables below.

Customary Units of Measure		Metric Units of Measure	
Smaller	**Larger**	**Smaller**	**Larger**
12 inches	1 foot	100 centimeters	1 meter
16 ounces	1 pound	1,000 grams	1 kilogram
8 pints	1 gallon	1,000 milliliters	1 liter
3 feet	1 yard	10 millimeters	1 centimeter
5,280 feet	1 mile	1,000 milligrams	1 gram

Each of the relationships in the tables can be written as a **unit ratio**. Like a unit rate, a unit ratio is one in which the denominator is 1 unit. Below are three examples of unit ratios.

$$\frac{12 \text{ inches}}{1 \text{ foot}} \qquad \frac{16 \text{ ounces}}{1 \text{ pound}} \qquad \frac{100 \text{ centimeters}}{1 \text{ meter}}$$

The numerator and denominator of each of the unit ratios shown are equal. So, the value of each ratio is 1.

You can convert one rate to an equivalent rate by multiplying by a unit ratio or its reciprocal. When you convert rates, you include the units in your computation.

The process of including units of measure as factors when you compute is called **dimensional analysis**.

$$\frac{10 \text{ ft}}{1 \text{ s}} = \frac{10 \; \cancel{\text{ft}}}{1 \text{ s}} \cdot \frac{12 \text{ in.}}{1 \; \cancel{\text{ft}}} = \frac{10 \cdot 12 \text{ in.}}{1 \text{ s} \cdot 1} = \frac{120 \text{ in.}}{1 \text{ s}}$$

 ## Example

1. A remote control car travels at a rate of 10 feet per second. How many inches per second is this?

$$\frac{10 \text{ ft}}{1 \text{ s}} = \frac{10 \text{ ft}}{1 \text{ s}} \cdot \frac{12 \text{ in.}}{1 \text{ ft}} \qquad \text{Use 1 foot} = 12 \text{ inches. Multiply by } \frac{12 \text{ in.}}{1 \text{ ft}}.$$

$$= \frac{10 \; \cancel{\text{ft}}}{1 \text{ s}} \cdot \frac{12 \text{ in.}}{1 \; \cancel{\text{ft}}} \qquad \text{Divide out common units.}$$

$$= \frac{10 \cdot 12 \text{ in.}}{1 \text{ s} \cdot 1} \qquad \text{Simplify.}$$

$$= \frac{120 \text{ in.}}{1 \text{ s}} \qquad \text{Simplify.}$$

So, 10 feet per second equals 120 inches per second.

Examples

2. **A swordfish can swim at a rate of 60 miles per hour. How many feet per hour is this?**

You can use 1 mile = 5,280 feet to convert the rates.

$$\frac{60 \text{ mi}}{1 \text{ h}} = \frac{60 \text{ mi}}{1 \text{ h}} \cdot \frac{5,280 \text{ ft}}{1 \text{ mi}} \qquad \text{Multiply by } \frac{5,280 \text{ ft}}{1 \text{ mi}}.$$

$$= \frac{60 \text{ mi}}{1 \text{ h}} \cdot \frac{5,280 \text{ ft}}{1 \text{ mi}} \qquad \text{Divide out common units.}$$

$$= \frac{60 \cdot 5,280 \text{ ft}}{1 \cdot 1 \text{ h}} \qquad \text{Simplify.}$$

$$= \frac{316,800 \text{ ft}}{1 \text{ h}} \qquad \text{Simplify.}$$

A swordfish can swim at a rate of 316,800 feet per hour.

3. **Marvin walks at a speed of 7 feet per second. How many feet per hour is this?**

You can use 60 seconds = 1 minute and you can use 60 minutes = 1 hour to convert the rates.

$$\frac{7 \text{ ft}}{1 \text{ s}} = \frac{7 \text{ ft}}{1 \text{ s}} \cdot \frac{60 \text{ s}}{1 \text{ min}} \cdot \frac{60 \text{ min}}{1 \text{ h}} \qquad \text{Multiply by } \frac{60 \text{ s}}{1 \text{ min}} \text{ and } \frac{60 \text{ min}}{1 \text{ h}}.$$

$$= \frac{7 \text{ ft}}{1 \text{ s}} \cdot \frac{60 \text{ s}}{1 \text{ min}} \cdot \frac{60 \text{ min}}{1 \text{ h}} \qquad \text{Divide out common units.}$$

$$= \frac{7 \cdot 60 \cdot 60 \text{ ft}}{1 \cdot 1 \cdot 1 \text{ h}} \qquad \text{Simplify.}$$

$$= \frac{25,200 \text{ ft}}{1 \text{ h}} \qquad \text{Simplify.}$$

Marvin walks 25,200 feet in 1 hour.

Got it? Do these problems to find out.

a. A gull can fly at a speed of 22 miles per hour. About how many feet per hour can the gull fly?

b. An AMTRAK train travels at 125 miles per hour. Convert the speed to miles per minute. Round to the nearest tenth.

 and Reflect

To convert meters per hour to kilometers per hour, circle the relationship you need to know.

100 cm = 1 m
60 s = 1 min
1,000 m = 1 km

Show your work.

a. _____

b. _____

Example

4. The average speed of one team in a relay race is about **10 miles per hour. What is this speed in feet per second?**

We can use 1 mile = 5,280 feet, 1 hour = 60 minutes, and 1 minute = 60 seconds to convert the rates.

$$\frac{10 \text{ mi}}{1 \text{ h}} = \frac{10 \text{ mi}}{1 \text{ h}} \cdot \frac{5,280 \text{ ft}}{1 \text{ mi}} \cdot \frac{1 \text{ h}}{60 \text{ min}} \cdot \frac{1 \text{ min}}{60 \text{ s}}$$ Multiply by distance and time unit ratios.

$$= \frac{10 \text{ mi}}{1 \text{ h}} \cdot \frac{5,280 \text{ ft}}{1 \text{ mi}} \cdot \frac{1 \text{ h}}{60 \text{ min}} \cdot \frac{1 \text{ min}}{60 \text{ s}}$$ Divide out common units.

$$= \frac{10 \cdot 5,280 \cdot 1 \cdot 1 \text{ ft}}{1 \cdot 1 \cdot 60 \cdot 60 \text{ s}}$$ Simplify.

$$= \frac{52,800 \text{ ft}}{3,600 \text{ s}}$$ Simplify.

$$\approx \frac{14.7 \text{ ft}}{1 \text{ s}}$$ Simplify.

The relay team runs at an average speed of about 14.7 feet per second.

Guided Practice

1. Water weighs about 8.34 pounds per gallon. About how many ounces per gallon is the weight of the water? (Examples 1 and 2)

_____

2. A skydiver is falling at about 176 feet per second. How many feet per minute is he falling? (Example 3)

_____

3. Lorenzo rides his bike at a rate of 5 yards per second. About how many miles per hour can Lorenzo ride his bike? (*Hint*: 1 mile = 1,760 yards) (Example 4)

_____

4. **Building on the Essential Question** Explain why the ratio $\frac{3 \text{ feet}}{1 \text{ yard}}$ has a value of one.

_____

_____

_____

Rate Yourself!

☐ I understand how to convert unit rates.

▶▶ Great! You're ready to move on!

☐ I still have questions about converting unit rates.

⫼ No Problem! Go online to access a Personal Tutor. Tutor

Independent Practice

Go online for Step-by-Step Solutions

1 A go-kart's top speed is 607,200 feet per hour. What is the speed in miles per hour? (Examples 1 and 2)

_____

_____

2. The fastest a human has ever run is 27 miles per hour. How many miles per minute did the human run? (Example 3)

3 A peregrine falcon can fly 322 kilometers per hour. How many meters per hour can the falcon fly? (Example 3)

_____

4. A pipe is leaking at 1.5 cups per day. About how many gallons per week is the pipe leaking? (*Hint*: 1 gallon = 16 cups) (Example 4)

_____

5. Charlie runs at a speed of 3 yards per second. About how many miles per hour does Charlie run? (Example 4)

_____

6. **PS** **Model with Mathematics** Refer to the graphic novel frame below. Seth traveled 1 mile in 57.1 seconds. About how fast does Seth travel in miles per hour?

_____

I can't believe how fast I was going.

7. The speed at which a certain computer can access the Internet is 2 megabytes per second. How fast is this in megabytes per hour?

_____

8. **PS Use Math Tools** The approximate metric measurement of length is given for a U.S. customary unit of length. Use your estimation skills to complete the graphic organizer below. Fill in each blank with _foot, yard, inch,_ or _mile_.

Metric		Customary
2.54 centimeters	⟶	1
0.30 meter	⟶	1
0.91 meter	⟶	1
1.61 kilometers	⟶	1

H.O.T. Problems Higher Order Thinking

9. **PS Which One Doesn't Belong?** Circle the rate that does not belong with the other three. Explain your reasoning.

60 mi/h		88 ft/s		500 ft/min		1,440 mi/day

_____

_____

10. **PS Reason Inductively** When you convert 100 feet per second to inches per second, will there be more or less than 100 inches. Explain.

_____

_____

11. **PS Persevere with Problems** Use the information in Exercise 8 to convert 7 meters per minute to yards per hour. Round to the nearest tenth.

_____

12. **PS Model with Mathematics** Write and solve a real-world problem in which a rate is converted.

_____

_____

Extra Practice

13. 20 mi/h = ⎡ 1,760 ⎤ ft/min

$$\frac{20\ \cancel{mi}}{1\ \cancel{h}} \cdot \frac{5{,}280\ ft}{1\ \cancel{mi}} \cdot \frac{1\ \cancel{h}}{60\ min} =$$

$$\frac{105{,}600\ ft}{60\ min} = 1{,}760\ ft/min$$

14. 16 cm/min = ⎡ 9.6 ⎤ m/h

$$\frac{16\ \cancel{cm}}{1\ \cancel{min}} \cdot \frac{1\ m}{100\ \cancel{cm}} \cdot \frac{60\ \cancel{min}}{1\ h} =$$

$$\frac{960\ m}{100\ h} = 9.6\ m/h$$

15. 45 mi/h = ⎡ ⎤ ft/s

16. 26 cm/s = ⎡ ⎤ m/min

17. 24 mi/h = ⎡ ⎤ ft/s

18. 105.6 L/h = ⎡ ⎤ L/min

19. The table shows the speed and number of wing beats per second for various flying insects.

   a. What is the speed of a housefly in feet per second? Round to the nearest hundredth.

_____

   b. How many times does a dragonfly's wing beat per minute?

_____

   c. About how many miles can a bumblebee travel in one minute?

_____

   d. How many times can a honeybee beat its wings in one hour?

_____

Flying Insects		
Insect	Speed (miles per hour)	Wing Beats per Second
Housefly	4.4	190
Honeybee	5.7	250
Dragonfly	15.6	38
Hornet	12.8	100
Bumblebee	6.4	130

20. A model airplane flew a distance of 330 feet in 15 seconds. Select all of the unit rates that are equivalent to the speed of the model airplane.

- ☐ 15 miles per hour
- ☐ 12 miles per hour
- ☐ 1320 feet per minute
- ☐ 1,056 feet per minute

21. The table shows how far some of the world's fastest animals can run in different lengths of time at their top speed.

Select the correct top speed to complete the table.

Animal	Top Speed (mph)
Cheetah	
Elk	
Lion	
Quarter Horse	

45	60
50	65
55	70

Fastest Animals on Land	
Animal	**Distance and Time**
Cheetah	3,080 feet in 30 seconds
Elk	2,970 feet in 45 seconds
Lion	4,400 feet in 60 seconds
Quarter Horse	6,050 feet in 75 seconds

Which animal had the fastest rate of speed? [   ]

Spiral Review

Determine if each pair of rates are equivalent. Explain your reasoning.

22. $36 for 4 baseball hats; $56 for 7 baseball hats

_____

_____

_____

23. 12 posters for 36 students; 21 posters for 63 students

_____

_____

_____

24. An employer pays $22 for 2 hours. Use the ratio table to determine how much she charges for 5 hours.

Payment	$22		
Hours	2		5

Proportional and Nonproportional Relationships

 Real-World Link

Pizza Party Ms. Cochran is planning a year-end pizza party for her students. Ace Pizza offers free delivery and charges $8 per medium pizza.

1. Complete the table to determine the cost for different numbers of pizzas ordered.

Cost ($)	8				
Pizza	1	2	3	4	5

2. For each number of pizzas, fill in the boxes to write the relationship of the cost and number of pizzas as a ratio in simplest form.

$$\frac{16}{2} = \frac{\boxed{}}{1} \qquad \frac{24}{3} = \frac{\boxed{}}{\boxed{}}$$

$$\frac{32}{\boxed{}} = \frac{\boxed{}}{\boxed{}} \qquad \frac{\boxed{}}{5} = \frac{\boxed{}}{\boxed{}}$$

3. What do you notice about the simplified ratios?

_____

_____

 Essential Question

HOW can you show that two objects are proportional?

 Vocabulary

proportional
nonproportional
equivalent ratios

Indiana Academic Standards
7.AF.6, 7.AF.7, 7.AF.9

PS Process Standards
1, 3, 4

Which **PS** **Process Standards** did you use?
Shade the circle(s) that applies.

① Persevere with Problems
② Reason Abstractly
③ Construct an Argument
④ Model with Mathematics

⑤ Use Math Tools
⑥ Attend to Precision
⑦ Make Use of Structure
⑧ Use Repeated Reasoning

Identify Proportional Relationships

Two quantities are **proportional** if they have a constant ratio or unit rate. For relationships in which this ratio is not constant, the two quantities are **nonproportional**.

In the pizza example on the previous page, the cost of an order is *proportional* to the number of pizzas ordered.

$$\frac{\text{cost of order}}{\text{pizzas ordered}} = \frac{8}{1} = \frac{16}{2} = \frac{24}{3} = \frac{32}{4} = \frac{40}{5} \text{ or } \$8 \text{ per pizza}$$

All of the ratios above are **equivalent ratios** because they all have the same value.

 ## Example

Tutor

1. **Andrew earns \$18 per hour for mowing lawns. Is the amount of money he earns proportional to the number of hours he spends mowing? Explain.**

Find the amount of money he earns for working a different number of hours. Make a table to show these amounts.

Earnings ($)	18	36	54	72
Time (h)	1	2	3	4

For each number of hours worked, write the relationship of the amount he earned and hour as a ratio in simplest form.

$$\frac{\text{amount earned}}{\text{number of hours}} \rightarrow \frac{18}{1} \text{ or } 18 \quad \frac{36}{2} \text{ or } 18 \quad \frac{54}{3} \text{ or } 18 \quad \frac{72}{4} \text{ or } 18$$

All of the ratios between the two quantities can be simplified to 18.

The amount of money he earns is proportional to the number of hours he spends mowing.

Show your work.

> **Got it?** Do this problem to find out.

a. At Lakeview Middle School, there are 2 homeroom teachers assigned to every 48 students. Is the number of students at this school proportional to the number of teachers? Explain your reasoning.

a. _____

Examples

2. Uptown Tickets charges $7 per baseball game ticket plus a $3 processing fee per order. Is the cost of an order proportional to the number of tickets ordered? Explain.

Cost ($)	10	17	24	31
Tickets Ordered	1	2	3	4

For each number of tickets, write the relationship of the cost and number of tickets as a ratio in simplest form.

$\dfrac{\text{cost of order}}{\text{tickets ordered}}$ → $\dfrac{10}{1}$ or 10 $\dfrac{17}{2}$ or 8.5 $\dfrac{24}{3}$ or 8 $\dfrac{31}{4}$ or 7.75

Since the ratios of the two quantities are not the same, the cost of an order is *not* proportional to the number of tickets ordered.

3. You can use the recipe shown to make a fruit punch. Is the amount of sugar used proportional to the amount of mix used? Explain.

Find the amount of sugar and mix needed for different numbers of batches. Make a table to help you solve.

Fruit Punch
$\frac{1}{2}$ cup sugar
1 envelope of mix
2 quarts of water

Cups of Sugar	$\frac{1}{2}$	1	$1\frac{1}{2}$	2
Envelopes of Mix	1	2	3	4

For each number of cups of sugar, write the relationship of the cups and number of envelopes of mix as a ratio in simplest form.

$\dfrac{\text{cups of sugar}}{\text{envelopes of mix}}$ → $\dfrac{\frac{1}{2}}{1}$ or 0.5 $\dfrac{1}{2}$ or 0.5 $\dfrac{1\frac{1}{2}}{3}$ or 0.5 $\dfrac{2}{4}$ or 0.5

All of the ratios between the two quantities can be simplified to 0.5. The amount of mix used is proportional to the amount of sugar used.

Got it? Do this problem to find out.

Show your work.

b. At the beginning of the year, Isabel had $120 in the bank. Each week, she deposits another $20. Is her account balance proportional to the number of weeks of deposits? Use the table below. Explain your reasoning.

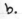
b. _____

Time (wk)	1	2	3
Balance ($)			

Example

Tutor

4. The tables shown represent the number of pages Martin and Gabriel read over time. Which situation represents a proportional relationship between the time spent reading and the number of pages read? Explain.

Pages Martin Read	2	4	6
Time (min)	5	10	15

Pages Gabriel Read	3	4	7
Time (min)	5	10	15

Write the ratios for each time period in simplest form.

$\frac{pages}{minutes} \rightarrow \frac{2}{5}, \frac{4}{10}$ or $\frac{2}{5}, \frac{6}{15}$ or $\frac{2}{5}$ $\frac{3}{5}, \frac{4}{10}$ or $\frac{2}{5}, \frac{7}{15}$

All of the ratios between Martin's quantities are $\frac{2}{5}$. So, Martin's reading rate represents a proportional relationship.

Guided Practice

Check ✓

1. The Vista Marina rents boats for $25 per hour. In addition to the rental fee, there is a $12 charge for fuel. Use a table to determine if the number of hours you rent the boat is proportional to the total cost. Explain. (Examples 1–3)

Rental Time (h)			
Cost ($)			

2. Which situation represents a proportional relationship between the hours worked and amount earned for Matt and Jane? Explain. (Example 4)

Matt's Earnings ($)	12	20	31
Time (h)	1	2	3

Jane's Earnings ($)	12	24	36
Time (h)	1	2	3

3. **Building on the Essential Question** Explain what makes two quantities proportional.

Rate Yourself!

How confident are you about determining proportional relationships? Shade the ring on the target.

I'm on target.

I need help.

For more help, go online to access a Personal Tutor.

Tutor

FOLDABLES Time to update your Foldable!

Independent Practice

Go online for Step-by-Step Solutions

For Exercises 1 and 2, use a table to solve. Then explain your reasoning.
(Examples 1 and 2)

1 An adult elephant drinks about 225 liters of water each day. Is the number of days the water supply lasts proportional to the number of liters of water the elephant drinks?

Time (days)	1	2	3	4
Water (L)				

2. An elevator *ascends*, or goes up, at a rate of 750 feet per minute. Is the height to which the elevator ascends proportional to the number of minutes it takes to get there? (Examples 1–3)

Time (min)	1	2	3	4
Height (ft)				

3. Which situation represents a proportional relationship between the number of laps run by each student and their time? (Example 4)

Desmond's Time (s)	146	292	584
Laps	2	4	8

Maria's Time (s)	150	320	580
Laps	2	4	6

Copy and Solve Use a table to help you solve. Then explain your reasoning. Show your work on a separate piece of paper.

4. Plant A is 18 inches tall after one week, 36 inches tall after two weeks, 56 inches tall after three weeks. Plant B is 18 inches tall after one week, 36 inches tall after two weeks, 54 inches tall after three weeks. Which situation represents a proportional relationship between the plants'

height and number of weeks? (Example 4) _____

5 Determine whether the measures for the figure shown are proportional.

a. the length of a side and the perimeter _____

b. the length of a side and the area _____

s

6. **(PS) Justify Conclusions** MegaMart collects a sales tax equal to $\frac{1}{16}$ of the retail price of each purchase. The tax is sent to the state government.

   a. Is the amount of tax collected proportional to the cost of an item before tax is added? Explain.

Retail Price ($)	16	32	48	64
Tax Collected ($)				

   b. Is the amount of tax collected proportional to the cost of an item after tax has been added? Explain.

Retail Price ($)	16	32	48	
Tax Collected ($)				
Cost Including Tax ($)				

H.O.T. Problems Higher Order Thinking

7. **(PS) Find the Error** Blake ran laps around the gym. His times are shown in the table. Blake is trying to decide whether the number of laps is proportional to the time. Find his mistake and correct it.

Time (min)	1	2	3	4
Laps	4	6	8	10

It is proportional because the number of laps always increases by 2.

8. **(PS) Persevere with Problems** Determine whether the cost for ordering multiple items that will be delivered is *sometimes*, *always*, or *never* proportional. Explain your reasoning.

9. **(PS) Model with Mathematics** Give real-world examples of two similar situations in which one is a proportional relationship and the second one is nonproportional.

Extra Practice

For Exercises 10–12, use a table to solve. Then explain your reasoning.

10. A vine grows 7.5 feet every 5 days. Is the length of the vine on the last day proportional to the number of days of growth?

Yes; the length to time ratios are all equal to 1.5 ft per day.

Time (days)	5	10	15	20
Length (ft)	7.5	15	22.5	30

11. **STEM** To convert a temperature in degrees Celsius to degrees Fahrenheit, multiply the Celsius temperature by $\frac{9}{5}$ and then add 32°. Is a temperature in degrees Celsius proportional to its equivalent temperature in degrees Fahrenheit?

Degrees Celsius	0	10	20	30
Degrees Fahrenheit				

12. On Saturday, Querida gave away 416 coupons for a free appetizer at a local restaurant. The next day, she gave away about 52 coupons an hour.

a. Is the number of coupons Querida gave away on Sunday proportional to the number of hours she worked that day?

Hours Worked on Sunday	1	2	3	4
Coupons Given Away on Sunday				

b. Is the total number of coupons Querida gave away on Saturday and Sunday proportional to the number of hours she worked on Sunday?

Hours Worked on Sunday	1	2	3	4
Coupons Given Away on Weekend				

13. **PS Justify Conclusions** The fee for ride tickets at a carnival is shown in the table at the right.

a. Is the fee for ride tickets proportional to the number of tickets? Explain your reasoning.

Tickets	5	10	15	20
Fee ($)	5	9.50	13.50	16

b. Can you determine the fee for 30 ride tickets? Explain.

14. Mr. Martinez is comparing the prices of oranges from several different markets. Determine whether each market uses proportional or nonproportional pricing. Place a checkmark in the column for the correct type of relationship.

Number of Oranges	5	10	15	20
Total Cost ($)	3.50	6.50	9.00	10.25

Number of Oranges	5	10	15	20
Total Cost ($)	3.25	6.50	9.75	13.00

Number of Oranges	5	10	15	20
Total Cost ($)	3.75	7.50	11.25	15.00

Number of Oranges	5	10	15	20
Total Cost ($)	3.65	7.30	10.80	14.30

Proportional   **Nonproportional**

15. A grocery store sells a 2.5-pound bag of mixed nuts for $9.25. The prices of mixed nuts are proportional. Determine if each of the following bags of mixed nuts could have been sold by the grocery store. Select yes or no.

   a. 4.4 pounds for $16.28   ☐ Yes   ☐ No

   b. 3.2 pounds for $12   ☐ Yes   ☐ No

   c. 2.8 pounds for $10.50   ☐ Yes   ☐ No

Spiral Review

Find the value of each expression if $x = 12$.

16. $3x$ _____

17. $2x - 4$ _____

18. $5x + 30$ _____

19. $3x - 2x$ _____

20. $x - 12$ _____

21. $\frac{x}{4}$ _____

Make a table to solve the situation.

22. Brianna downloads 9 songs each month onto her MP3 player. Show the total number of songs downloaded after 1, 2, 3, and 4 months.

Month				
Number of Songs				

PS Problem-Solving Investigation
The Four-Step Plan

Indiana Academic Standards
7.AF.6

PS **Process Standards**
1, 3, 4

Case #1 'Round and 'Round

The Forte family visited the Mall of America in Minneapolis. The Ferris wheel in the mall's amusement park is about 22.5 meters tall.

What is the approximate height of the Mall of America Ferris wheel in feet if 1 foot is about 0.3 meter?

In mathematics, there is a *four-step problem-solving plan* you can use to help you solve any problem. The four steps are *Understand, Plan, Solve,* and *Check.*

Understand *What are the facts?*

- The Mall of America Ferris wheel is about 22.5 meters tall.
- You need to find the height of the Ferris wheel in feet.

Plan *What is your strategy to solve this problem?*

To solve the problem, write an expression that converts meters to feet. Then divide out common units.

Solve *How can you apply the strategy?*

One foot is about 0.3 meter. Convert 22.5 meters to feet.

$$22.5 \text{ meters} \cdot \frac{1 \text{ foot}}{0.3 \text{ meter}} \approx \frac{22.5}{0.3} \text{ or } \boxed{} \text{ feet}$$

So, the Ferris wheel is about 75 feet tall.

Check *Does the answer make sense?*

There is a little more than 3 feet in a meter.

Since $3 \cdot 22.5$ is 67.5 and 75 feet is a little more than 67.5 feet, the answer is reasonable.

Analyze the Strategy Tutor

PS **Reason Inductively** Explain in your own words how the four-step plan helps you solve real-world problems.

_____

_____

_____

Case #2 Cool Treats

Mr. Martino's class learned the average American consumes about 23 quarts of ice cream every year. The class also learned the average American in the north-central United States consumes about 19 quarts more.

How much ice cream in gallons is consumed every year by the average American in the north-central United States?

Understand

Read the problem. What are you being asked to find?

I need to find _____

_____.

Fill in each box with the information you know.

The average American consumes about ☐ quarts of ice cream.

The average American in the north-central United States consumes

about ☐ quarts more.

Plan

Choose two operations to solve the problem.

I will _____.

Solve

How will you use the operations?

I will _____.

Find total quarts.   Convert to gallons.

☐ + ☐ = ☐   ☐ quarts • $\dfrac{1 \text{ gallon}}{☐ \text{ quarts}}$ = _____ gallons

The average American in the north-central United States consumes

about ☐ gallons of ice cream each year.

Check

Use information from the problem to check your solution.

_____.

Work with a small group to solve the following cases.
Show your work on a separate piece of paper.

Case #3 Financial Literacy

Terry opened a savings account in December with $150 and deposited $30 each month beginning in January.

What is the value of Terry's account at the end of July?

Case #4 STEM

About how many centimeters longer is the average femur than the average tibia? (Hint: 1 inch ≈ 2.54 centimeters)

Bones in a Human Leg	
Bone	Length (in.)
Femur (upper leg)	19.88
Tibia (inner lower leg)	16.94
Fibula (outer lower leg)	15.94

Case #5 Patterns

Numbers that can be represented by a triangular arrangement of dots are called *triangular numbers*. The first four triangular numbers are shown.

Describe the pattern in the first four numbers. Then list the next three triangular numbers.

1   3   6   10

Case #6 Transportation

Mr. Norman has agreed to drive 4 students to their gymnastics practice.

If one student rides in the front seat and three students ride in the back, in how many ways can the 4 students be arranged in the car?

Use any strategy!

Mid-Chapter Check

Vocabulary Check

1. **PS** **Be Precise** Define *complex fraction*. Give two examples of a complex fraction. (Lesson 2)

_____

_____

2. Fill in the blank in the sentence below with the correct term. (Lesson 1)

When a rate is simplified so that it has a denominator of 1 unit, it is

called a(n) _____ rate.

Skills Check and Problem Solving

Find each unit rate. Round to the nearest hundredth if necessary. (Lesson 1)

3. 750 yards in 25 minutes _____

4. $420 for 15 tickets _____

Simplify. (Lesson 2)

5. $\dfrac{9}{\frac{1}{3}}$ = _____

6. $\dfrac{\frac{1}{2}}{4}$ = _____

7. $\dfrac{\frac{1}{6}}{1\frac{3}{8}}$ = _____

8. A tourist information center charges $10 per hour to rent a bicycle. Is the rental charge proportional to the number of hours you rent the bicycle? Justify your response. (Lesson 4)

_____

9. **PS** **Persevere with Problems** A cruise ship is traveling at a speed of 20 knots. A knot is approximately equal to 1.151 miles per hour. What is the approximate speed the ship is traveling in yards per second? Round to the nearest tenth. (Lesson 3) _____

Graph Proportional Relationships

Vocabulary Start-Up

Maps have grids to locate cities. The **coordinate plane** is a type of grid that is formed when two number lines intersect at their zero points. The number lines separate the coordinate plane into four regions called **quadrants**.

An **ordered pair** is a pair of numbers, such as (1, 2), used to locate or graph points on the coordinate plane.

The **x-coordinate** corresponds to a number on the *x*-axis. →**(1, 2)**← The **y-coordinate** corresponds to a number on the *y*-axis.

Label the coordinate plane with the terms *ordered pair*, *x-coordinate*, and *y-coordinate*.

y-axis

origin

x-axis

Graph points (2, 3) and (−3, −2) above. Connect the three points on the coordinate plane. Describe the graph.

Essential Question

HOW can you show that two objects are proportional?

Vocabulary

coordinate plane
quadrants
ordered pair
x-coordinate
y-coordinate
y-axis
origin
x-axis

Indiana Academic Standards
7.AF.6, 7.AF.9

PS Process Standards
1, 2, 3, 4

Which PS Process Standards did you use?
Shade the circle(s) that applies.

① Persevere with Problems
② Reason Abstractly
③ Construct an Argument
④ Model with Mathematics
⑤ Use Math Tools
⑥ Attend to Precision
⑦ Make Use of Structure
⑧ Use Repeated Reasoning

Identify Proportional Relationships

Another way to determine whether two quantities are proportional is to graph the quantities on the coordinate plane. If the graph of the two quantities is a straight line through the origin, then the two quantities are proportional.

Linear Relationships

Relationships that have straight-line graphs are called linear relationships.

Example

1. The slowest mammal on Earth is the tree sloth. It moves at a speed of 6 feet per minute. Determine whether the number of feet the sloth moves is proportional to the number of minutes it moves by graphing on the coordinate plane. Explain your reasoning.

Step 1 Make a table to find the number of feet walked for 0, 1, 2, 3, and 4 minutes.

Time (min)	0	1	2	3	4
Distance (ft)	0	6	12	18	24

Step 2 Graph the ordered pairs (time, distance) on the coordinate plane. Then connect the ordered pairs.

The line passes through the origin and is a straight line. So, the number of feet traveled is proportional to the number of minutes.

Got it? Do this problem to find out.

a. James earns $5 an hour babysitting. Determine whether the amount of money James earns babysitting is proportional to the number of hours he babysits by graphing on the coordinate plane. Explain your reasoning in the work zone.

a. _____

Example

 Tutor

2. The cost of renting video games from Games Inc. is shown in the table. Determine whether the cost is proportional to the number of games rented by graphing on the coordinate plane. Explain your reasoning.

Video Game Rental Rates

Number of Games	Cost ($)
1	3
2	5
3	7
4	9

Step 1 Write the two quantities as ordered pairs (number of games, cost).

The ordered pairs are (1, 3), (2, 5), (3, 7), and (4, 9).

Step 2 Graph the ordered pairs on the coordinate plane. Then connect the ordered pairs and extend the line to the y-axis.

The line does not pass through the origin. So, the cost of the video games is not proportional to the number of games rented.

Check The ratios are not constant. $\frac{1}{3} \neq \frac{2}{5}$ ✔

Number of Games

Got it? Do this problem to find out.

b. The table shows the number of Calories an athlete burned per minute of exercise. Determine whether the number of Calories burned is proportional to the number of minutes by graphing on the coordinate plane. Explain your reasoning in the Work Zone.

Calories Burned

Number of Minutes	Number of Calories
0	0
1	4
2	8
3	13

Time (min)

Show your work.

b. _____

Example

3. Which batting cage represents a proportional relationship between the number of pitches thrown and the cost? Explain.

The graph for Softball Plus is a straight line, but it does not pass through the origin. So, the relationship is not proportional.

The graph for the Fun Center is a straight line through the origin. So, the relationship between the number of the pitches thrown and the cost is proportional.

Guided Practice

Check

1. The cost of 3-D movie tickets is $12 for 1 ticket, $24 for 2 tickets, and $36 for 3 tickets. Determine whether the cost is proportional to the number of tickets by graphing on the coordinate plane. Explain your reasoning. (Examples 1 and 2)

_____

_____

2. The number of books two stores sell after 1, 2, and 3 days is shown. Which book sale represents a proportional relationship between time and books? Explain. (Example 3)

_____

_____

3. **Building on the Essential Question** How does graphing relationships help you determine whether the relationship is proportional or not? _____

_____

_____

Independent Practice

Go online for Step-by-Step Solutions

PS Model with Mathematics Determine whether the relationship between the two quantities shown in each table are proportional by graphing on the coordinate plane. **Explain your reasoning.** (Examples 1 and 2)

1

Savings Account	
Week	Account Balance ($)
1	125
2	150
3	175

_____

_____

2.

Calories in Fruit Cups	
Servings	Calories
1	70
3	210
5	350

_____

_____

3 The height of two plants is recorded after 1, 2, and 3 weeks as shown in the graph at the right. Which plants' growth represents a proportional relationship between time and height? Explain. (Example 3)

_____

_____

4. The perimeter of a square is 4 times as great as the length of any of its sides. Determine if the perimeter of a square is proportional to its side length. Explain.

_____

_____

5. A health club charges $35 a month for membership fees. Determine whether the cost of membership is proportional to the number of months. Explain your reasoning.

_____

_____

_____

🔥 H.O.T. Problems Higher Order Thinking

6. (PS) **Reason Abstractly** Describe some data that when graphed would represent a proportional relationship. Explain your reasoning.

_____

_____

_____

7. (PS) **Persevere with Problems** The greenhouse temperatures at certain times are shown in the table. The greenhouse maintains temperatures between 65°F and 85°F. Suppose the temperature increases at a constant rate. Create a graph of the time and temperatures at each hour from 1:00 P.M. to 8:00 P.M. Is the relationship proportional? Explain.

Time	Temperature (°F)
1:00 P.M.	66
6:00 P.M.	78.5
8:00 P.M.	83.5

_____

_____

_____

8. (PS) **Model with Mathematics** Write a real-world problem that describes a proportional relationship. Make a table of values and graph the ordered pairs on the coordinate plane.

Extra Practice

Determine whether the relationship between the two quantities shown in each table are proportional by graphing on the coordinate plane. Explain your reasoning.

9.

Cooling Water	
Time (min)	Temperature (°F)
5	95
10	90
15	85

Not proportional; The graph does not pass through the origin.

10.

Pizza Recipe	
Number of Pizzas	Cheese (oz)
1	8
4	32
7	56

_____

Copy and Solve Determine if each situation represents a proportional relationship. Graph on a separate piece of paper. Write an explanation for each situation.

11. **PS Justify Conclusions** An airplane is flying at an altitude of 4,000 feet and descends at a rate of 200 feet per minute. Determine whether the altitude is proportional to number of minutes. Explain your reasoning.

_____

12. Frank and Allie purchased cell phone plans through different providers. Their costs for several minutes are shown. Graph each plan to determine whose plan is proportional to the number of minutes the phone is used. Explain your reasoning.

Cell Phone Plans		
Time (min)	Frank's Cost ($)	Allie's Cost ($)
0	0	4.00
3	1.50	4.50
6	3.00	5.00

13. The relationship between the number of heartbeats and the time shown in the graph is proportional. Determine if each ordered pair represents a point from this relationship. Select yes or no.

a. (5, 10) ☐ Yes ☐ No

b. (14, 7) ☐ Yes ☐ No

c. (8, 16) ☐ Yes ☐ No

14. The table shows the rental costs for a moving truck.

Rental Costs				
Miles Driven	50	100	150	200
Total Cost ($)	40	60	80	100

Graph the data on the coordinate plane and explain whether the relationship between the number of miles and the total cost is proportional or nonproportional.

Spiral Review

Write each ratio as a fraction in simplest form.

15. A class has 10 boys and 15 girls. What is the ratio of boys to girls? _____

16. A car dealership has 55 cars and 11 vans. What is the ratio of cars to vans? _____

17. A drawer has 4 red shirts and 8 green shirts. What is the ratio of red shirts to the total number of shirts? _____

18. A store sells 13 coffees and 65 hot chocolates. What is the ratio of coffees to hot chocolates? _____

Inquiry Lab
Proportional and Nonproportional Relationships

 Inquiry HOW are proportional and nonproportional linear relationships alike? HOW are they different?

Indiana Academic Standards
7.AF.6

PS **Process Standards**
1, 3, 4

Albert and Bianca joined an online discussion group. Each student posted four comments. The number of replies to each of their comments is shown in the table. Determine if each data set represents a proportional relationship.

Hands-On Activity

Tools

Step 1 Arrange centimeter cubes to model the number of replies per comment as shown in the diagram below.

Student	Albert				Bianca			
Comment Number	1	2	3	4	1	2	3	4
Number of Replies								

Step 2 Complete each table. Then graph the data on the coordinate plane. You may wish to use a different color pencil for each data set.

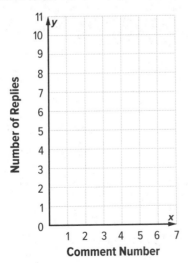

Albert's Comments

Comment Number (x)	Number of Replies (y)
1	2
2	4
3	
4	

Bianca's Comments

Comment Number (x)	Number of Replies (y)
1	1
2	4
3	
4	

Analyze and Reflect

Collaborate

Work with a partner to answer the following questions.

1. Describe any patterns in the data.

   _____

   _____

2. Connect the ordered pairs with a straight line for each graph. Then describe the graphs.

   _____

   _____

   _____

3. Predict the next three points on the graph for each data.

   _____

   _____

   _____

4. Compare and contrast the relationship shown in each graph. What do you notice?

   _____

   _____

   _____

Create

On Your Own

5. **PS Model with Mathematics** Use a table and graph to describe a real-world situation that represents a proportional relationship. Then explain how you could change your situation so that it represents a nonproportional relationship.

   _____

   _____

   _____

6. **Inquiry** HOW are proportional and nonproportional linear relationships alike? HOW are they different?

   _____

   _____

Solve Proportional Relationships

 Real-World Link

Fruit Smoothies Katie and some friends want to buy fruit smoothies. They go to a health food store that advertises a sale of 2 fruit smoothies for $5.

1. Fill in the boxes to write a ratio that compares the cost to the number of fruit smoothies.

$$\frac{\$\boxed{}}{\boxed{} \text{ smoothies}}$$

2. Suppose Katie and her friends buy 6 fruit smoothies. Complete the ratio that compares the cost to the number of fruit smoothies.

$$\frac{\$\boxed{}}{6 \text{ smoothies}}$$

3. Is the cost proportional to the number of fruit smoothies for two and six smoothies? Explain.

_____

_____

_____

 Essential Question

HOW can you show that two objects are proportional?

Vocab **Vocabulary**

proportion
cross product

🟡 **Indiana Academic Standards**
7.AF.6

PS **Process Standards**
1, 2, 3, 4

 Which **PS** **Process Standards** **did you use?**
Shade the circle(s) that applies.

① Persevere with Problems
② Reason Abstractly
③ Construct an Argument
④ Model with Mathematics

⑤ Use Math Tools
⑥ Attend to Precision
⑦ Make Use of Structure
⑧ Use Repeated Reasoning

Write and Solve Proportions

Work Zone

Words
A **proportion** is an equation stating that two ratios or rates are equivalent.

Numbers	Algebra
$\frac{6}{8} = \frac{3}{4}$	$\frac{a}{b} = \frac{c}{d}, b \neq 0, d \neq 0$

Consider the following proportion.

$$\frac{a}{b} = \frac{c}{d}$$

$$\frac{a}{\overset{1}{\cancel{b}}} \cdot \overset{1}{\cancel{b}}d = \frac{c}{\overset{1}{\cancel{d}}} \cdot b\overset{1}{\cancel{d}} \qquad \text{Multiply each side by } bd \text{ and divide out common factors.}$$

$$ad = bc \qquad \text{Simplify.}$$

The products ad and bc are called the **cross products** of this proportion. The cross products of any proportion are equal.

$$\frac{6}{8} \diagtimes \frac{3}{4} \longrightarrow \frac{8 \cdot 3}{6 \cdot 4} \equiv \frac{24}{24}$$

Example

1. After 2 hours, the air temperature had risen 7°F. Write and solve a proportion to find the amount of time it will take at this rate for the temperature to rise an additional 13°F.

Write a proportion. Let t represent the time in hours.

$$\text{temperature} \longrightarrow \quad \frac{7}{2} = \frac{13}{t} \quad \longleftarrow \text{temperature}$$
$$\text{time} \longrightarrow \qquad\qquad\qquad \longleftarrow \text{time}$$

$$7 \cdot t = 2 \cdot 13 \qquad \text{Find the cross products.}$$

$$7t = 26 \qquad \text{Multiply}$$

$$\frac{7t}{7} = \frac{26}{7} \qquad \text{Divide each side by 7.}$$

$$t \approx 3.7 \qquad \text{Simplify.}$$

It will take about 3.7 hours to rise an additional 13°F.

Got it? Do these problems to find out.

Show your work.

a. _____

b. _____

c. _____

Solve each proportion.

a. $\frac{x}{4} = \frac{9}{10}$ **b.** $\frac{2}{34} = \frac{5}{y}$ **c.** $\frac{7}{3} = \frac{n}{21}$

Example

Tutor

2. If the ratio of Type O to non-Type O donors at a blood drive was 37:43, how many donors would be Type O, out of 300 donors?

Type O donors → $\dfrac{37}{37+43}$ or $\dfrac{37}{80}$
total donors →

Write a proportion. Let t represent the number of Type O donors.

Type O donors → $\dfrac{37}{80} = \dfrac{t}{300}$ ← Type O donors
total donors → ← total donors

$37 \cdot 300 = 80t$ Find the cross products.

$11{,}100 = 80t$ Multiply.

$\dfrac{11{,}100}{80} = \dfrac{80t}{80}$ Divide each side by 80.

$138.75 = t$ Simplify.

There would be about 139 Type O donors.

Show your work.

Got it? Do this problem to find out.

d. The ratio of 7th grade students to 8th grade students in a soccer league is 17:23. If there are 200 students in all, how many are in the 7th grade?

d. _____

Use Unit Rate

You can also use the unit rate to write an equation expressing the relationship between two proportional quantities.

Examples

Tutor

3. Olivia bought 6 containers of yogurt for $7.68. Write an equation relating the cost c to the number of yogurts y. How much would Olivia pay for 10 yogurts at this same rate?

Find the unit rate between cost and containers of yogurt.

$\dfrac{\text{cost in dollars}}{\text{containers of yogurt}} = \dfrac{7.68}{6}$ or $1.28 per container

The cost is $1.28 times the number of containers of yogurt.

$c = 1.28y$ Let c represent the cost. Let y represent the number of yogurts.

$= 1.28(10)$ Replace y with 10.

$= 12.80$ Multiply.

The cost for 10 containers of yogurt is $12.80.

STOP and Reflect

Consider the proportion $\frac{6}{b} = \frac{c}{7}$. What is true about bc?

4. Jaycee bought 8 gallons of gas for $31.12. Write an equation relating the cost c to the number of gallons g of gas. How much would Jaycee pay for 11 gallons at this same rate?

Find the unit rate between cost and gallons.

$$\frac{\text{cost in dollars}}{\text{gasoline in gallons}} = \frac{31.12}{8} \text{ or } \$3.89 \text{ per gallon}$$

The cost is $3.89 times the number of gallons.

$c = 3.89g$ Let c represent the cost. Let g represent the number of gallons.

$\quad\quad = 3.89(11)$ Replace g with 11.

$\quad\quad = 42.79$ Multiply.

The cost for 11 gallons of gas is $42.79.

Got it? Do this problem to find out.

e. Olivia typed 2 pages in 15 minutes. Write an equation relating the number of minutes m to the number of pages p typed. How long will it take her to type 10 pages at this rate?

e. _____

Guided Practice

Solve each proportion. (Examples 1 and 2)

1. $\frac{k}{7} = \frac{32}{56}$ $k = $ _____

2. $\frac{3.2}{9} = \frac{n}{36}$ $n = $ _____

3. $\frac{41}{x} = \frac{5}{2}$ $x = $ _____

4. Trina earns $28.50 tutoring for 3 hours. Write an equation relating her earnings m to the number of hours h she tutors. Assuming the situation is proportional, how much would Trina earn tutoring for 2 hours? for 4.5 hours? (Examples 3 and 4)

_____

_____

5. Ⓠ **Building on the Essential Question** How do you solve a proportion?

_____

_____

Rate Yourself!

How confident are you about solving proportions? Check the box that applies.

For more help, go online to access a Personal Tutor.

FOLDABLES Time to update your Foldable!

Independent Practice

Go online for Step-by-Step Solutions

Solve each proportion. (Examples 1 and 2)

1 $\frac{1.5}{6} = \frac{10}{p}$ $p =$ _____

2. $\frac{44}{p} = \frac{11}{5}$ $p =$ _____

3. $\frac{2}{w} = \frac{0.4}{0.7}$ $w =$ _____

Assume the situations are proportional. Write and solve by using a proportion. (Examples 1 and 2)

4. Evarado paid $1.12 for a dozen eggs at his local grocery store. Determine the cost of 3 eggs.

_____

5. Sheila mixed 3 ounces of blue paint with 2 ounces of yellow paint. She decided to create 20 ounces of the same mixture. How many ounces of yellow paint does Sheila need for the new mixture?

_____

Assume the situations are proportional. Use the unit rate to write an equation, then solve. (Examples 3 and 4)

6. A car can travel 476 miles on 14 gallons of gas. Write an equation relating the distance d to the number of gallons g. How many gallons of gas does this car need to travel 578 miles.

_____

7 Mrs. Baker paid $2.50 for 5 pounds of bananas. Write an equation relating the cost c to the number of pounds p of bananas. How much would Mrs. Baker pay for 8 pounds of bananas?

_____

8. A woman who is 64 inches tall has a shoulder width of 16 inches. Write an equation relating the height h to the width w. Find the height of a woman who has a shoulder width of 18.5 inches.

_____

16 in.

64 in.

9. At an amusement park, 360 visitors rode the roller coaster in 3 hours. Write and solve a proportion to find the number of visitors at this rate who will ride the roller coaster in 7 hours. (Examples 3 and 4)

_____

10. (PS) **Reason Abstractly** Use the table to write a proportion relating the weights on two planets. Then find the missing weight. Round to the nearest tenth.

Weights on Different Planets Earth Weight = 120 pounds	
Mercury	45.6 pounds
Venus	109.2 pounds
Uranus	96 pounds
Jupiter	304.8 pounds

  a. Earth: 90 pounds; Venus: ⬚ pounds

  b. Mercury: 55 pounds; Earth: ⬚ pounds

  c. Jupiter: 350 pounds; Uranus: ⬚ pounds

  d. Venus: 115 pounds; Mercury: ⬚ pounds

H.O.T. Problems Higher Order Thinking

11. (PS) **Justify Conclusions** A powdered drink mix calls for a ratio of powder to water of 1:8. If there are 32 cups of powder, how many total cups of water are

needed? Explain your reasoning. _____

_____

_____

_____

(PS) **Persevere with Problems** Solve each equation.

12. $\frac{2}{3} = \frac{18}{x+5}$ _____

13. $\frac{x-4}{10} = \frac{7}{5}$ _____

14. $\frac{4.5}{17-x} = \frac{3}{8}$ _____

15. (PS) **Justify Conclusions** A rectangle has an area of 36 square units. As the length and the width change, what do you know about their product? Is the length proportional to the width? Justify your reasoning.

Rectangle	Length	Width	Area (units²)
A	3	12	36
B	6	6	36
C	9	4	36

_____

_____

_____

Extra Practice

Solve each proportion.

16. $\dfrac{x}{13} = \dfrac{18}{39}$ $x = 6$ _____

Homework Help

$x \cdot 39 = 13 \cdot 18$

$39x = 234$

$\dfrac{39x}{39} = \dfrac{234}{39}$

$x = 6$

17. $\dfrac{6}{25} = \dfrac{d}{30}$ $d = $ _____

18. $\dfrac{2.5}{6} = \dfrac{h}{9}$ $h = $ _____

Assume the situations are proportional. Write and solve by using a proportion.

19. For every person who has the flu, there are 6 people who have only flu-like symptoms. If a doctor sees 40 patients, determine approximately how many patients you would expect to have only flu-like symptoms.

_____

20. For every left-handed person, there are about 4 right-handed people. If there are 30 students in a class, predict the number of students who are right-handed.

_____

21. Jeremiah is saving money from a tutoring job. After the first three weeks, he saved $135. Assume the situation is proportional. Use the unit rate to write an equation relating the amount saved s to the number of weeks w worked. At this rate, how much will Jeremiah save after eight weeks?

_____

22. **PS** **Make a Prediction** A speed limit of 100 kilometers per hour (kph) is approximately equal to 62 miles per hour (mph). Write an equation relating kilometers per hour k to miles per hour m. Then predict the following measures. Round to the nearest tenth.

a. a speed limit in mph for a speed limit of 75 kph

_____

b. a speed limit in kph for a speed limit of 20 mph

_____

23. Part of Nicole's pumpkin muffin recipe is shown. How many cups of flour are needed to make

5 dozen muffins? [   ]

> **Pumpkin Muffin Recipe**
> Yield: 2 dozen muffins
> 4.5 cups flour
> 1.5 cups sugar
> 1 teaspoon nutmeg

24. An amusement park line for passengers waiting to ride a rollercoaster is moving about 16 feet every 10 minutes. Jason and his friends are standing 40 feet from the front of the line. Select values to set up a proportion to represents this situation.

16	40
10	x

$$\frac{\square}{\square} = \frac{\square}{\square}$$

Solve the proportion to determine how long it will take for Jason and his friends to reach the front of the line.

[   ]

Spiral Review

25. The table shows the cost to have various numbers of pizzas delivered from Papa's Slice of Italy pizzeria. Is the relationship between the cost and the number of pizzas proportional? Explain.

Number of Pizzas	Cost ($)
1	12.50
2	20
3	27.50
4	35

_____

26. Brenna charges $15, $30, $45, and $60 for babysitting 1, 2, 3, and 4 hours, respectively. Is the relationship between the amount charged and the number of hours proportional? If so, find the unit rate. If not, explain why not.

_____

Find each unit rate.

27. 50 miles on 2.5 gallons _____

28. 2,500 kilobytes in 5 minutes _____

Inquiry Lab
Rate of Change

 Inquiry HOW is unit rate related to rate of change?

Indiana Academic Standards
7.AF.6, 7.AF.7

PS Process Standards
1, 3

Happy Hound is a doggie daycare where people drop off their dogs while they are at work. It costs $3 for 1 hour, $6 for 2 hours, and $9 for 3 hours of doggie daycare. Farah takes her dog to Happy Hound several days a week. Farah wants to determine if the number of hours of daycare is related to the cost.

Hands-On Activity

Step 1 Assume the pattern in the table continues. Complete the table shown.

Happy Hound Doggie Daycare	
Number of Hours	Cost ($)
1	3
2	6
3	9
4	
5	

Step 2 The cost depends on the number of hours. So, the cost is the output *y*, and

the number of hours is the _____.
Graph the data on the coordinate plane below.

Investigate

Collaborate

Refer to the Investigation. Work with a partner.

1. **PS Justify Conclusions** Describe the graph.

_____

2. What is the cost per hour, or unit rate, charged by Happy Hound?

_____

3. Use the graph to examine any two consecutive points. By how much does y change? By how much does x change?

_____

4. The first two ordered pairs on the graph are (1, 3) and (2, 6). You can find the *rate of change* by writing the ratio of the change in y to the change in x.

   Find the rate of change shown in the graph. _____

Analyze and Reflect

Collaborate

Work with a partner to answer the following question.

5. Pampered Pooch charges $5 for 1 hour of doggie daycare, $10 for 2 hours, and $15 for 3 hours.

   a. What is the unit rate? _____

   b. What is the rate of change? _____

   c. **PS Reason Inductively** How do the rates of change for doggie daycare at Pampered Pooch and Happy Hound compare?

   _____

   _____

Create

On Your Own

6. **PS Model with Mathematics** Describe a doggie daycare situation that has a rate of change less than that of Happy Hound.

_____

_____

7. **Inquiry** HOW is unit rate related to rate of change?

_____

_____

Constant Rate of Change

Vocabulary Start-Up

A **rate of change** is a rate that describes how one quantity changes in relation to another. In a linear relationship, the rate of change between any two quantities is the same. A linear relationship has a **constant rate of change**.

 Real-World Link

A computer programmer charges customers per line of code written. Fill in the blanks with the amount of change between consecutive numbers.

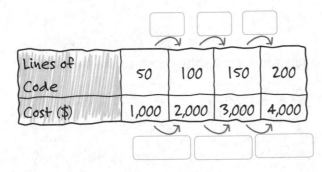

Lines of Code	50	100	150	200
Cost ($)	1,000	2,000	3,000	4,000

Label the diagram below with the terms *change in lines, change in dollars,* and *constant rate of change.*

$$\frac{\boxed{}}{\boxed{}} = \frac{\$1,000}{50 \text{ lines}}$$

$$= \frac{\$20}{1 \text{ line}} \Big\} \text{ unit rate}$$

The _____ is $20 per line of programming code.

 Essential Question

HOW can you show that two objects are proportional?

 Vocabulary

rate of change
constant rate of change

🔹 **Indiana Academic Standards**
7.AF.4, 7.AF.6, 7.AF.7, 7.AF.8

PS **Process Standards**
1, 3, 4

Which **PS** **Process Standards** did you use?
Shade the circle(s) that applies.

① Persevere with Problems

② Reason Abstractly

③ Construct an Argument

④ Model with Mathematics

⑤ Use Math Tools

⑥ Attend to Precision

⑦ Make Use of Structure

⑧ Use Repeated Reasoning

Use a Table

You can use a table to find a constant rate of change.

 Example

1. The table shows the amount of money a booster club makes washing cars for a fundraiser. Use the information to find the constant rate of change in dollars per car.

Cars Washed	
Number	Money ($)
5	40
10	80
15	120
20	160

+5 ... +40

Find the unit rate to determine the constant rate of change.

$$\frac{\text{change in money}}{\text{change in cars}} = \frac{40 \text{ dollars}}{5 \text{ cars}}$$ The money earned increases by $40 for every 5 cars.

$$= \frac{8 \text{ dollars}}{1 \text{ car}}$$ Write as a unit rate.

So, the number of dollars earned increases by $8 for every car washed.

Unit Rate

A rate of change is usually expressed as a unit rate.

Got it? Do these problems to find out.

a. The table shows the number of miles a plane traveled while in flight. Use the information to find the approximate constant rate of change in miles per minute.

Time (min)	30	60	90	120
Distance (mi)	290	580	870	1,160

b. The table shows the number of students that buses can transport. Use the table to find the constant rate of change in students per school bus.

Number of Buses	2	3	4	5
Number of Students	144	216	288	360

Show your work.

a. _____

b. _____

Use a Graph

You can also use a graph to find a constant rate of change and to analyze points on the graph.

Examples

 Tutor

2. **The graph represents the distance traveled while driving on a highway. Find the constant rate of change.**

To find the rate of change, pick any two points on the line, such as (0, 0) and (1, 60).

$$\frac{\text{change in miles}}{\text{change in hours}} = \frac{(60 - 0)\text{ miles}}{(1 - 0)\text{ hours}}$$

$$= \frac{60\text{ miles}}{1\text{ hour}}$$

> **Ordered Pairs**
> The ordered pair (2, 120) represents traveling 120 miles in 2 hours.

3. **Explain what the points (0, 0) and (1, 60) represent.**

The point (0, 0) represents traveling zero miles in zero hours. The point (1, 60) represents traveling 60 miles in 1 hour. Notice that this is the constant rate of change.

Got it? **Do these problems to find out.**

c. Use the graph to find the constant rate of change in miles per hour while driving in the city.

d. On the lines below, explain what the points (0, 0) and (1, 30) represent.

 Show your work.

c. _____

_____

_____

_____

4. The table and graph below show the hourly charge to rent a bicycle at two different stores. Which store charges more per bicycle? Explain.

Pedals Rentals

Time (hour)	Cost ($)
2	24
3	36
4	48

+1 +12
+1 +12

Super Cycles

The cost at Pedals Rentals increases by $12 every hour. The cost at Super Cycles increases by $8 every hour.

So, Pedals Rentals charges more per hour to rent a bicycle.

Guided Practice

1. The table and graph below show the amount of money Mi-Ling and Daniel save each week. Who saves more each week? Explain. (Examples 1, 2, and 4)

Mi-Ling's Savings

Time (weeks)	Savings ($)
2	$30
3	$45
4	$60

Daniel's Savings

2. Refer to the graph in Exercise 1. Explain what the points (0, 0) and (1, 10) represent. (Example 3)

3. **Building on the Essential Question** How can you find the unit rate on a graph that goes through the origin?

Independent Practice

Go online for Step-by-Step Solutions

Find the constant rate of change for each table. (Example 1)

1

Time (s)	Distance (m)
1	6
2	12
3	18
4	24

2.

Items	Cost ($)
2	18
4	36
6	54
8	72

3 The graph shows the cost of purchasing T-shirts. Find the constant rate of change for the graph. Then explain what points (0, 0) and (1, 9) represent. (Examples 2 and 3)

_____

_____

_____

_____

4. The Guzman and Hashimoto families each took a 4-hour road trip. The distances traveled by each family are shown in the table and graph below. Which family averaged fewer miles per hour? Explain. (Example 4)

Guzman's Road Trip	
Time (hours)	Distance (miles)
2	90
3	135
4	180

Hashimoto's Road Trip

_____

_____

_____

5. At 1:00 P.M., the water level in a pool is 13 inches. At 1:30 P.M., the water level is 18 inches. At 2:30 P.M., the water level is 28 inches. What is the constant rate of change?

_____

6 (PS) **Model with Mathematics** Refer to the lap times for Exercises **a** and **b**.

The race is 20 laps, which is 5 miles. Assuming your speed is constant...

Let's calculate Seth's times.

Lap	4	8	12	16	20
Distance(mi)	1	2	3	4	5
Time (s)	57.1	114.2	171.3		

a. How long does it take Seth to race 1 mile? Write the constant rate of change in miles per second. Round to the nearest hundredth. _____

b. Graph the ordered pairs (time, distance) on the coordinate plane at the right. Connect the points with a solid line.

H.O.T. Problems

7. (PS) **Model with Mathematics** Make a table where the constant rate of change is 6 inches for every foot.

Feet	Inches

8. (PS) **Justify Conclusions** The terms in sequence A increase by 3. The terms in sequence B increase by 8. In which sequence do the terms form a steeper line when graphed as points on a coordinate plane? Justify your reasoning.

_____

_____

_____

9. (PS) **Persevere with Problems** The constant rate of change for the relationship shown in the table is $8 per hour. Find the missing values.

Time (h)	1	2	3
Earnings ($)	x	y	z

$x =$ _____ $y =$ _____ $z =$ _____

Extra Practice

Find the constant rate of change for each table.

10.

Time (h)	0	1	2	3
Wage ($)	0	9	18	27

$9 per hour

$$\frac{\text{change in wages}}{\text{change in hours}} = \frac{\$9}{1 \text{ hour}}$$

◄ Homework Help

11.

Minutes	1,000	1,500	2,000	2,500
Cost ($)	38	53	68	83

_____

12. Use the graph to find the constant rate of change. Then, explain what the points (0, 0) and (6, 72) represent.

_____

_____

_____

_____

13. **PS Justify Conclusions** Ramona and Josh earn money by babysitting. The amounts earned for one evening are shown in the table and graph. Who charged more per hour? Explain.

Ramona's Earnings

Time (hours)	Earnings ($)
2	18
3	27
4	36

Josh's Earnings

_____

_____

14. The cost of 1 movie ticket is $7.50. The cost of 2 movie tickets is $15. Based on this constant rate of change, what is the cost of 4 movie

tickets? _____

Power Up! Test Practice

15. Reggie started a running program to prepare for track season. He ran a half hour each morning for 60 days. He averaged 6.5 miles per hour. What is the total number of miles Reggie ran over the 60-day period? ☐

16. Select the correct constant rate of change for each table of data.

Number of Apples	3	7	11
Number of Seeds	30	70	110

☐ $\dfrac{1}{12}$ ☐ $\dfrac{1}{10}$ ☐ $\dfrac{12}{1}$ ☐ $\dfrac{10}{1}$

Number of Tables	4	6	9
Number of Chairs	48	72	108

☐ $\dfrac{1}{12}$ ☐ $\dfrac{1}{10}$ ☐ $\dfrac{12}{1}$ ☐ $\dfrac{10}{1}$

Number of Passengers	24	60	120
Number of Vans	2	5	10

☐ $\dfrac{1}{12}$ ☐ $\dfrac{1}{10}$ ☐ $\dfrac{12}{1}$ ☐ $\dfrac{10}{1}$

Number of Booklets	20	50	100
Number of Pages	2	5	10

☐ $\dfrac{1}{12}$ ☐ $\dfrac{1}{10}$ ☐ $\dfrac{12}{1}$ ☐ $\dfrac{10}{1}$

Spiral Review

Write the output for each given input in the tables below.

17.

Input	Add 4	Output
1	1 + 4	
2	2 + 4	
3	3 + 4	
4	4 + 4	

18.

Input	Subtract 5	Output
30	30 − 5	
40	40 − 5	
50	50 − 5	
60	60 − 5	

19.

Input	Multiply by 2	Output
1	1 × 2	
2	2 × 2	
3	3 × 2	
4	4 × 2	

20.

Input	Divide by 3	Output
3	3 ÷ 3	
6	6 ÷ 3	
9	9 ÷ 3	
12	12 ÷ 3	

Slope

 Real-World Link

Recycling Hero Comics prints on recycled paper. The table shows the total number of pounds of recycled paper that has been used each day during the month.

Day of Month	Total Recycled (lbs)
3	36
5	60
6	72
7	84
12	144

Essentinal Question

HOW can you show that two objects are proportional?

Vocabulary

slope

Indiana Academic Standards
7.AF.4, 7.AF.5, 7.AF.6, 7.AF.7

PS Process Standards
1, 3, 4

1. Graph the ordered pairs on the coordinate plane.

2. Explain why the graph is linear. _____

_____

3. Use two points to find the constant rate of change.

Point 1: _____   change in pounds ⟶ ▢ pounds

Point 2: _____   change in days ⟶ ▢ days

So, the constant rate of change is $\dfrac{24}{2}$ or ▢ pounds per day.

 Which PS Process Standards did you use?
Shade the circle(s) that applies.

① Persevere with Problems

② Reason Abstractly

③ Construct an Argument

④ Model with Mathematics

⑤ Use Math Tools

⑥ Attend to Precision

⑦ Make Use of Structure

⑧ Use Repeated Reasoning

Slope is the rate of change between any two points on a line.

$$\text{slope} = \frac{\text{change in } y}{\text{change in } x} \quad \longleftarrow \text{vertical change}$$
$$\longleftarrow \text{horizontal change}$$

$$= \frac{2}{1} \text{ or } 2$$

In a linear relationship, the vertical change (change in y-value) per unit of horizontal change (change in x-value) is always the same. This ratio is called the **slope** of the function. The constant rate of change, or unit rate, is the same as the slope of the related linear relationship.

The slope tells how steep the line is. The vertical change is sometimes called "rise" while the horizontal change is called "run." You can say that slope $= \frac{\text{rise}}{\text{run}}$.

Count the number of units that make up the rise of the line in the graph shown above. Write this number for the numerator of the fraction below. Count the number of units that make up the run of the line. Write this number for the denominator of the fraction below.

$$\frac{\text{rise}}{\text{run}} = \frac{\boxed{}}{\boxed{}}$$

So, the slope of the line is $\frac{3}{2}$.

Example

Watch | Tutor

1. The table below shows the relationship between the number of seconds *y* it takes to hear thunder after a lightning strike and the miles *x* you are from the lightning. Graph the data and find the slope. Explain what the slope represents.

Miles (*x*)	0	1	2	3	4	5
Seconds (*y*)	0	5	10	15	20	25

$$\text{slope} = \frac{\text{change in } y}{\text{change in } x} \quad \text{Definition of slope}$$

$$= \frac{25 - 15}{5 - 3} \quad \text{Use (3, 15) and (5, 25).}$$

$$= \frac{10}{2} \quad \leftarrow \text{seconds} \quad \leftarrow \text{miles}$$

$$= \frac{5}{1} \quad \text{Simplify.}$$

So, for every 5 seconds between a lightning flash and the sound of thunder, there is 1 mile between you and the lightning strike.

Got it? Do this problem to find out.

a. Graph the data about plant height for a science fair project. Then find the slope of the line. Explain what the slope represents in the work zone.

Week	Plant Height (cm)
1	1.5
2	3
3	4.5
4	6

Show your work.

a. _____

Example

2. Renaldo opened a savings account. Each week he deposits $300. Draw a graph of the the account balance versus time. Find the numerical value of the slope and interpret it in words.

The slope of the line is the rate at which the account balance rises, or $\dfrac{\$300}{1\text{ week}}$.

Got it? Do this problem to find out.

b. _____

b. Jessica has a balance of $35 on her cell phone account. She adds $10 each week for the next four weeks. In the work zone, graph the account balance versus time. Find the numerical value of the slope and interpret it in words.

Guided Practice

1. The table at the right shows the number of small packs of fruit snacks y per box x. Graph the data. Then find the slope of the line. Explain what the slope represents. (Examples 1 and 2)

Boxes, x	3	5	7
Fruit Snacks, y	12	20	28

2. (Q) **Building on the Essential Question** How is rate of change related to slope? _____

_____

_____

Rate Yourself!

How well do you understand slope? Circle the image.

Clear   Somewhat Clear   Not So Clear

For more help, go online to access a Personal Tutor.

Independent Practice

Go online for Step-by-Step Solutions

1 The table shows the number of pages Adriano read in *x* hours. Graph the data. Then find the slope of the line. Explain what the slope represents. (Example 1)

Time (h)	1	2	3	4
Number of pages	50	100	150	200

_____

_____

2. Graph the data. Find the numerical value of the slope and interpret it in words. (Example 2)

Number of Yards	1	2	3
Number of Feet	3	6	9

_____

_____

3 The graph shows the average speed of two cars on the highway.

a. What does (2, 120) represent? _____

_____

b. What does (1.5, 67.5) represent? _____

_____

c. What does the ratio of the *y*-coordinate to the *x*-coordinate for each pair of points on the graph represent?

_____

d. What does the slope of each line represent?

_____

e. Which car is traveling faster? How can you tell from the graph?

_____

4. **PS Multiple Representations** Complete the graphic organizer on slope.

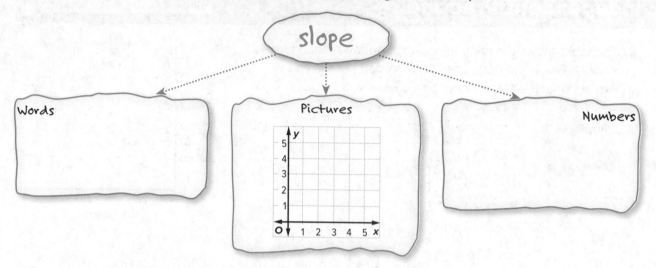

slope

Words

Pictures

Numbers

H.O.T. Problems Higher Order Thinking

5. **PS Find The Error** Marisol is finding the slope of the line containing the points (3, 7) and (5, 10). Find her mistake and correct it.

The slope between the two points (3, 7) and (5, 10) is found like this:
$$slope = \frac{rise}{run} = \frac{5-3}{10-7}$$
$$= \frac{2}{3}$$

6. **PS Persevere with Problems** Kaya is saving money at a rate of $30 per month. Eduardo is saving money at a rate of $35 per month. They both started saving at the same time. If you were to create a table of values and graph each function, what would be the slope of each graph?

7. **PS Reason Inductively** Without graphing, determine whether $A(5, 1)$, $B(1, 0)$, and $C(3, 3)$ lie on the same line. Explain your reasoning.

8. **PS Model with Mathematics** Name two points on a line that has a slope of $\frac{5}{8}$.

Extra Practice

9. **PS** **Justify Conclusions** The table to the right shows the number of markers per box. Graph the data. Then find the slope of the line. Explain what the slope represents.

Boxes	1	2	3	4
Markers	8	16	24	32

Use (1, 8) and (2, 16).

slope = $\dfrac{\text{change in } y}{\text{change in } x}$

$= \dfrac{16 - 8}{2 - 1}$

$= \dfrac{8}{1}$

Homework Help

So, there are 8 markers in every box.

10. The table shows the cost to rent a paddle boat from two businesses.

a. What does (1, 20) represent?

_____

_____

b. What does (2, 50) represent?

_____

_____

Paddle Boat Rentals		
Number of Hours	Water Wheels Cost ($)	Fun in the Sun Cost ($)
1	20	25
2	40	50
3	60	75
4	80	100

Copy and Solve For Exercises 11–14, draw a graph on a separate sheet of grid paper to find each slope. Then record each slope and interpret its meaning.

11. Joshua swims 25 meters in 1 minute. Draw a graph of meters swam versus time. Find the value of the slope and interpret it in words.

12. The table shows the amount Maggie earns for various numbers of hours she babysits. Graph the data. Then find the slope of the line. Explain what the slope represents.

Number of Hours	Earnings ($)
1	8
2	16
3	24
4	32

13. Zack completes 20 homework problems in 1 hour. Draw a graph of homework problems versus time. Find the value of the slope and interpret it in words.

14. The Jackson family rents 6 movies each month. Draw a graph of movies rented versus time. Find the value of the slope and interpret it in words.

15. Two weeks ago, Audrey earned $84 for 7 hours of work. This week, she earned $132 for 11 hours of work. Find the numerical value of the slope of the line that represents Audrey's earnings.

16. The ordered pairs (1, 4), (3, 12), and (5, 20) represent the distance y that Jairo walks after x seconds. Plot the ordered pairs on the coordinate plane and draw a line through the points.

Find the slope of the line and explain what the slope represents.

Spiral Review

Determine if each situation is proportional. Explain your reasoning.

17. Taxi cab passengers are charged $2.50 upon entering a cab. They are then charged $1.00 for every mile traveled.

18. A restaurant charges $5 for one sandwich, $9.90 for two sandwiches, and $14.25 for three sandwiches.

19.

Tickets Purchased	1	2	3	4
Cost ($)	7.50	15	22.50	30

20.

Cups of Flour	3	6	9	12
Cups of Sugar	2	4	6	8

Lesson 9
Direct Variation

 Real-World Link

Speed The distance y a car travels after x hours can be represented by $y = 65x$. The table and graph also represent the situation.

Time (hours)	Distance (miles)
2	130
3	195
4	260

 Essential Question

HOW can you show that two objects are proportional?

 Vocabulary

direct variation
constant of variation
constant of proportionality

Indiana Academic Standards
7.AF.6, 7.AF.7

PS Process Standards
1, 2, 3, 4

1. Fill in the blanks to find the constant ratio.

$$\frac{\text{distance traveled}}{\text{driving time}} = \frac{130}{2} = \frac{195}{\boxed{}} = \frac{\boxed{}}{4}$$

The constant ratio is $\boxed{}$ miles per hour.

2. The constant rate of change, or slope, of the line is $\dfrac{\text{change in miles}}{\text{change in time}}$, which is equal to $\dfrac{195 - 130}{3 - 2}$

or $\boxed{}$ miles per hour.

3. Write a sentence that compares the constant rate of change and the constant ratio.

_____

 Which **PS** **Process Standards** did you use?
Shade the circle(s) that applies.

① Persevere with Problems
② Reason Abstractly
③ Construct an Argument
④ Model with Mathematics

⑤ Use Math Tools
⑥ Attend to Precision
⑦ Make Use of Structure
⑧ Use Repeated Reasoning

Direct Variation

Words   A linear relationship is a direct variation when the ratio of y to x is a constant, k. We say y varies directly with x.

Model

Symbols $\dfrac{y}{x} = k$ or $y = kx$, where $k \neq 0$

Example $y = 2x$

When two variable quantities have a constant ratio, their relationship is called a **direct variation**. The constant ratio is called the **constant of variation**. The constant of variation is also known as the **constant of proportionality**.

In a direct variation equation, the constant rate of change, or slope, is assigned a special variable, k.

Real World Example

1. The height of the water as a pool is being filled is shown in the graph. Determine the rate in inches per minute.

Since the graph of the data forms a line, the rate of change is constant. Use the graph to find the constant of proportionality.

$$\frac{\text{height}}{\text{time}} \longrightarrow \quad \frac{2}{5} \text{ or } \frac{0.4}{1} \qquad \frac{4}{10} \text{ or } \frac{0.4}{1} \qquad \frac{6}{15} \text{ or } \frac{0.4}{1} \qquad \frac{8}{20} \text{ or } \frac{0.4}{1}$$

The pool fills at a rate of 0.4 inch every minute.

Got it? Do this problem to find out.

> **Direct Variation**
> When a relationship varies directly, the graph of the function will always go through the origin, (0, 0). Also, the unit rate r is located at $(1, r)$.

Show your work.

a. Two minutes after a diver enters the water, he has descended 52 feet. After 5 minutes, he has descended 130 feet. At what rate is the scuba diver descending?

a. _____

Example

Tutor

2. The equation $y = 10x$ represents the amount of money y Julio earns for x hours of work. Identify the constant of proportionality. Explain what it represents in this situation.

$y = kx$
$\downarrow$
$y = 10x$

Compare the equation to $y = kx$, where k is the constant of proportionality.

The constant of proportionality is 10. So, Julio earns $10 for every hour that he works.

Got it? Do this problem to find out.

b. The distance y traveled in miles by the Chang family in x hours is represented by the equation $y = 55x$. Identify the constant of proportionality. Then explain what it represents.

Show your work.

b. _____

Determine Direct Variation

Not all situations with a constant rate of change are proportional relationships. Likewise, not all linear functions are direct variations.

Weight (lb)	Cost ($)

Example

3. Pizzas cost $8 each plus a $3 delivery charge. Show the cost of 1, 2, 3, and 4 pizzas. Is there a direct variation?

Number of Pizzas	1	2	3	4
Cost ($)	$11	$19	$27	$35

$\dfrac{\text{cost}}{\text{number of pizzas}} \longrightarrow \dfrac{11}{1}, \dfrac{19}{2}$ or 9.5,

$\dfrac{27}{3}$ or 9, $\dfrac{35}{4}$ or 8.75

There is no constant ratio and the line does not go through the origin. So, there is no direct variation.

Got it? Do this problem to find out.

c. Two pounds of cheese cost $8.40. Show the cost of 1, 2, 3, and 4 pounds of cheese. Is there a direct variation? Explain.

c. _____

Example

4. Determine whether the linear relationship is a direct variation. If so, state the constant of proportionality.

Time, x	1	2	3	4
Wages ($), y	12	24	36	48

Compare the ratios to check for a common ratio.

$\dfrac{\text{wages}}{\text{time}} \longrightarrow$ $\dfrac{12}{1}$ $\dfrac{24}{2}$ or $\dfrac{12}{1}$ $\dfrac{36}{3}$ or $\dfrac{12}{1}$ $\dfrac{48}{4}$ or $\dfrac{12}{1}$

Since the ratios are the same, the relationship is a direct variation. The constant of proportionality is $\dfrac{12}{1}$.

Guided Practice

1. The number of cakes baked varies directly with the number of hours the caterers work. What is the ratio of cakes baked to hours worked? (Examples 1 and 2) _____

2. An airplane travels 780 miles in 4 hours. Make a table and graph to show the mileage for 2, 8, and 12 hours. Is there a direct variation? Explain.

(Examples 3 and 4) _____

_____

Hours			
Miles			

3. **Building on the Essential Question** How can you determine if a linear relationship is a direct variation from an equation? a table? a graph? _____

_____

_____

Rate Yourself!

How confident are you about direct variation? Check the box that applies.

For more help, go online to access a Personal Tutor.

Independent Practice

Go online for Step-by-Step Solutions

1. Veronica is mulching her front yard. The total weight of mulch varies directly with the number of bags of mulch.

What is the rate of change? (Example 1) _____

2. The Spanish club held a car wash to raise money. The equation $y = 5x$ represents the amount of money y club members made for washing x cars. Identify the constant of proportionality. Then explain

what it represents in this situation. (Example 2) _____

_____

3. A technician charges $25 per hour plus $50 for a house call to repair home computers. Make a table and a graph to show the cost for 1, 2, 3, and 4 hours of home computer repair service. Is there a direct variation? (Example 3)

Time (h)				
Charge ($)				

_____

_____

Determine whether each linear relationship is a direct variation. If so, state the constant of proportionality. (Example 4)

4.

Pictures, x	3	4	5	6
Profit, y	24	32	40	48

_____

5.

Minutes, x	185	235	285	335
Cost, y	60	100	140	180

_____

6.

Year, x	5	10	15	20
Height, y	12.5	25	37.5	50

_____

7.

Game, x	2	3	4	5
Points, y	4	5	6	7

_____

8. At a 33-foot depth underwater, the pressure is 29.55 pounds per square inch (psi). At a depth of 66 feet, the pressure reaches 44.4 psi. At what rate is the pressure increasing? _____

(PS) Reason Abstractly If y varies directly with x, write an equation for the direct variation. Then find each value.

9. If $y = 14$ when $x = 8$, find y when $x = 12$.

_____

10. Find y when $x = 15$ if $y = 6$ when $x = 30$.

_____

11. If $y = 6$ when $x = 24$, what is the value of x when $y = 7$?

_____

12. Find x when $y = 14$, if $y = 7$ when $x = 8$.

_____

H.O.T. Problems Higher Order Thinking

13. **(PS) Reason Inductively** Identify two additional values for x and y in a direct variation relationship where $y = 11$ when $x = 18$.

$x =$ _____ $y =$ _____   and $x =$ _____ $y =$ _____

14. **(PS) Persevere with Problems** Find y when $x = 14$ if y varies directly with x^2, and $y = 72$ when $x = 6$. _____

15. **(PS) Model with Mathematics** Tom is drawing rectangles in which the length varies directly with the width. One of his rectangles has a width of 2 centimeters and a length of 3.6 centimeters. Draw and label a rectangle with a width of 3.5 centimeters that could be one of Tom's rectangles. Then find the perimeter.

Show your work.

Extra Practice

16. The money Shelley earns varies directly with the number of dogs she walks. How much does Shelley earn for each dog she walks?

Since the points on the graph lie in a straight line, the rate of change is a constant. The constant ratio is what Shelley earns per dog.

$$\text{pay (\$)} \rightarrow \text{number of dogs} \rightarrow \frac{2}{1}, \frac{4}{2} \text{ or } \frac{2}{1}, \frac{6}{3} \text{ or } \frac{2}{1}, \frac{8}{4} \text{ or } \frac{2}{1}$$

Shelley earns $2.00 per dog.

17. A cake recipe requires $3\frac{1}{4}$ cups of flour for 13 servings and $4\frac{1}{2}$ cups of flour for 18 servings. How much flour is required to make a cake that serves 28? _____

Determine whether each linear relationship is a direct variation. If so, state the constant of variation.

18.

Age, x	11	13	15	19
Grade, y	5	7	9	11

_____

19.

Price, x	20	25	30	35
Tax, y	4	5	6	7

_____

20. **PS** **Multiple Representations** Robert is in charge of the community swimming pool. Each spring he drains it in order to clean it. Then he refills the pool, which holds 120,000 gallons of water. Robert fills the pool at a rate of 10 gallons each minute.

a. Words What is the rate at which Robert will fill the

pool? Is it constant? _____

b. Graph Graph the relationship on the grid shown.

c. Algebra Write an equation for the direct variation.

_____

_____

21. Determine if each equation represents a direct variation. Select yes or no.

a. $y = 4x + 1$ ☐ Yes ☐ No

b. $y = 7.5x$ ☐ Yes ☐ No

c. $y = \frac{1}{15}x$ ☐ Yes ☐ No

d. $y = \frac{6}{x}$ ☐ Yes ☐ No

22. Place a checkmark in the column below the correct direct variation equation, if possible.

					$y = 18x$	$y = 15x$	not a direct variation
Price, x	20	30	40	50	☐	☐	☐
Discount, y	2	4	6	8			

					$y = 18x$	$y = 15x$	not a direct variation
Seconds, x	2	6	7	11	☐	☐	☐
Feet, y	30	90	105	165			

					$y = 18x$	$y = 15x$	not a direct variation
Packages, x	3	5	7	9	☐	☐	☐
Crayons, y	54	90	126	162			

					$y = 18x$	$y = 15x$	not a direct variation
Hours, x	1	4	7	10	☐	☐	☐
Cost, y	15	30	45	60			

Spiral Review

23. The table below shows the number of sheets of paper in various numbers of packages. Graph the data.

Number of Packages	1	2	3	4
Number of Sheets	50	100	150	200

24. The cost of various numbers of tickets to a festival is shown in the table. Graph the data. Then find the slope of the line. Explain what the slope represents.

Number of Tickets	5	10	20	25
Cost ($)	40	80	160	200

21ST CENTURY CAREER
in Engineering

Biomechanical Engineering

Did you know that more than 700 pounds of force are exerted on a 140-pound long-jumper during the landing? Biomechanical engineers understand how forces travel through the shoe to an athlete's foot and how the shoes can help reduce the impact of those forces on the legs.
If you are curious about how engineering can be applied to the human body, a career in biomechanical engineering might be a great fit for you.

Is This the Career for You?

Are you interested in a career as a biomechanical engineer? Take some of the following courses in high school.

◆ Biology
◆ Calculus
◆ Physics
◆ Trigonometry

Find out how math relates to a career in Biomechanical Engineering.

PS Start Off on the Right Foot

Use the information in the graph to solve each problem.

1. Find the constant rate of change for the data shown in the graph below Exercise 2. Interpret its meaning.

_____

_____

_____

2. Is there a proportional relationship between the weight of an athlete and the forces that are generated from running? Explain your reasoning. _____

_____

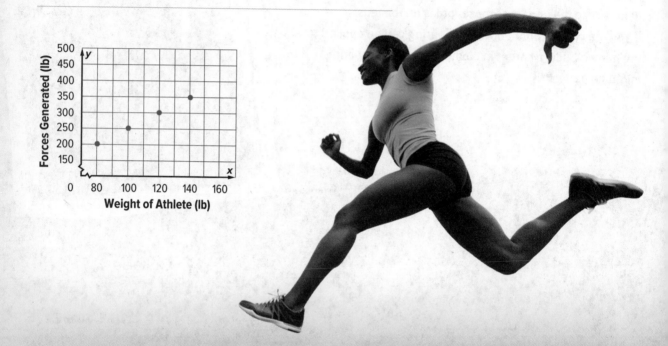

PS Career Project

It's time to update your career portfolio! Use the Internet or another source to research the fields of biomechanical engineering, biomedical engineering, and mechanical engineering. Write a brief summary comparing and contrasting the fields. Describe how they are all related.

_____

_____

_____

What subject in school is the most important to you? How would you use that subject in this career?

_____

_____

_____

_____

Chapter Review

Vocabulary Check

Complete each sentence using the vocabulary list at the beginning of the chapter. Then circle the word that completes the sentence in the word search.

1. A _____ is a ratio that compares two quantities with different kinds of units.

2. A rate that has a denominator of 1 unit is called a _____ rate.

3. A pair of numbers used to locate a point in the coordinate plane is an _____ pair.

4. (0, 0) represents the _____.

5. A _____ fraction has a fraction in the numerator, denominator, or both.

6. A _____ variation is the relationship between two variable quantities with a constant ratio.

7. The _____ is the rate of change between any two points on a line.

8. One of the four regions into which a coordinate plane is separated is called a _____.

9. A _____ is an equation stating that two ratios or rates are equal.

10. The rate of _____ describes how one quantity changes in relation to another.

11. _____ analysis is the process of including units of measurement when you compute.

I	U	M	H	P	G	N	B	W	Z	A	F	X	O	Q	G	H	W	M	E	M	P
L	Z	E	O	X	V	D	H	B	T	U	S	A	A	U	X	E	L	P	M	O	C
U	Y	K	N	N	U	L	S	N	H	K	D	Z	A	J	U	R	W	X	T	I
G	A	B	V	X	Y	X	P	C	Y	E	L	M	E	D	C	H	A	N	G	E	U
G	O	J	Y	L	C	S	T	F	G	P	Y	J	V	R	T	R	T	Y	F	O	V
A	Q	N	N	L	W	I	L	T	M	R	R	F	J	A	E	D	E	V	O	Y	M
M	N	I	P	U	O	I	C	Z	J	M	W	O	C	N	Z	D	X	X	C	A	A
A	T	G	N	N	I	E	L	B	A	M	K	B	P	T	O	T	R	G	Z	U	F
R	H	I	A	E	R	Z	G	A	T	R	U	O	X	O	S	G	M	O	N	H	M
U	T	R	Z	I	A	H	R	S	A	Y	F	Y	Z	F	R	L	U	E	R	D	E
N	C	O	D	T	G	C	F	A	O	X	O	M	W	B	T	T	O	K	W	X	W
I	L	S	E	M	G	D	I	M	E	N	S	I	O	N	A	L	I	P	T	Z	N
Y	H	M	R	L	C	O	I	E	Z	R	S	A	V	L	Z	B	P	O	E	Y	L
X	S	W	C	C	W	G	J	W	U	D	G	A	I	W	I	E	Y	C	N	O	D
J	U	U	V	K	O	Z	Z	D	H	J	K	G	W	Z	P	U	K	M	F	W	J
A	G	A	L	R	B	K	Z	X	X	Q	M	H	P	L	P	M	N	B	W	T	V

Use Your FOLDABLES®

Use your Foldable to help review the chapter.

Got it?

Identify the Correct Choice Write the correct term or number to complete each sentence.

1. When a rate is simplified so that it has a (numerator, denominator) of 1 unit, it is called a unit rate.

2. If Dinah can skate $\frac{1}{2}$ lap in 15 seconds, she can skate 1 lap in (7.5, 30) seconds.

3. Slope is the ratio of (horizontal change to vertical change, vertical change to horizontal change).

4. When two quantities have a constant ratio, their relationship is called a (direct, linear) variation.

Power Up! Performance Task

Road Trip

The Jensen family took a trip in September. Sally is calculating the gas mileage in miles per gallon for her dad's SUV. When he fills the tank, her dad records the miles on the SUV as 24,033. Her dad pays $83.58 to fill up the empty gas tank of the SUV.

Write your answers on another piece of paper. Show all of your work to receive full credit.

Part A

What is the size of the SUV's tank in gallons? Round your answer to the nearest whole number.

Part B

At the destination, there was a quarter-tank of gas left in the vehicle and the miles were recorded as 24,297. Use a ratio equation to determine the gas mileage in miles per gallon for the trip. Round your answer to the nearest whole number.

Part C

Two months later, the Jensen family takes their mom's sedan on a different trip. When she fills the tank, Sally's mom records the miles on the sedan as 15,004. It takes $71.98 to fill up the vehicle's empty gas tank. What is the size of the sedan's tank in gallons? Round your answer to the nearest whole number.

Part D

At one point on the trip, the miles are recorded as 15,121 when the gas tank is 75% full. Use a ratio equation to determine the miles per gallon the sedan averages. Round your answer to the nearest whole number.

Part E

Which vehicle has the better gas mileage? Explain your reasoning.

Reflect

 Answering the Essential Question

Use what you learned about ratios and proportional reasoning to complete the graphic organizer.

Essential Question

HOW can you show that two objects are proportional...

... with a table?	... with a graph?	... with an equation?

Answer the Essential Question. HOW can you show that two objects are proportional?

_____

_____

Chapter 2
Percents

Essential Question

HOW can percent help you understand situations involving money?

Indiana Academic Standards
7.C.6, 7.AF.6

PS Process Standards
1, 2, 3, 4, 5, 6

Math in the Real World

Biking The class goal for a biking fundraiser was to make $300 by the end of the pledge week. Halfway through the week, the students had made $210. Fill in the graph below to show the percent of the goal achieved.

Biking Fundraiser
Help Us Reach Our Goal
100%
90%
80%
70%
60%
50%
40%
30%
20%
10%
0%

FOLDABLES
Study Organizer

 Cut out the Foldable on page FL5 of this book.

 Place your Foldable on page 180.

 Use the Foldable throughout this chapter to help you learn about percents.

Vocabulary

discount	percent equation	percent of increase	selling price
gratuity	percent error	percent proportion	simple interest
markdown	percent of change	principal	tip
markup	percent of decrease	sales tax	

Study Skill: Studying Math

Draw a Picture Drawing a picture can help you better understand numbers. For example, a *number map* shows how numbers are related to each other.

In the space below, make a number map for 0.75.

What Do You Already Know?

List three things you already know about percents in the first section. Then list three things you would like to learn about percents in the second section.

Percents

What I know	What I want to find out

When Will You Use This?

Here are a few examples of how percents are used in the real world.

Activity 1 Have you ever seen something offered at a discounted price? Look in a newspaper to find an advertisement for an item that is on sale for a certain percentage off its original price. Describe the ad and explain why you think it is or is not a good deal.

_____

_____

_____

_____

Activity 2 Go online at **connectED.mcgraw-hill.com** to read the graphic novel **Amusement Park Prices**. What is the full price of admission for each park?

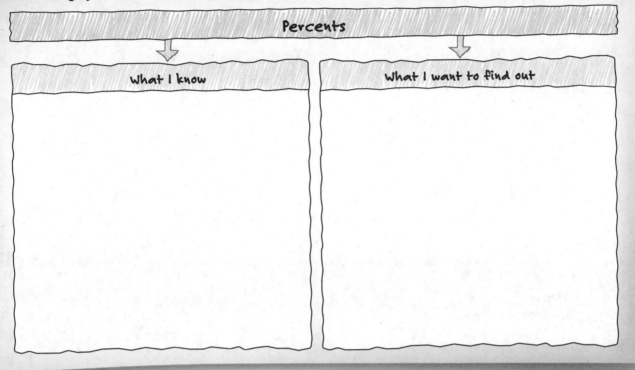

Marisol, Blake, and Hiroshi in
Amusement Park Prices

Well, let's take a look...

There. Got it!

Are You Ready?

Try the Quick Check below.
Or, take the Online Readiness Quiz.

Quick Review

Example 1

Evaluate 240 × 0.03 × 5.

240 × 0.03 × 5
= 7.2 × 5   Multiply 240 by 0.03.
= 36   Simplify.

Example 2

Write 0.35 as a percent.

0.35 = 35%   Move the decimal point two places to the right and add the percent symbol.

Quick Check

Multiply Decimals Find each product.

1. 300 × 0.02 × 8 = _____

2. 85 × 0.25 × 3 = _____

3. Suppose Nicole saves $2.50 every day. How much money will she have in 4 weeks? _____

Decimals and Percents Write each decimal as a percent.

4. 0.675 = _____

5. 0.725 = _____

6. 0.95 = _____

7. Approximately 0.92 of a watermelon is water. What percent represents this decimal? _____

How Did You Do?

Which problems did you answer correctly in the Quick Check?
Shade those exercise numbers below.

① ② ③ ④ ⑤ ⑥ ⑦

Inquiry Lab
Percent Diagrams

Indiana Academic
Standards
7.C.6

PS Process
Standards
1, 3, 4

 Inquiry HOW are percent diagrams used to solve real-world problems?

One fourth of the students in Mrs. Singh's music class chose a guitar as their favorite musical instrument. There are 24 students in Mrs. Singh's music class. How many students chose a guitar as their favorite musical instrument?

What do you know? _____

_____

_____

What do you need to find? _____

_____

Hands-On Activity 1

Bar diagrams can be used to represent a part of a whole as a fraction and as a percent.

Step 1 The bar diagram represents 100% of the class. Shade the bar diagram to show that $\frac{1}{4}$ or ☐ % of the class chose guitar as their favorite instrument.

| | | | | 100% |

├--- ☐ % ---┤

Step 2 There are ☐ students in Mrs. Singh's music class. Divide the number of students equally into 4 sections. Fill in the number in each section.

├------------------ 24 students ------------------┤

| | | | | 100% |

├--- ☐ % ---┤

So, ☐ students chose a guitar as their favorite musical instrument.

Hands-On Activity 2

There are 500 seventh-grade students at Heritage Middle School. Sixty percent of them play a musical instrument. How many seventh-grade students play a musical instrument?

Step 1   Supply the missing information for the second bar.

percent [   ] 100%

students [   ] [   ] total students

Step 2   Divide each bar into ten equal parts. Write 10% in each section of the first bar.

percent **10%** [   ] 100%

students [   ] [   ] [   ] total students

Step 3   Determine what number to write in each section of the second bar. Fill in that number.

percent **10%** [   ] 100%

students [   ] [   ] [   ] total students

Step 4   Shade 60% of the first bar and an equal amount on the second bar.

percent **10%** [   ] 100%

students [   ] [   ] [   ] total students

Since [   ] % corresponds to 6 sections, count the number of students in

6 sections. There are [   ] seventh-grade students who play a musical instrument.

Investigate

Work with a partner. Use bar diagrams to solve each problem.

1. The seventh-grade class at Fort Couch Middle School has a goal of selling 300 tickets to the annual student versus teacher basketball game. The eighth-grade class has a goal of selling 400 tickets.

   a. By the end of the first week, the eighth-grade students sold 30% of their goal. How many tickets has the eighth grade sold? _____

percent		100%
tickets		

   b. The seventh grade sold 60% of their goal. How many tickets do the students still need to sell? Explain. _____

   _____

   _____

		100%

2. **PS Justify Conclusions** The graph shows the results of a survey asking 500 teens about their allowances. How many teens did *not* receive between $10 and $20? Explain.

   _____

   _____

   Weekly Allowance

   10%
   more
   than $20

   15%
   less
   than $10

   75%
   $10–$20

		%

Work with a partner to complete the graphic organizer about percent and bar diagrams. The first one is done for you.

	Percent	Rate per 100	Whole	Part
	30%	$\frac{30}{100}$	150	45
3.	40%	$\frac{40}{100}$	150	
4.	50%	$\frac{50}{100}$	150	

5. Describe the pattern in the table above. Use the pattern to find 80% of 150.

_____

On Your Own

Create

PS Model with Mathematics Write a real-world problem for the bar diagrams shown. Then solve your problem.

6.

10%	10%	10%	10%	10%	10%	10%	10%	10%	10%	100%

25	25	25	25	25	25	25	25	25	25	250

_____

_____

7.

25%	25%	25%	25%	100%

15	15	15	15	60

_____

_____

8. **Inquiry** HOW are percent diagrams used to solve real-world problems?

_____

_____

_____

Percent of a Number

Real-World Link

Pets Some students are collecting money for a local pet shelter. The model shows that they have raised 60% of their $2,000 goal or $1,200.

 Essential Question

HOW can percent help you understand situations involving money?

🄸 **Indiana Academic Standards**
7.C.6

PS Process Standards
1, 3, 4

	Percent	Decimal	Fractions
$2,000	100% ⇨	1 ⇨	$\frac{5}{5}$ or 1
$1,600	80% ⇨	⇨	
$1,200	60% ⇨	⇨	
$800	40% ⇨	⇨	
$400	20% ⇨	⇨	$\frac{1}{5}$
$0	0% ⇨	0 ⇨	0

FIDO

1. Fill in the decimal and fractional equivalents for each of the percents shown in the model.

2. Use the model to write two multiplication sentences that are equivalent to 60% of 2,000 = 1,200.

Which PS Process Standards did you use?
Shade the circle(s) that applies.

① Persevere with Problems
② Reason Abstractly
③ Construct an Argument
④ Model with Mathematics

⑤ Use Math Tools
⑥ Attend to Precision
⑦ Make Use of Structure
⑧ Use Repeated Reasoning

Find the Percent of a Number

To find the percent of a number such as 60% of 2,000, you can use either of the following methods.

- Write the percent as a fraction and then multiply.
- Write the percent as a decimal and then multiply.

Examples

Tutor

1. **Find 5% of 300 by writing the percent as a fraction.**

Write 5% as $\frac{5}{100}$ or $\frac{1}{20}$. Then find $\frac{1}{20}$ of 300.

$$\frac{1}{20} \text{ of } 300 = \frac{1}{20} \times 300 \qquad \text{Write a multiplication expression.}$$

$$= \frac{1}{\cancel{20}_{1}} \times \frac{\cancel{300}^{15}}{1} \qquad \text{Write 300 as } \frac{300}{1}. \text{ Divide out common factors.}$$

$$= \frac{1 \times 15}{1 \times 1} \qquad \text{Multiply numerators and denominators.}$$

$$= \frac{15}{1} \text{ or } 15 \qquad \text{Simplify.}$$

So, 5% of 300 is 15.

2. **Find 25% of 180 by writing the percent as a decimal.**

Write 25% as 0.25. Then multiply 0.25 and 180.

$$
\begin{array}{r}
180 \\
\times\ 0.25 \quad \leftarrow \text{two decimal places} \\
\hline
900 \\
+\ 360 \\
\hline
45.00 \quad \leftarrow \text{two decimal places}
\end{array}
$$

So, 25% of 180 is 45.

Got it? Do these problems to find out.

Find the percent of each number.

    a. 40% of 70   **b.** 15% of 100

    c. 55% of 160   **d.** 75% of 280

Percent as a Rate

Find a percent of a quantity as a rate per 100. For example, 5% of a quantity means $\frac{5}{100}$ times the quantity.

Show your work.

a. _____

b. _____

c. _____

d. _____

Use Percents Greater Than 100%

Percents that are greater than 100% can be written as improper fractions, mixed numbers, or decimals greater than 1.

$$150\% = \frac{150}{100} = \frac{3}{2} = 1\frac{1}{2} = 1.5$$

Examples

3. **Find 120% of 75 by writing the percent as a fraction.**

Write 120% as $\frac{120}{100}$ or $\frac{6}{5}$. Then find $\frac{6}{5}$ of 75.

$\frac{6}{5}$ of $75 = \frac{6}{5} \times 75$ Write a multiplication expression.

$= \frac{6}{\cancel{5}_{1}} \times \frac{\cancel{75}^{15}}{1}$ Write 75 as $\frac{75}{1}$. Divide out common factors.

$= \frac{6 \times 15}{1 \times 1}$ Multiply numerators and denominators.

$= \frac{90}{1}$ or 90   Simplify.

So, 120% of 75 is 90.

> **Alternate Method**
> You can solve Example 3 using a decimal, and you can solve Example 4 using a fraction.

4. **Find 150% of 28 by writing the percent as a decimal.**

Write 150% as 1.5. Then find 1.5 of 28.

$$
\begin{array}{r}
28 \\
\times\ 1.5 \quad \leftarrow \text{one decimal place} \\
\hline
140 \\
+\ 28 \\
\hline
42.0 \quad \leftarrow \text{one decimal place}
\end{array}
$$

So, 150% of 28 is 42.

Got it? Do these problems to find out.

Find each number.

e. 150% of 20

f. 160% of 35

e. _____

f. _____

Example

5. Refer to the graph. If 275 students took the survey, how many can be expected to have 3 televisions each in their houses?

Write the percent as a decimal. Then multiply.

$$23\% \text{ of } 275 = 23\% \times 275$$
$$= 0.23 \times 275$$
$$= 63.25$$

So, about 63 students can be expected to have 3 televisions each.

Got it? Do this problem to find out.

g. Mr. Sudimack earned a 4% commission on the sale of a hot tub that cost $3,755. How much did he earn?

Commission
Refer to Exercise g. It is common for people who work in the sales industry to earn a commission on the products they sell.

Show your work.

g. _____

Guided Practice

 Check

Find each number. Round to the nearest tenth if necessary. (Examples 1–4)

1. 8% of 50 = _____

2. 95% of 40 = _____

3. 110% of 70 = _____

Show your work.

4. Mackenzie wants to buy a backpack that costs $50. If the tax rate is 6.5%, how much tax will she pay? (Example 5)

_____

5. **Building on the Essential Question** Give an example of a real-world situation in which you would find the percent of a number. _____

_____

Rate Yourself!

Are you ready to move on? Shade the section that applies.

I have a few questions.

I'm ready to move on.

I have a lot of questions.

For more help, go online to access a Personal Tutor.

 Tutor

Independent Practice

Go online for Step-by-Step Solutions eHelp

Find each number. Round to the nearest tenth if necessary. (Examples 1–4)

1. 65% of 186 = _____

Show your work.

2. 45% of $432 = _____

3. 23% of $640 = _____

4. 130% of 20 = _____

5 175% of 10 = _____

6. 150% of 128 = _____

7. 32% of 4 = _____

8. 5.4% of 65 = _____

9. 23.5% of 128 = _____

10. Suppose there are 20 questions on a multiple-choice test. If 25% of the answers are choice B, how many of the answers are *not* choice B?

(Example 5) _____

11. PS **Model with Mathematics** Refer to the graphic novel frame below. Find the dollar amount of the group discount each student would receive at each park.

_____

12. In addition to her salary, Ms. Lopez earns a 3% *commission,* or fee paid based on a percent of her sales, on every vacation package that she sells. One day, she sold the three vacation packages shown. Fill in the table for each packages' commission. What was her total commission?

Package	Sale Price	Commission
#1	$2,375	
#2	$3,950	
#3	$1,725	

Copy and Solve For Exercises 13–21, find each number. Round to the nearest hundredth. Show your work on a separate piece of paper.

13. $\frac{4}{5}$% of 500

14. $5\frac{1}{2}$% of 60

15. $20\frac{1}{4}$% of 3

16. 1,000% of 99

17. 520% of 100

18. 0.15% of 250

19. 200% of 79

20. 0.3% of 80

21. 0.28% of 50

H.O.T. Problems Higher Order Thinking

22. (PS) **Persevere with Problems** Suppose you add 10% of a number to the number, and then you subtract 10% of the total. Is the result *greater than, less than,* or *equal to* the original number? Explain your reasoning.

_____

_____

23. (PS) **Reason Inductively** When is it easiest to find the percent of a number using a fraction? using a decimal? _____

_____

_____

24. (PS) **Reason Inductively** If you found the percent of a number and the product is greater than the number, what do you know about the percent? Explain. _____

_____

Extra Practice

Find each number. Round to the nearest tenth if necessary.

25. 54% of 85 = _45.9_

Homework Help ➡

$0.54 \times 85 = 45.9$

26. 12% of $230 = _$27.60_

$$\frac{\overset{3}{\cancel{12}}}{\underset{25}{\cancel{100}}} \times 230 = \frac{3}{\cancel{25}} \times \overset{46}{\cancel{230}}$$

$$= \frac{3}{5} \times 46$$

$$= \frac{138}{5} \text{ or } 27.6$$

27. 98% of 15 = _____

28. 250% of 25 = _____

29. 108% of $50 = _____

30. 75.2% of 130 = _____

31. 0.5% of 60 = _____

32. 2.4% of 20 = _____

33. 7.5% of 30 = _____

34. In a recent year, 17.7% of households watched the finals of a popular reality series. There are 110.2 million households in the United States. How many households watched the finals?

_____

35. A family pays $19 each month for Internet access. Next month, the cost will increase by 5% because of an equipment fee. After this increase, what will be the cost for the Internet access?

_____

36. **PS Persevere with Problems** 250 people were asked to name their favorite fruit.
  a. Of those surveyed, how many people prefer peaches?

  _____

  b. Which type of fruit did more than 100 people prefer?

  _____

Favorite Fruit	
Berries	44%
Peaches	32%
Cherries	24%

37. The table shows the results of a survey of 200 movie rental customers. How many customers prefer horror movies?

Favorite Type of Movie	Percent of Customers
Comedy	15
Mystery	10
Horror	46
Science Fiction	29

38. The graph shows the Ramirez family budget. Their budget is based on a monthly income of $4,000.

Determine if each statement is true or false.

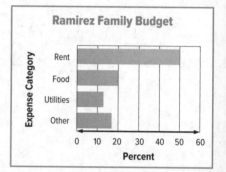

a. The family budgeted $1,500 for rent. ☐ True ☐ False

b. The family budgeted $800 for food. ☐ True ☐ False

c. The family budgeted $200 more for utilities than for other expenses. ☐ True ☐ False

d. The family budgeted $1,200 more for rent than for food. ☐ True ☐ False

Spiral Review

Multiply.

39. $1.7 \times 54 =$ _____

40. $1.5 \times 3.65 =$ _____

41. $49.6 \times 2.7 =$ _____

42. Trent spent 50 minutes at the neighbor's house. He spent $\frac{2}{5}$ of the time swimming. How many minutes did Trent spend swimming? _____

Percent and Estimation

Real-World Link

Music Suppose 200 people are surveyed to find out how they learned to play an instrument. The results are shown in the table below.

Type of Teaching	Actual Percent	Estimated Percent	Fraction
Private Lessons	42%	40%	$\frac{2}{5}$
Lessons at School	32%		
Self-Taught	26%		

Essential Question

HOW can percent help you understand situations involving money?

🇺🇸 **Indiana Academic Standards**
7.C.6

PS Process Standards
1, 3, 4, 5

1. Estimate each percent. Choose an estimate that can be represented by a fraction that is easy to use. Then, write each estimated percent as a fraction in simplest form.

2. About how many people took lessons at school?

_____

3. Sarah estimates the percent of people who taught themselves to play an instrument as 25%, and then she found $\frac{1}{4}$ of 200. Would her answer be less than or greater than the actual number of people who were self taught? Explain. _____

_____

_____

_____

Which PS Process Standards did you use?
Shade the circle(s) that applies.

①Persevere with Problems
②Reason Abstractly
③Construct an Argument
④Model with Mathematics
⑤Use Math Tools
⑥Attend to Precision
⑦Make Use of Structure
⑧Use Repeated Reasoning

Estimate the Percent of a Number

Sometimes an exact answer is not needed when using percents. One way to estimate the percent of a number is to use a fraction.

Another method for estimating the percent of a number is first to find 10% of the number and then multiply.

$$70\% = 7 \cdot 10\%$$

So, 70% equals 7 times 10% of a number.

 Examples

1. **Jodi has paid 62% of the $500 she owes for her loan. Estimate 62% of 500.**

62% of $500 \approx 60\%$ of 500 $62\% \approx 60\%$

$\approx \dfrac{3}{5} \cdot 500$ $60\% = \dfrac{6}{10}$ or $\dfrac{3}{5}$

≈ 300 Multiply.

So, 62% of 500 is about 300.

What are two ways to estimate 22% of 130? Explain below.

2. **Marita and four of her friends ordered a pizza that cost $14.72. She is responsible for 20% of the bill. About how much money will she need to pay?**

Step 1   Find 10% of $15.00.

10% of $\$15.00 = 0.1 \cdot \$15.00$

$= \$1.50$ To multiply by 10%, move the decimal point one place to the left.

Step 2   Multiply.

20% of $15.00 is 2 times 10% of $15.00.

$2 \cdot \$1.50 = \$3.00$

So, Marita should pay about $3.00.

Show your work.

Got it? **Do these problems to find out.**

a. _____

a. Estimate 42% of 120.

b. _____

b. Dante plans to put 80% of his paycheck into a savings account and spend the other 20%. His paycheck this week was $295. About how much money will he put into his savings account?

Percents Greater Than 100 or Less Than 1

You can also estimate percents of numbers when the percent is greater than 100 or less than 1.

Example

3. **Estimate 122% of 50.**

122% is about 120%.

120% of 50 = 100% of 50 + 20% of 50   120% = 100% + 20%

$= (1 \cdot 50) + \left(\frac{1}{5} \cdot 50\right)$ 100% = 1 and 20% = $\frac{1}{5}$

$= 50 + 10$ or 60   Simplify.

So, 122% of 50 is about 60.

Got it? Do these problems to find out.

c. 174% of 200   d. 298% of 45   e. 347% of 80

Example

4. There are 789 seventh grade students at Washington Middle School. About $\frac{1}{4}$% of the seventh grade students have traveled overseas. What is the approximate number of seventh grade students that have traveled overseas? Explain.

$\frac{1}{4}$% is one fourth of 1%. 789 is about 800.

1% of 800 = 0.01 · 800   Write 1% as 0.01.

$= 8$ To multiply by 1%, move the decimal point two places to the left.

One fourth of 8 is $\frac{1}{4} \cdot 8$ or 2.

So, about 2 seventh grade students have traveled overseas.

Got it? Do this problem to find out.

f. A county receives $\frac{3}{4}$% of a state sales tax. About how much money would the county receive from the sale of a computer that costs $1,020?

Tutor

5. Last year, 639 students attended a summer camp. Of those who attended this year, 0.5% also attended summer camp last year. About how many students attended the summer camp two years in a row?

0.5% is half of 1%.

$$1\% \text{ of } 639 = 0.01 \cdot 639$$
$$\approx 6$$

So, 0.5% of 639 is about $\frac{1}{2}$ of 6 or 3.

About 3 students attended summer camp 2 years in a row.

Guided Practice

Check ✓

Estimate. (Examples 1–4)

1. 52% of 10 ≈ _____

2. 79% of 489 ≈ _____

3. 151% of 70 ≈ _____

4. $\frac{1}{2}$% of 82 ≈ _____

5. Of the 78 teenagers at a youth camp, 63% have birthdays in the spring. About how many teenagers have birthdays in the spring? (Example 2)

_____

6. About 0.8% of the land in Maine is federally owned. If Maine has 19,847,680 acres, about how many acres are federally owned? (Example 5) _____

_____

_____

Rate Yourself!

How confident are you about estimating percents? Shade the ring on the target.

7. **Building on the Essential Question** How can you estimate the percent of a number? _____

_____

_____

For more help, go online to access a Personal Tutor.

Tutor

Independent Practice

Go online for Step-by-Step Solutions eHelp

Estimate. (Examples 1–4)

1. 47% of 70 ≈ _____

 Show your work.

2. 39% of 120 ≈ _____

3 21% of 90 ≈ _____

4. 65% of 152 ≈ _____

5. 72% of 238 ≈ _____

6. 132% of 54 ≈ _____

7. 224% of 320 ≈ _____

8. $\frac{3}{4}$% of 168 ≈ _____

9. 0.4% of 510 ≈ _____

10. **Financial Literacy** Carlie spent $42 at the salon. Her mother loaned her the money. Carlie will pay her mother 15% of $42 each week until the loan is repaid. About how much will Carlie pay each week? (Example 2)

_____

11 The United States has 12,383 miles of coastline. If 0.8% of the coastline is located in Georgia, about how many miles of coastline are in Georgia? (Example 5)

_____

_____

12. **PS** **Persevere with Problems** Use the graph shown.

a. About how many more hours does Avery spend sleeping than doing the activities in the "other" category? Justify your answer.

_____

b. What is the approximate number of minutes Avery spends each day on extracurricular activities?

_____

Avery's Day

Extracurricular Activities 8%

Sleep 33%

Other 19%

School 27%

Homework 13%

Estimate.

13. 67% of 8.7 ≈ _____

14. 54% of 76.8 ≈ _____

15. 10.5% of 238 ≈ _____

16. The average white rhinoceros gives birth to a single calf that weighs about 3.8% as much as its mother. If the mother rhinoceros weighs 3.75 tons,

about how many pounds does its calf weigh? _____

17. The students at Monroe Junior High sponsored a canned food drive. The seventh-grade class collected 129% of its canned food goal.

    a. About how many canned foods did the seventh-graders collect if their goal

       was 200 cans? _____

    b. About how many canned foods did the seventh-graders collect if their goal

       was 595 cans? _____

H.O.T. Problems Higher Order Thinking

18. **PS** **Persevere with Problems** Explain how you could find $\frac{3}{8}$% of $800.

_____

_____

19. **PS** **Use Math Tools** Is an estimate for the percent of a number *always*, *sometimes*, or *never* greater than the actual percent of the number? Give an example or a counterexample to support your answer.

_____

_____

20. **PS** **Model with Mathematics** Write a multi-step real-world problem in which the answer can be found by estimating 18% of 30. Then explain how you would solve the problem.

_____

_____

_____

_____

Extra Practice

Estimate.

21. 76% of 180 ≈ _135_

$\frac{3}{4} \cdot 180 = 135$ or

$0.1 \cdot 180 = 18$

$7.5 \cdot 18 = 135$

22. 57% of 29 ≈ _18_

$\frac{3}{5} \cdot 30 = 18$ or

$0.1 \cdot 30 = 3$

$6 \cdot 3 = 18$

23. 92% of 104 ≈ _____

24. $\frac{1}{2}$% of 412 ≈ _____

25. 0.9% of 74 ≈ _____

26. 32% of 89.9 ≈ _____

27. You use 43 muscles to frown. When you smile, you use 32% of these same muscles. About how many muscles do you use when you smile?

_____

28. (PS) **Justify Conclusions** The coastline of the Atlantic Coast is 2,069 miles long. Approximately $\frac{6}{10}$% of the coastline lies in New Hampshire. About how many miles of the coastline lie in New Hampshire? Explain how you estimated.

_____

_____

29. The table shows the number of passes attempted and the percent completed by the top quarterbacks in the NFL for a recent season.

NFL Quarterbacks		
Player	Passes Attempted	Percent Completed
T. Brady	578	69
P. Manning	515	65
T. Romo	520	64
D. Garrard	325	64

a. Estimate the number of passes that Tom Brady completed.

_____

b. Is your estimate greater or less than the actual number of passes he completed? Explain. _____

_____

c. Without calculating, determine whether Tony Romo or David Garrard completed more passes. Justify your reasoning.

_____

_____

30. The table shows the fundraising goals for three different activities and the percent of the goal that was actually raised.

Estimate the amount raised by each activity. Sort the estimates from least to greatest.

Activity	Goal	Percent of Goal Raised
Car Wash	$250	112%
Raffle	$200	143%
Magazine Sales	$240	102%

	Activity	Estimate
Least		
Greatest		

31. The graph shows the results of a survey of 510 students. Determine if each of the following are good estimates. Select yes or no.

Pet Preferences

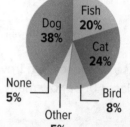

a. about 125 students prefer cats   Yes   ☐ No

b. about 200 students prefer dogs   Yes   ☐ No

c. about 150 students prefer fish   ☐ Yes   No

Spiral Review

Solve each equation. Show your work.

32. $5n = 120$

33. $1,200 = 4a$

34. $6x = 39$

35. Marquita created the design at the right. She created the design from 8 equal-size rectangles. Write a fraction in simplest form that represents the yellow portion of the design.

36. Write three fractions equivalent to $\frac{3}{5}$.

Inquiry Lab

Find Percents

Indiana Academic Standards
7.C.6

PS **Process Standards**
1, 3, 4

Inquiry HOW is percent used to solve real-world problems?

The eighth grade had 300 tickets to sell to the school play and the seventh grade had 250 tickets to sell. One hour before the show, the eighth grade had sold 225 tickets and the seventh grade had sold 200 tickets. Complete the investigation below to find which grade sold the greater percent of tickets.

Hands-On Activity

Step 1 The bar diagrams below show 100% for each grade. Label the total tickets to be sold above each bar. Divide each bar into 10 equal sections. So, each section will represent 10%.

eighth grade ⌐——————————⌐ tickets ——————————⌐ 100%

seventh grade ⌐——————————⌐ tickets ——————————⌐ 100%

Step 2 Find the number that belongs in each section for both of the bars. Then write that number in the sections.

Eighth grade:

$300 \div 10 = \boxed{}$

Seventh grade:

$250 \div 10 = \boxed{}$

Step 3 Find the number of sections to shade for each bar. Then shade the sections.

Eighth grade:

$225 \div 30 = \boxed{}$

Seventh grade:

$200 \div 25 = \boxed{}$

The eighth grade sold $\boxed{}$ % of their tickets. The seventh grade

sold $\boxed{}$ % of their tickets.

The _____ grade sold the greater percent of their tickets.

Investigate

Collaborate

Work with a partner. Show your work using bar diagrams.

1. **PS Model with Mathematics** Vanlue Middle School has 600 students and Memorial Middle School has 450 students. Vanlue has 270 girls and Memorial has 225 girls. Which school has the greater percent of girls? Explain. _____

_____

_____

_____

```
                 |------------ [    ] students -----------|
    Vanlue       |                                        |
                 |_____| 100%

                 |-------- [    ] students ----------|
    Memorial     |                                   |
                 |_____| 100%
```

Create

On Your Own

Work with a partner to answer the following question.

2. **PS Model with Mathematics** Seventy-five students were in the audience for a 3-D screening of a movie. Fifty students were in the audience for a 2-D screening of the same movie. Describe a situation in which the percent of students who went to the 2-D screening is greater than the percent of students who went to the 3-D screening. _____

_____

_____

_____

3. **Inquiry** HOW is percent used to solve real-world problems? _____

_____

_____

_____

The Percent Proportion

 ## Real-World Link

Monster Trucks The tires on a monster truck weigh approximately 2 tons. The entire truck weighs about 6 tons.

1. Write the ratio of tire weight to total weight as a fraction.

$$\frac{Part}{Whole} = \underline{\hspace{3cm}} = \frac{\square}{\square}$$

2. Represent the fraction above by shading in the model.

3. Write the fraction as a decimal to the nearest hundredth.

4. About what percent of the monster truck's weight is the tires?

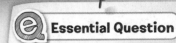 **Essential Question**

HOW can percent help you understand situations involving money?

Vocabulary

percent proportion

Indiana Academic Standards
7.C.6

PS Process Standards
1, 3, 4

Which PS **Process Standards** did you use?
Shade the circle(s) that applies.

① Persevere with Problems
② Reason Abstractly
③ Construct an Argument
④ Model with Mathematics
⑤ Use Math Tools
⑥ Attend to Precision
⑦ Make Use of Structure
⑧ Use Repeated Reasoning

Use the Percent Proportion

Type	Example	Proportion
Find the Percent	What percent of 5 is 4?	$\frac{4}{5} = \frac{n}{100}$
Find the Part	What number is 80% of 5?	$\frac{p}{5} = \frac{80}{100}$
Find the Whole	4 is 80% of what number?	$\frac{4}{w} = \frac{80}{100}$

In a **percent proportion**, one ratio or fraction compares part of a quantity to the whole quantity. The other ratio is the equivalent percent written as a fraction with a denominator of 100.

$$4 \text{ out of } 5 \text{ is } 80\%$$

$$\frac{\text{part}}{\text{whole}} \cdots\!\!\rightarrow \left.\frac{4}{5} = \frac{80}{100}\right\} \text{percent}$$

Example

1. What percent of $15 is $9?

Words	What percent of $15 is $9?
Variable	Let n represent the percent.
Proportion	$\dfrac{\text{part}}{\text{whole}} \rightarrow \left.\dfrac{9}{15} = \dfrac{n}{100}\right\}$ percent

$\dfrac{9}{15} = \dfrac{n}{100}$ Write the proportion.

$9 \cdot 100 = 15 \cdot n$ Find the cross products.

$900 = 15n$ Simplify.

$\dfrac{900}{15} = \dfrac{15n}{15}$ Divide each side by 15.

$60 = n$

So, $9 is 60% of $15.

Got it? Do these problems to find out.

a. What percent of 25 is 20?   b. $12.75 is what percent of $50?

Work Zone

The Percent Proportion

The word of is usually followed by the whole.

Show your work.

a. _____

b. _____

Example

2. **What number is 40% of 120?**

Words	What number is 40% of 120?
Variable	Let p represent the part.
Proportion	$\dfrac{\text{part} \longrightarrow}{\text{whole} \longrightarrow} \dfrac{p}{120} = \dfrac{40}{100} \Big\}$ percent

$$\dfrac{p}{120} = \dfrac{40}{100}$$ Write the proportion.

$p \cdot 100 = 120 \cdot 40$ Find the cross products.

$100p = 4,800$ Simplify.

$\dfrac{100p}{100} = \dfrac{4,800}{100}$ Divide each side by 100.

$p = 48$ So, 48 is 40% of 120.

Got it? Do these problems to find out.

c. What number is 5% of 60? **d.** 12% of 85 is what number?

c. _____

d. _____

Example

3. **18 is 25% of what number?**

Words	18 is 25% of what number?
Variable	Let w represent the whole.
Proportion	$\dfrac{\text{part} \longrightarrow}{\text{whole} \longrightarrow} \dfrac{18}{w} = \dfrac{25}{100} \Big\}$ percent

$$\dfrac{18}{w} = \dfrac{25}{100}$$ Write the proportion.

$18 \cdot 100 = w \cdot 25$ Find the cross products.

$1,800 = 25w$ Simplify.

$\dfrac{1,800}{25} = \dfrac{25w}{25}$ Divide each side by 25.

$72 = w$ So, 18 is 25% of 72.

Got it? Do these problems to find out.

e. 40% of what number is 26? **f.** 84 is 75% of what number?

STOP and Reflect

In the proportion $\dfrac{3}{20} = \dfrac{15}{100}$, identify the part, whole, and percent.

part = _____

whole = _____

percent = _____

Show your work.

e. _____

f. _____

Watch | Tutor

4. The average adult male Western Lowland gorilla eats about 33.5 pounds of fruit each day. How much food does the average adult male gorilla eat each day?

You know that 33.5 pounds is the part. You need to find the whole.

$$\frac{33.5}{w} = \frac{67}{100}$$ Write the proportion.

$33.5 \cdot 100 = w \cdot 67$ Find the cross products.

$3{,}350 = 67w$ Simplify.

$$\frac{3{,}350}{67} = \frac{67w}{67}$$ Divide each side by 67.

$50 = w$

The average adult male gorilla eats 50 pounds of food each day.

Western Lowland Gorilla's Diet	
Food	**Percent**
Fruit	67%
Seeds, leaves, stems, and pith	17%
Insects/ insect larvae	16%

Guided Practice

Check ✓

Find each number. Round to the nearest tenth if necessary. (Examples 1–3)

1. What percent of $90 is $9?

2. What number is 2% of 35?

3. 62 is 90.5% of what number?

Show your work.

4. Brand A cereal contains 10 cups of cereal. How many more cups of cereal are in Brand B cereal?

(Example 4)

5. **Building on the Essential Question** How can you use the percent proportion to solve real-world problems?

Rate Yourself!

How confident are you about using the percent proportion? Shade the ring on the target.

I'm on target.

I need help.

For more help, go online to access a Personal Tutor.

Tutor

FOLDABLES Time to update your Foldable!

Independent Practice

Go online for Step-by-Step Solutions

Find each number. Round to the nearest tenth if necessary. (Examples 1–3)

1. What percent of 60 is 15? _____

2. What number is 15% of 60? _____

Show your work.

3. 9 is 12% of which number? _____

4. 12% of 72 is what number? _____

5. What percent of 50 is 18? _____

6. 12 is 90% of what number? _____

7. A pair of sneakers is on sale as shown. This is 75% of the original price. What was the original price of the shoes? (Example 4) _____

Sale Price
$51

8. Of the 60 books on a bookshelf, 24 are nonfiction. What percent of the books are nonfiction? (Example 4) _____

Find each number. Round to the nearest hundredth if necessary.

9. 40 is 50% of what number? _____

10. 12.5% of what number is 24? _____

11. What percent of 300 is 0.6? _____

12. What number is 0.5% of 8? _____

Find each number. Round to the nearest hundredth if necessary.

13. **STEM** Use the table shown. Mercury's radius is 2,440 kilometers.

Planet	Radius (km)
Mercury	r
Mars	$r + 957$
Jupiter	$29.3r$

a. Mercury's radius is what percent of Jupiter's radius?

_____

b. If the radius of Mars is about 13.7% of Neptune's radius, what is the radius of Neptune?

_____

c. Earth's radius is about 261.4% of Mercury's radius. What is the radius of Earth?

_____

H.O.T. Problems Higher Order Thinking

14. **PS Reason Inductively** Seventy percent of the 100 students in a middle school cafeteria bought their lunch. Some of the students that bought their lunch leave the cafeteria to attend an assembly. Now only 60% of the remaining students bought their lunch. How many students are remaining in the cafeteria? Explain. _____

_____

_____

_____

15. **PS Persevere with Problems** Without calculating, arrange the following from greatest to least value. Justify your reasoning.

20% of 100, 20% of 500, 5% of 100

_____

_____

_____

_____

16. **PS Model with Mathematics** Write a real-world problem involving a percent that can be solved by using the proportion $\frac{3}{b} = \frac{60}{100}$. Then solve the proportion.

_____

_____

_____

_____

Extra Practice

Find each number. Round to the nearest tenth if necessary.

17. What number is 25% of 180? _45_____

$$\frac{n}{180} = \frac{25}{100}$$

$$\frac{n}{180} = \frac{1}{4}$$

$$4n = 180$$

$$n = 45$$

Homework Help

18. $3 is what percent of $40? _7.5%_____

$$\frac{3}{40} = \frac{P}{100}$$

$$40p = 300$$

$$p = 7.5\%$$

19. 9 is 45% of what number? _____

20. 75 is 20% of what number? _____

21. What percent of 60 is 12? _____

22. What number is 5% of 46? _____

23. **PS Justify Conclusions** Roman has 2 red pencils in his backpack. If this is 25% of the total number of pencils, how many pencils are in his backpack? Explain.

_____

24. **PS Justify Conclusions** Eileen and Michelle scored 48% of their team's points. If their team had a total of 50 points, how many points did they score? Explain.

_____

Find each number. Round to the nearest hundredth if necessary.

25. What percent of 25 is 30? _____

26. What number is 8.2% of 50? _____

27. The types of flowers shown in the table make up an arrangement. What percent of the flowers in the arrangement are roses?

Flower Arrangement	
Lilies	4
Roses	15
Snapdragons	6

[   ]

28. Select values to set up a percent proportion that represents each situation. Then solve each problem. Round to the nearest tenth if necessary.

Situation 1: A pair of shoes is on sale for 80% of the original price. The sale price is $60. What was the original price?

[   ]

$$\frac{\square}{\square} = \frac{\square}{\square}$$

Situation 2: Maggie's goal was to collect 60 canned goods for a food drive. She actually collected 80. What percent of her goal did Maggie reach?

[   ]

$$\frac{\square}{\square} = \frac{\square}{\square}$$

Situation 3: Craig has made 60% of 80 free throw attempts this season. How many free throws has he made?

[   ]

$$\frac{\square}{\square} = \frac{\square}{\square}$$

Spiral Review

Multiply.

29. $\frac{1}{2} \times \frac{2}{3} =$ _____

30. $\frac{3}{5} \times \frac{1}{4} =$ _____

31. $\frac{2}{7} \times \frac{1}{6} =$ _____

Divide.

32. $\frac{2}{5} \div \frac{3}{4} =$ _____

33. $\frac{1}{3} \div \frac{5}{6} =$ _____

34. $\frac{1}{5} \div \frac{5}{7} =$ _____

The Percent Equation

Vocabulary Start-Up

You have used a percent proportion to find the missing part (*p*), percent (*n*), or whole (*w*). You can also use a **percent equation**. The percent equation is part = percent • whole.

Label the diagram that shows the relationship between the percent proportion and the percent equation with the terms *part, whole,* and *percent.* Use each term once.

$$\frac{part}{whole} = \text{_____}$$ Write the percent proportion.

$$\frac{part}{whole} \cdot whole = percent \cdot \text{_____}$$ Multiply each side by the whole.

$$\text{_____} = percent \cdot whole$$ Divide out common factors to obtain the percent equation.

Essential Question

HOW can percent help you understand situations involving money?

 Vocabulary

percent equation

🅘 **Indiana Academic Standards**
7.AF.6

PS **Process Standards**
1, 2, 3, 4

Real-World Link

A survey found that 16% of all seventh-graders at Lincoln Middle school think that tarantulas are the scariest creatures. There are 150 seventh-graders at the school. How would you write a percent equation to find how many seventh-graders said that tarantulas are the scariest creatures?

$$\boxed{} = 0.16 \cdot \boxed{}$$

Boo!

Which **PS** **Process Standards** did you use?
Shade the circle(s) that applies.

① Persevere with Problems   ⑤ Use Math Tools

② Reason Abstractly   ⑥ Attend to Precision

③ Construct an Argument   ⑦ Make Use of Structure

④ Model with Mathematics   ⑧ Use Repeated Reasoning

Use the Percent Equation

Type	Example	Equation
Find the Percent	3 is what percent of 6?	$3 = n \cdot 6$
Find the Part	What number is 50% of 6?	$p = 0.5 \cdot 6$
Find the Whole	3 is 50% of what number?	$3 = 0.5 \cdot w$

You can use the percent equation to solve problems that involve percent.

$$\textbf{3 is 50\% of 6}$$

$$\underline{\text{part}} \quad \underline{\text{percent}} \quad \underline{\text{whole}}$$
$$3 \;\; = \;\; 0.5 \;\; \times \;\; 6$$

Note that the percent is written as a decimal.

Example

1. What number is 12% of 150?

Do you need to find the percent, part, or whole? _____

Estimate $0.10 \cdot 150 = 15$

$\underline{\text{part}} = \underline{\text{percent}} \cdot \underline{\text{whole}}$

$p = 0.12 \cdot 150$ Write the percent equation. 12% = 0.12

$p = 18$ Multiply.

So, 18 is 12% of 150.

18 is close to the estimate of 15. So, the answer is reasonable. You can also check your answer using the percent proportion.

Check $\dfrac{18}{150} \stackrel{?}{=} \dfrac{12}{100}$

$18 \cdot 100 \stackrel{?}{=} 150 \cdot 12$

$1,800 = 1,800 \checkmark$

Percent Equation
A percent must always be converted to a decimal or a fraction when it is used in an equation.

a. _____

b. _____

c. _____

d. _____

Got it? Do these problems to find out.

Write an equation for each problem. Then solve.

    a. What is 6% of 200?   **b.** Find 72% of 50.

    c. What is 14% of 150?   **d.** Find 50% of 70.

Example

Tutor

2. **21 is what percent of 40?**

Do you need to find the percent, part, or whole? _____

Estimate $\frac{21}{40} \approx \frac{1}{2}$ or 50%

$$\underbrace{\text{part}} = \underbrace{\text{percent}} \cdot \underbrace{\text{whole}}$$

21 =	n	·	40	Write the percent equation.

$\frac{21}{40} = \frac{40n}{40}$ Divide each side by 40.

$0.525 = n$ Simplify.

So, 21 is 52.5% of 40.

Check   52.5% ≈ 50% ✓

> **Percent**
> Remember to write the decimal as a percent in your final answer.

Got it? Do these problems to find out.

Show your work.

Write an equation for each problem. Then solve. Round to the nearest tenth if necessary.

e. What percent of 40 is 9?   **f.** 27 is what percent of 150?

e. _____

f. _____

Example

Tutor

3. **13 is 26% of what number?**

Do you need to find the percent, part, or whole? _____

Estimate $\frac{1}{4}$ of 48 = 12

$$\underbrace{\text{part}} = \underbrace{\text{percent}} \cdot \underbrace{\text{whole}}$$

13 = 0.26 · w   Write the percent equation. 26% = 0.26

$\frac{13}{0.26} = \frac{0.26w}{0.26}$ Divide each side by 0.26.

50 = w   Simplify.

So, 13 is 26% of 50.

Check   50 ≈ 48. ✓

Got it? Do these problems to find out.

Write an equation for each problem. Then solve. Round to the nearest tenth if necessary.

g. 39 is 84% of what number?   **h.** 26% of what number is 45?

g. _____

h. _____

4. A survey found that 25% of people aged 18–24 gave up their home phone and only use a cell phone. If 3,264 people only use a cell phone, how many people were surveyed?

Words	3,264 people is 25% of what number of people?
Variable	Let w represent the number of people.
Equation	3,264 $=$ 0.25 $\cdot$ w

$3,264 = 0.25 \cdot w$ Write the percent equation. 25% = 0.25

$\dfrac{3,264}{0.25} = \dfrac{0.25w}{0.25}$ Divide each side by 0.25. Use a calculator.

$13,056 = w$ Simplify.

About 13,056 people were surveyed.

Guided Practice

 Check ✓

Write an equation for each problem. Then solve. Round to the nearest tenth if necessary. (Examples 1–3)

1. What number is 88% of 300?

2. 24 is what percent of 120?

3. 3 is 12% of what number?

4. A local bakery sold 60 loaves of bread in one day. If 65% of these were sold in the afternoon, how many loaves were sold in the afternoon? (Example 4) _____

5. **Building on the Essential Question** When might it be easier to use the percent equation rather than the percent proportion? _____

_____

Rate Yourself!

Are you ready to move on? Shade the section that applies.

YES ? NO

For more help, go online to access a Personal Tutor.   Tutor

FOLDABLES Time to update your Foldable!

Independent Practice

Go online for Step-by-Step Solutions

Write an equation for each problem. Then solve. Round to the nearest tenth if necessary. (Examples 1–3)

1. 75 is what percent of 150? _____

2. 84 is 60% of what number? _____

3. What number is 65% of 98? _____

4. Find 39% of 65. _____

5. Find 24% of 25. _____

6. What number is 53% of 470? _____

7. Ruben bought 6 new books for his collection. This increased his collection by 12%. How many books did he have before his purchases? (Example 4)

_____

8. A store sold 550 video games during the month of December. If this made up 12.5% of its yearly video game sales, about how many video games did the store sell all year? (Example 4)

_____

9. **PS** **Persevere with Problems** About 142 million people in the United States watch online videos. Use the graph that shows what type of videos they watch.

a. About what percent of viewers watch comedy, jokes, and bloopers? _____

b. About what percent watch news stories?

_____

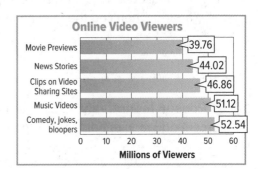

Online Video Viewers

Movie Previews	39.76
News Stories	44.02
Clips on Video Sharing Sites	46.86
Music Videos	51.12
Comedy, jokes, bloopers	52.54

Millions of Viewers

Write an equation for each problem. Then solve. Round to the nearest tenth if necessary.

10. Find 135% of 64. _____

11. What number is 0.4% of 82.1? _____

12. 450 is 75.2% of what number? _____

13. What percent of 200 is 230? _____

H.O.T. Problems Higher Order Thinking

14. (PS) **Model with Mathematics** Write a percent problem for which the percent is greater than 100 and the part is known. Use the percent equation to solve your problem to find the whole.

_____

15. (PS) **Persevere with Problems** If you need to find the percent of a number, explain how you can predict whether the part will be *less than*, *greater than*, or *equal* to the number.

_____

_____

_____

16. (PS) **Reason Abstractly** A museum has 50 pieces of art to display in an exhibit. Of these, 11 are photographs and 39 are color paintings. The manager wants to add more photographs so that they represent 25% of the pieces of art at the museum. Write and solve an equation to find the number of photos to be added. Then find the total number of pieces of art in the exhibit.

_____

_____

17. (PS) **Reason Inductively** Explain when it might be more efficient to use the percent equation rather than the percent proportion.

_____

_____

_____

_____

Extra Practice

Write an equation for each problem. Then solve. Round to the nearest tenth if necessary.

18. 9 is what percent of 45? _20%_

$$9 = n \times 45$$

$$\frac{9}{45} = \frac{45n}{45}$$

$$0.2 \text{ or } 20\% = n$$

Homework Help →

19. What percent of 96 is 26? _27.1%_

$$26 = n \times 96$$

$$\frac{26}{96} = \frac{96n}{96}$$

$$0.271 \text{ or } 27.1\% = n$$

20. What percent of 392 is 98? _____

21. 30 is what percent of 64? _____

22. 33% of what number is 1.45? _____

23. 84 is 75% of what number? _____

24. 17 is 40% of what number? _____

25. 80% of what number is 64? _____

26. The length of Giselle's arm is 27 inches. The length of her lower arm is 17 inches. About what percent of Giselle's arm is her lower arm?

_____

27. Approximately 0.02% of North Atlantic lobsters are born bright blue in color. Out of 5,000 North Atlantic lobsters, how many would you expect to be blue in color?

_____

28. Financial Literacy Suppose you earn $6 per hour at your part-time job. What will your new hourly rate be after a 2.5% raise? Explain.

_____

_____

29. Taryn's grandmother took her family out to dinner. The receipt shows the total amount spent. Taryn's dinner was 20% of the total bill after tax and tip. How much was Taryn's dinner?

Le Bistro

Subtotal $58.38

Tax......................$3.38

Tip...................$12.24

30. Model each situation below with a percent equation. Select the correct equation for each situation. Then solve each problem.

a. Of the 300 students in a homeroom, 120 play a school sport. What percent of students play a school sport?

Equation: _____   Solution: _____

$x = 0.3 \cdot 120$

$x = 0.12 \cdot 300$

$120 = 300 \cdot x$

b. A survey of 120 middle schools showed that 30% have a foreign language program. How many schools have a foreign language program?

Equation: _____   Solution: _____

c. Katrina saved $300 last summer. Of that amount, 12% came from her allowance. How much came from her allowance?

Equation: _____   Solution: _____

Spiral Review

Fill in each ◯ with <, >, or = to make a true statement.

31. 5.56 ◯ $5\frac{5}{7}$

32. 4.027 ◯ 4.0092

33. 88% ◯ 0.9

Use the graph to solve.

34. What number represents 100% of the fall student athletes?

Explain. _____

_____

Student Participation in Fall Sports

Bar graph — Number of Student Athletes vs. Fall Sports: Field Hockey 12, Soccer 21, Football 62, Volleyball 45.

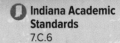

PS Problem-Solving Investigation
Determine Reasonable Answers

Indiana Academic Standards
7.C.6

PS Process Standards
1, 3, 4

Case #1 Vacations

Wesley's family spent $1,400 on a trip to the Grand Canyon. They spent 30% of the total on a sightseeing helicopter flight. Wesley estimates that his family spent about $450 on the flight.

Determine whether Wesley's estimate is reasonable.

Understand *What are the facts?*

- Wesley's family spent $1,400 on vacation.
- Thirty percent of the total was spent on a helicopter flight.
- Wesley estimates that 30% is about $450.

Plan *What is your strategy to solve this problem?*

Make a bar diagram that represents 100%.

Solve *How can you apply the strategy?*

Fill in each section of the diagram with 10% of $1,400.

Add three sections to get a total of ⬚.
So, the helicopter flight cost $420.

Check *Does the answer make sense?*

Wesley estimated the cost of the helicopter flight to be $450.
Since $450 is close to $420, his estimate was reasonable.

Analyze the Strategy Tutor 💬

PS **Make a Conjecture** How can you use $\frac{1}{3}$ to determine if Wesley's estimate is reasonable? Explain.

_____

_____

Case #2 Don't forget the tip!

At a local Italian restaurant, Brett's bill was $17.50.
He decides to leave a 20% tip for the server.

Is $4 a reasonable tip?

Understand

Read the problem. What are you being asked to find?

I need to _____ .

Is there any information that you do *not* need to know?

I do not need to know _____ .

Plan

Choose a problem-solving strategy.

I will use the _____ strategy.

Solve

Use your problem-solving strategy to solve the problem.

Use a bar diagram to represent 100%. Divide it into [   ] parts. Each part

represents [   ] % or $ [   ] .

```
|-------------- $17.50 --------------|
|  |  |  |  |  |  |  |  |  |  | 100%
|-- tip --|
```

Two parts, or [   ] %, equal $ [   ] + $ [   ] = $ [   ] .

Is $4 a reasonable tip? _____

Check

Use information from the problem to check your answer.

_____

_____

**Work with a small group to solve the following cases.
Show your work on a separate piece of paper.**

Case #3 Travel

A travel agency surveyed 140 families about their favorite vacation spots.

Is it reasonable to say that 24 more families chose Hawaii over Florida? Explain.

Favorite Vacation Spots

13% Other
15% California
48% Hawaii
24% Florida

Case #4 Exercise

A survey showed that 61% of middle school students do some kind of physical activity every day. Of those students, 9% play on the football team.

Suppose there are 828 middle school students in your school. About how many students would play on the football team?

Case #5 Clubs

Of the 36 students in the environmental club, 15 are boys and 21 are girls. The president of the club wants to add more boys so that the boys represent 50% of the students in the club.

Write and solve an equation to find the number of boys to be added. Then find the total number of students in the club.

Use any strategy!

Case #6 Bowling

In bowling, you get a spare when you knock down the ten pins in two throws.

How many possible ways are there to get a spare?

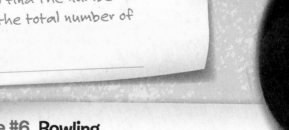

Mid-Chapter Check

Vocabulary Check

1. Fill in the blank in the sentence below with the correct term. (Lesson 4)

The _____ states that the part equals the percent multiplied by the whole.

Skills Check and Problem Solving

Find each number. Round to the nearest tenth if necessary. (Lessons 1 and 3)

2. What percent of 84 is 12? _____

Show your work →

3. 15 is 25% of what number? _____

Estimate. (Lesson 2)

4. 20% of 392 _____

5. 78% of 112 _____

Write an equation for each problem. Then solve. Round to the nearest tenth if necessary. (Lesson 4)

6. **PS Use Math Tools** A computer costs $849.75 and the hard drive is 61.3% of the total cost. What is a reasonable estimate for the cost of the hard drive? (Lesson 2)

_____

7. What number is 35% of 72? _____

8. 16.1 is what percent of 70? _____

9. **PS Persevere with Problems** Ayana has 220 coins in her piggy bank. Of those, 40% are pennies. Out of the coins that are *not* pennies, 25% are quarters. How many of the coins are quarters? (Lesson 4)

_____

Inquiry Lab
Percent of Change

Indiana Academic Standards
7.C.6

PS Process Standards
1, 3, 4

 Inquiry HOW can you use a bar diagram to show a percent of change?

The admission price for the state fair has increased by 50% in the last five years. The admission price was $6 five years ago. What is the current admission price? Do the Activity below to find out.

Hands-On Activity

Use a bar diagram to solve.

Step 1 The bar diagram represents 100%.

price 5 years ago = $6	100%

Since 50% = $\frac{1}{2}$, divide the bar diagram in half. Fill in the missing information.

price 5 years ago = ☐

$3		100%

Step 2 The admission price increased by 50%. Complete the bar diagram that represents 150% of the price 5 years ago.

price 5 years ago = ☐ ----- increase -----

$3			150%

current price = ☐

So, the current admission price is ☐ + ☐ or ☐ .

Investigate

Work with a partner to solve the following problems.

1. The height of a tree was 8 feet. After a year, the tree's height increased by

   25%. Draw a bar diagram to find the new height of the tree. _____

2. **PS Model with Mathematics** The model below describes the following scenario: Ryan put $160 in a bank account. After 2 months, the total in his account decreased by 25%. Fill in the amount in Ryan's account after 2 months.

The amount in Ryan's
account after 2 months
is ⬚ .

Collaborate

Analyze and Reflect

Work with a partner to answer the following question.

3. **PS Reason Inductively** Refer to Exercise 1. How can you find the new amount of a quantity that has increased over a period of time?

   _____

   _____

   _____

On Your Own

Create

4. Write two different ways you can find 125% of 8.

   _____

   _____

5. **inquiry** HOW can you use a bar diagram to show a percent of change?

   _____

   _____

   _____

Percent of Change

 Real-World Link

Speed Racer The Indy 500 is one of the world's great motor races. The table shows the average speed of the winning race cars for various years.

Year	Speed (mph)
1922	94
1955	128
2010	162

Essential Question

HOW can percent help you understand situations involving money?

Vocab

Vocabulary

percent of change
percent of increase
percent of decrease
percent error

Indiana Academic Standards
7.C.6

PS Process Standards
1, 3, 4, 5, 6

1. Write the ratio

$$\frac{\text{speed increase from 1922 to 1955}}{\text{speed in 1922}}.$$

Then write the ratio as a percent. Round to the nearest whole percent.

$$\frac{\boxed{}}{94} = \boxed{} \%$$

2. Write the ratio

$$\frac{\text{speed increase from 1955 to 2010}}{\text{speed in 1955}}.$$

Then write the ratio as a percent. Round to the nearest whole percent.

$$\frac{\boxed{}}{128} = \boxed{} \%$$

3. Why are the amounts of increase the same but the percents different?

_____

_____

Which PS Process Standards did you use?
Shade the circle(s) that applies.

① Persevere with Problems
② Reason Abstractly
③ Construct an Argument
④ Model with Mathematics

⑤ Use Math Tools
⑥ Attend to Precision
⑦ Make Use of Structure
⑧ Use Repeated Reasoning

Percent of Change

Words	A **percent of change** is a ratio that compares the change in quantity to the original amount.
Equation	$\text{percent of change} = \dfrac{\text{amount of change}}{\text{original amount}}$

When you compare the amount of change to the original amount in a ratio, you are finding the percent of change. The percent of change is based on the original amount.

If the original quantity is increased, then it is called a **percent of increase**. If the original quantity is decreased, then it is called a **percent of decrease**.

$$\text{percent of increase} = \dfrac{\text{amount of increase}}{\text{original amount}}$$

$$\text{percent of decrease} = \dfrac{\text{amount of decrease}}{\text{original amount}}$$

 Examples Watch | Tutor

1. **Find the percent of change in the cost of gasoline from 1970 to 2010. Round to the nearest whole percent if necessary.**

1970 · GAS · $1.30
2010 · GAS · $2.95

Since the 2010 price is greater than the 1970 price, this is a percent of increase.

Step 1 Find the amount of increase.
$\$2.95 - \$1.30 = \$1.65$

Step 2 Find the percent of increase.

$$\text{percent of increase} = \dfrac{\text{amount of increase}}{\text{original amount}}$$

$$= \dfrac{\$1.65}{\$1.30} \qquad \text{Substitution}$$

$$\approx 1.27 \qquad \text{Simplify.}$$

$$\approx 127\% \qquad \text{Write 1.27 as a percent.}$$

The cost of gasoline increased by about 127% from 1970 to 2010.

Percents

In the percent of change formula, the decimal repesenting the percent of change must be written as a percent.

2. Yusuf bought a DVD recorder for $280. Now, it is on sale for $220. Find the percent of change in the price. Round to the nearest whole percent if necessary.

Since the new price is less than the original price, this is a percent of decrease.

Step 1 Find the amount of decrease.
$280 − $220 = $60

Step 2 Find the percent of decrease.

$$\text{percent of decrease} = \frac{\text{amount of decrease}}{\text{original amount}}$$

$$= \frac{\$60}{\$280} \qquad \text{Substitution}$$

$$\approx 0.21 \qquad \text{Simplify.}$$

$$\approx 21\% \qquad \text{Write 0.21 as a percent.}$$

The price of the DVD recorder decreased by about 21%.

> **Percent of Change**
> Always use the original amount as the whole when finding percent of change.

Got it? Do these problems to find out.

Show your work.

a. Find the percent of change from 10 yards to 13 yards.

a. _____

b. The price of a radio was $20. It is on sale for $15. What is the percent of change in the price of a radio?

b. _____

Percent Error

Key Concept

Words The **percent error** is a ratio that compares the inaccuracy of an estimate, or amount of error, to the actual amount.

Equation $\text{percent error} = \dfrac{\text{amount of error}}{\text{actual amount}}$

Finding the percent error is similar to finding the percent of change. Instead of finding the amount of increase or decrease, you will find the amount an estimate is greater or less than the actual amount.

Suppose you guess there are 300 gum balls in a jar, but there are actually 400.

Error → 400 Actual amount
→ 300 Guess

$\text{Percent error} = \dfrac{100}{400}$ or 25%

Example

STOP and Reflect

How is finding a percent error like finding a percent of change?

3. Ahmed wants to practice free-throws. He estimates the distance from the free-throw line to the hoop and marks it with chalk. Ahmed's estimate was 13.5 feet. The actual distance should be 15 feet. Find the percent error.

Step 1 Find the amount of error.
15 feet − 13.5 feet = 1.5 feet

Step 2 Find the percent error.

$$\text{percent error} = \frac{\text{amount of error}}{\text{actual amount}}$$

$$= \frac{1.5}{15} \qquad \text{Substitution.}$$

$$= 0.1 \text{ or } 10\% \qquad \text{Simplify.}$$

So, the percent error is 10%.

Got it? Do this problem to find out.

c. Find the percent error if the estimate is $230 and the actual amount is $245. Round to the nearest whole percent.

c. _____

Guided Practice

Check

Find each percent of change. Round to the nearest whole percent if necessary. State whether the percent of change is an *increase* or a *decrease*. (Examples 1 and 2)

1. 30 inches to 24 inches _____

2. $126 to $150 _____

3. Jessie estimates the weight of her cat to be 10 pounds. The actual weight of the cat is 13.75 pounds. Find the percent error. (Example 3) _____

4. **Building on the Essential Question** Explain how two amounts of change can be the same but the percents of change can be different.

_____

_____

_____

Rate Yourself!

How confident are you about percent of change? Check the box that applies.

For more help, go online to access a Personal Tutor.

Independent Practice

Go online for Step-by-Step Solutions

Find each percent of change. Round to the nearest whole percent if necessary. State whether the percent of change is an *increase* or a *decrease*. (Examples 1 and 2)

1. 15 yards to 18 yards

2. 100 acres to 140 acres

 Show your work.

3. $15.60 to $11.70

4. 125 centimeters to 87.5 centimeters

5. 1.6 hours to 0.95 hour

6. 132 days to 125.4 days

PS **Be Precise** Find the percent error. Round to the nearest whole percent if necessary. (Example 3)

7. Each week, Mr. Jones goes to the grocery store. Mr. Jones estimates that he will spend $120 when he goes to the grocery store this week. He actually spends $94.

8. Marcus estimates that 230 people will attend the choir concert. There was an actual total of 300 people who attended the choir concert.

For each situation, find each percent of change. Round to the nearest whole percent if necessary. State whether the percent of change is an *increase* or a *decrease*. (Examples 1 and 2)

9. Three months ago, Santos could walk 2 miles in 40 minutes. Today he can walk 2 miles in 25 minutes.

10. Last school year the enrollment of Genoa Middle School was 465 students. This year the enrollment is 525.

11. Refer to the rectangle at the right. Suppose the side lengths are doubled.

4 in.

2 in.

   a. Find the percent of change in the perimeter. _____

   b. Find the percent of change in the area. _____

12. **PS Use Math Tools** Find examples of data reflecting change over a period of time in a newspaper or magazine, on television, or on the Internet. Determine the percent of change. Explain whether the data show a percent of increase or decrease.

13. Use the graph shown to find the percent of change in CD

    sales from 2011 to 2012. _____

Drop in CD Sales

Year

2011 — 283 million

2012 — 271 million

270   275   280   285   290

Sale of CDs (in millions)

🔥 H.O.T. Problems Higher Order Thinking

14. **PS Persevere with Problems** The costs of two sound systems were decreased by $10. The original costs of the systems were $90 and $60. Without calculating, which had a greater percent of decrease? Explain.

   _____

   _____

15. **PS Find the Error** Dario is finding the percent of change from $52 to $125. Find his mistake and correct it.

$$\frac{\$125 - \$52}{\$125} \approx 0.58$$

or 58%

   _____

   _____

   _____

16. **PS Reason Inductively** If a quantity increases by 25% and then decreases by 25%, will the result be the original quantity? Explain.

   _____

   _____

   _____

Extra Practice

Find each percent of change. Round to the nearest whole percent. State whether the percent of the change is an *increase* or *decrease*.

17. $12 to $6

    50%; decrease

    12 − 6 = 6

    $\frac{6}{12}$ = 0.5 or 50%

Homework Help

18. 48 notebooks to 14 notebooks

19. $240 to $320

20. 624 feet to 702 feet

21. The table shows the number of youth 7 years and older who played soccer from 2004 to 2012.

  a. Find the percent of change from 2008 to 2012. Round to the nearest tenth of a percent. Is it an increase or decrease?

  b. Find the percent of change from 2006 to 2008. Round to the nearest tenth of a percent. Is it an increase or decrease?

Playing Soccer	
Year	Number (millions)
2004	12.9
2006	13.7
2008	13.3
2010	14.0
2012	13.8

22. Shoe sales for a certain company were $25.9 billion. Sales are expected to increase by about 20% in the next year. Find the projected amount of shoe sales next year. _____

23. **PS Be Precise** Eva estimates that 475 songs will fit on her MP3 player. The actual amount of songs that fit is 380. Find the percent error. _____

24. The table shows Catalina's babysitting hours. She charges $6.50 per hour. Write a sentence that compares the percent of change in the amount of money earned from April to May to the percent of change in the amount of money earned from May to June. Round to the nearest percent if needed.

Month	Hours Worked
April	30
May	35
June	45

25. Dario increased his savings from $350 to $413, while Monica increased her savings from $225 to $270. Fill in each blank below to write a true statement.

[   ] had a higher percent of increase in savings. The difference

in the percents of increase is [   ].

26. The line graph shows the level of the Elk River during a period of heavy rainfall.

Find the percent of increase in the river level from Monday to Tuesday, from Tuesday to Wednesday, from Wednesday to Thursday, and from Thursday to Friday. Round to the nearest tenth of a percent if necessary. Sort the percents of increase between consecutive days from least to greatest.

Elk River

	Consecutive Days	Percent of Increase
Least		
Greatest		

Spiral Review

Find each sum.

27. $1.5 + 2.25 =$ _____

28. $32.5 + 13.43 =$ _____

29. $\$66.99 + \$8.15 =$ _____

30. The distances around Earth at the equator and through the North and South Poles are shown at the right. How many miles would you travel if you circled Earth along both routes?

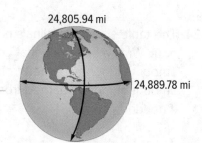

24,805.94 mi

24,889.78 mi

_____

Sales Tax, Tips, and Markup

 Real-World Link

Kayaks Alonso plans to buy a new kayak that costs $2,100. But when he buys the kayak, it actually costs more because he lives in a county where there is a 7% sales tax.

You can find the amount of tax on an item by multiplying the price by the tax percentage.

1. Circle the amount below that shows the amount of tax Alonso will pay for the kayak.

   $350 $235 $147

2. Use the amount of tax from Exercise 1 to fill in the receipt at the right. Then find the total cost Alonso will pay for the kayak.

3. Multiply 1.07 and $2,100. How does the result compare to your answer in Exercise 2?

   _____

4. On Alonso's kayaking trip, hiring a guide costs $50. Alonso wants to give the guide a 10% tip. Explain how to find the amount of the tip.

   _____

   _____

Jimmie's Kayaks

Kayak _____

Sales Tax + _____

Total _____

 Essential Question

HOW can percent help you understand situations involving money.

Vocab
Vocabulary

sales tax
tip
gratuity
markup
selling price

 Indiana Academic Standards
7.C.6

PS Process Standards
1, 3, 4

Which PS Process Standards did you use?
Shade the circle(s) that applies.

① Persevere with Problems   ⑤ Use Math Tools

② Reason Abstractly   ⑥ Attend to Precision

③ Construct an Argument   ⑦ Make Use of Structure

④ Model with Mathematics   ⑧ Use Repeated Reasoning

Sales Tax and Total Cost

Sales tax is an additional amount of money charged on items that people buy. The total cost of an item is the regular price plus the sales tax.

Example

1. Drew wants to buy exercise equipment that costs $140 and the sales tax is 5.75%. What is the total cost of the equipment?

> **Method 1** Add sales tax to the regular price.
>
> First, find the sales tax.
>
> Let t represent the sales tax.
>
> $\underbrace{\text{part}} = \underbrace{\text{percent}} \times \underbrace{\text{whole}}$ Write the percent equation.
>
> $t = 0.0575 \times 140$ 5.75% = 0.0575
>
> $t = 8.05$ Multiply.
>
> Next, add the sales tax to the regular price.
> $8.05 + 140 = 148.05$

> **Method 2** Add the percent of tax to 100%.
>
> $100\% + 5.75\% = 105.75\%$ Add the percent of tax to 100%.
>
> Let t represent the total.
>
> $\underbrace{\text{part}} = \underbrace{\text{percent}} \times \underbrace{\text{whole}}$ Write the percent equation.
>
> $t = 1.0575 \times 140$ 105.75% = 1.0575
>
> $t = \$148.05$ Multiply.
>
> The total cost of the exercise equipment is $148.05.

Show your work.

Got it? Do this problem to find out.

a. _____

a. What is the total cost of a sweatshirt if the regular price is $42 and the sales tax is $5\frac{1}{2}\%$?

Tips and Markups

A **tip** or **gratuity** is a small amount of money in return for a service. The total price is the regular price of the service plus the tip.

A store sells items for more than it pays for those items. The amount of increase is called the **markup**. The **selling price** is the amount the customer pays for an item.

Examples

Tutor

2. A customer wants to tip 15% on a restaurant bill that is $35. What will be the total bill with tip?

Method 1 Add the tip to the regular price.

First, find the tip. Let t represent the tip.

part = percent × whole

t = 0.15 × 35   15% = 0.15

t = 5.25   Multiply.

Next, add the tip to the bill.

$5.25 + $35 = $40.25   Add.

Method 2 Add the percent of tip to 100%.

100% + 15% = 115%   Add the percent of tip to 100%.

The total cost is 115% of the bill. Let t represent the total.

part = percent × whole

t = 1.15 ×35   115% = 1.15

t = 40.25   Multiply.

Using either method, the total cost of the bill with tip is $40.25.

3. A haircut costs $20. Sales tax is 4.75%. Is $25 sufficient to cover the haircut with tax and a 15% tip?

Sales tax is 4.75% and the tip is 15%, so together they will be 19.75%. Let t represent the tax and tip.

part = percent × whole

t = 0.1975 × 20   0.15 + 0.0475 = 0.1975

t = 3.95   Multiply.

$20 + $3.95 = $23.95   Add.

Since $23.95 < $25, $25 is sufficient to cover the total cost.

Got it? Do these problems to find out.

b. Scott wants to tip his taxicab driver 20%. If his commute costs $15, what is the total cost?

c. Find the total cost of a spa treatment of $42 including 6% tax and 20% tip.

Mental Math

10% of a number can be found by moving the decimal one place to the left. 10% of $20 is $2. So, 20% of $20 is $4.

Show your work.

b. _____

c. _____

Example

4. **A store pays $56 for a GPS navigation system. The markup is 25%. Find the selling price.**

First, find the markup. Let m represent the markup.

$\underbrace{\text{part}} = \underbrace{\text{percent}} \times \underbrace{\text{whole}}$ Write the percent equation.

$m \ = \ 0.25 \ \times \ 56$ $25\% = 0.25$

$m \ = \ 14$ Mulitply.

Next, add the markup to the amount the store pays.

$\$14 + \$56 = \$70$ Add.

The selling price of the GPS navigation system is $70.

> **Markup**
>
> In Example 4, you could find the selling price by finding 125% of the amount the store pays.

Got it? **Do this problem to find out.**

d. A store pays $150 for a portable basketball backboard and the markup is 40%. What is the selling price?

d. _____

Guided Practice

Find the total cost to the nearest cent. (Examples 1 and 2)

1. $2.95 notebook; 5% tax _____

2. $28 lunch; 15% tip _____

3. Jaimi went to have a manicure that cost $30. She wanted to tip the technician 20% and tax is 5.75%. How much did she spend total for the manicure? (Example 3)

_____

4. Find the selling price of a $62.25 karaoke machine with

a 60.5% markup. (Example 4) _____

5. **Building on the Essential Question** Describe two methods for finding the total price of a bill that includes a

20% tip. Which method do you prefer? _____

_____

> **Rate Yourself!**
>
> How well do you understand finding sales tax, tips, and markups? Circle the image that applies.
>
>
>
> Clear   Somewhat   Not So
>   Clear   Clear
>
> For more help, go online to access a Personal Tutor.

Independent Practice

Go online for Step-by-Step Solutions

eHelp

Find the total cost to the nearest cent. (Examples 1 and 2)

1. $58 bill; 20% tip _____

Show your work.

2. $43 dinner; 18% gratuity _____

3 $1,500 computer; 7% tax _____

4. $46 shoes; 2.9% tax _____

5 **Financial Literacy** A restaurant bill comes to $28.35. Find the total cost if the tax is 6.25% and a 20% tip is left on the amount before tax.

(Example 3) _____

6. Toru takes his dog to be groomed. The fee to groom the dog is $75 plus 6.75% tax. Is $80 enough to pay for the service? Explain.

(Example 3) _____

_____

7. Find the selling price of a $270 bicycle with a 24% markup. (Example 4) _____

8. Find the selling price of a $450 painting with a 45% markup. (Example 4) _____

9. What is the sales tax on the chair shown if the tax rate is 5.75%? _____

$178.90

10. A store pays $10 for a bracelet, and the markup is 115%. A customer will also pay a $5\frac{1}{2}$% sales tax. What will be the total cost of the bracelet to the nearest cent? _____

H.O.T. Problems Higher Order Thinking

11. (PS) **Persevere with Problems** The Leather Depot buys a coat from a supplier for $90 wholesale and marks up the price by 40%. If the retail price is $134.82, what is the sales tax? _____

12. (PS) **Model with Mathematics** Give an example of the regular price of an item and the total cost including sales tax if the tax rate is 5.75%.

_____

_____

13. (PS) **Which One Doesn't Belong?** In each pair, the first value is the regular price of an item and the second value is the price with gratuity. Identify the pair that does not belong with the other three. Explain your reasoning to a classmate.

| $30, $34.50 | $54, $64.80 | $16, $18.40 | $90, $103.50 |

_____

_____

14. (PS) **Reason Abstractly** Prices for several cell phones are listed in the table. The table shows the regular price p and the price with tax t. The sales tax is 8%. Write a formula that could be used to calculate the price with tax.

Phone	Regular Price (p)	Price with Tax (t)
Flip phone	$80	$86.40
Slide phone	$110	$118.80
Video phone	$120	$129.60

_____

15. (PS) **Use a Counterexample** Is the following statement *true* or *false*? If *false*, provide a counterexample.

It is impossible to increase the cost of an item by more than 100%.

_____

_____

Extra Practice

Find the total cost to the nearest cent.

16. $99 CD player; 5% tax $103.95

Homework
Help

$$0.05 \times 99 = 4.95$$

$99.00
+ 4.95
$103.95

17. $13 haircut; 15% tip $14.95

$$0.15 \times 13 = 1.95$$

$13.00
+ 1.95
$14.95

18. $7.50 meal; 6.5% tax _____

19. $39 pizza order; 15% tip _____

20. $89.75 scooter; $7\frac{1}{4}$% tax _____

21. $8.50 yoga mat; 75% markup _____

22. **(PS) Reason Inductively** Diana and Sujit clean homes for a summer job. They charge $70 for the job plus 5% for supplies. A homeowner gave them a 15% tip. Did they receive more than $82 for their job? Explain.

_____

_____

23. **(PS) Find the Error** Jamar is finding the selling price of a pair of $40 skates with a 30% markup. Find his mistake and correct it.

$$0.3 \times \$40 = 12$$
$$\$40 - 12 = \$28$$

_____

_____

_____

24. The same pair of boots is sold at four stores in different counties. The costs and sales tax rates are shown in the table.

Sort the total costs after sales tax from least to greatest.

	Store	Total Cost
Least		
Greatest		

Store	Price	Tax Rate
Boot World	$54.90	5.5%
Shoes 'n More	$53.25	7%
Nos Zapatos	$52.20	6.25%
Frank's Footwear	$53.95	6.5%

Which store has the lowest price after sales tax? [ ]

25. An office supply store marks up their prices by 30%. Which of the following could be items sold by the store? Select all of that apply.

- ☐ office chair: cost: $72, selling price: $94.50
- ☐ printer paper: cost: $4.60, selling price: $5.98
- ☐ box of paper clips: cost: $1.20, selling price: $1.65
- ☐ file cabinet: cost: $60, selling price: $78

Spiral Review

Solve.

26. $45 - 4.5 =$ _____

27. $89 - 31.15 =$ _____

28. $102 - $25.75 =$ _____

29. Renata paid $35.99 for a dress. The dress was on sale for $14.01 off its regular price. What was the regular price of the dress?

_____

30. Mr. Durant bought Console B for $20.99 off the advertised price. Find the total amount Mr. Durant paid.

_____

Game Console	Advertised Price ($)
A	128.99
B	138.99
C	148.99

Real-World Link

Water Parks A pass at a water park is $58 dollars at the beginning of the season. The cost of the pass decreases each month.

1. Each month 10% is taken off the price of a season pass. Find the discounted price for August by completing the fill-ins below.

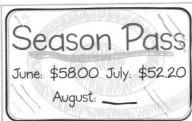

Season Pass

June: $58.00   July: $52.20

August: _____

Price in July   Write 10% as a decimal.   Amount of discount

_____ × _____ = _____

Price in July   Amount of discount   Discounted price for August

_____ − _____ = _____

2. Multiply 0.9 and $52.20. How does the result compare to your answer in Exercise 1?

_____

_____

3. Write the definition of *discount* in your own words. _____

_____

Essential Question

HOW can percent help you understand situations involving money?

Vocab

Vocabulary

discount
markdown

 Indiana Academic Standards
7.C.6

PS Process Standards
1, 3, 4, 5

Which PS Process Standards did you use?
Shade the circle(s) that applies.

① Persevere with Problems

② Reason Abstractly

③ Construct an Argument

④ Model with Mathematics

⑤ Use Math Tools

⑥ Attend to Precision

⑦ Make Use of Structure

⑧ Use Repeated Reasoning

Find Sale Price and Original Price

Discount or **markdown** is the amount by which the regular price of an item is reduced. The sale price is the regular price minus the discount.

 Example

Tutor

1. A DVD normally costs $22. This week it is on sale for 25% off the original price. What is the sale price of the DVD?

```
        Original Price
              $22
|----------        ----------|
|                            |        |
|-------- Sale Price -----|-- 25% --|
```

Method 1 Subtract the discount from the regular price.

First, find the amount of the discount.

Let *d* represent the discount.

$\underbrace{\text{part}} = \underbrace{\text{percent}} \times \underbrace{\text{whole}}$ Write the percent equation.

$d = 0.25 \times 22$ $25\% = 0.25.$

$d = 5.50$ Multiply.

Next, subtract the discount from the regular price.

$\$22 - \$5.50 = \$16.50$

Method 2 Subtract the percent of discount from 100%.

$100\% - 25\% = 75\%$ Subtract the discount from 100%.

The sale price is 75% of the regular price.

Let *s* represent the sale price.

$\underbrace{\text{part}} = \underbrace{\text{percent}} \times \underbrace{\text{whole}}$ Write the percent equation.

$s = 0.75 \times 22$ $75\% = 0.75$

$s = 16.50$ Multiply.

The sale price of the DVD is $16.50.

Show your work.

Got it? Do this problem to find out.

a. _____

a. A shirt is regularly priced at $42. It is on sale for 15% off of the regular price. What is the sale price of the shirt?

Example

Tutor

2. A boogie board that has a regular price of $69 is on sale at a 35% discount. What is the sale price with 7% tax?

Step 1 Find the amount of the discount.

Let *d* represent the discount.

$$\underbrace{\text{part}} = \underbrace{\text{percent}} \times \underbrace{\text{whole}} \qquad \text{Write the percent equation.}$$
$$d = 0.35 \times 69 \qquad 35\% = 0.35$$
$$d = 24.15 \qquad \text{Multiply.}$$

Step 2 Subtract the discount from the regular price.

$69 - $24.15 = $44.85

Step 3 The percent of tax is applied after the discount is taken.

7% of $44.85 = 0.07 · 44.85   Write 7% as a decimal.

$= 3.14$ The tax is $3.14.

$44.85 + $3.14 = $47.99   Add the tax to the sale price.

The sale price of the boogie board including tax is $47.99.

Got it? Do this problem to find out.

Show your work.

b. A CD that has a regular price of $15.50 is on sale at a 25% discount. What is the sale price with 6.5% tax?

b. _____

Example

Tutor

3. A cell phone is on sale for 30% off. If the sale price is $239.89, what is the original price?

The sale price is 100% − 30% or 70% of the original price.

Let *p* represent the original price.

$$\underbrace{\text{part}} = \underbrace{\text{percent}} \times \underbrace{\text{whole}}$$
$$239.89 = 0.7 \times p$$
$$\frac{239.89}{0.7} = \frac{0.7p}{0.7} \qquad \text{Divide each side by 0.7.}$$
$$342.70 = p \qquad \text{Simplify.}$$

The original price is $342.70.

Got it? Do this problem to find out.

c. Find the original price if the sale price of the cell phone is $205.50.

c. _____

Percent Equation

Remember that in the percent equation, the percent must be written as a decimal. Since the sale price is 70% of the original price, use 0.7 to represent 70% in the percent equation.

Example

Tutor

4. **Clothes Are Us and Ratcliffe's are having sales. At Clothes Are Us, a pair of sneakers is on sale for 40% off the regular price of $50. At Ratcliffe's, the same brand of sneakers is discounted by 30% off of the regular price of $40. Which store has the better sale price? Explain.**

Find the sale price of the sneakers at each store.

Clothes Are Us

60% of $50 = 0.6 × $50

= $30

The sale price is $30.

Ratcliffe's

70% of $40 = 0.7 × $40

= $28

The sale price is $28.

Since $28 < $30, the sale price at Ratcliffe's is the better buy.

 Show your work.

Got it? Do this problem to find out.

d. _____

d. If the sale at Clothes Are Us was 50% off, which store would have the better buy? Explain.

Guided Practice

 Check

1. Mary and Roberto bought identical backpacks at different stores. Mary's backpack originally cost $65 and was discounted 25%. Roberto's backpack originally cost $75 and was on sale for 30% off of the original price. Which backpack was the better buy? Explain. (Examples 1, 2, and 4)

 Show your work.

_____

2. A pair of in-line skates is on sale for $90. If this price represents a 9% discount from the original price, what is the original price to the nearest cent? (Example 3)

_____

3. **Building on the Essential Question** Describe two methods for finding the sale price of an item that is discounted 30%.

_____

_____

_____

Name _____ My Homework _____

Find the sale price to the nearest cent. (Examples 1 and 2)

1. $64 jacket; 20% discount _____

Show
your
work.

2. $1,200 TV; 10% discount _____

3. $7.50 admission; 20% off;

5.75% tax _____

4. $4.30 makeup; 40% discount;

6% tax _____

5. A bottle of hand lotion is on sale for $2.25. If this price represents a 50% discount from the original price, what is the original price to the nearest cent? (Example 3)

_____

6. A tennis racket at Sport City costs $180 and is discounted 15%. The same model racket costs $200 at Tennis World and is on sale for 20% off. Which store is offering the better deal? Explain. (Example 4)

_____

_____

7. (PS) **Model with Mathematics** Refer to the graphic novel frame below.

I think we have it! Guess where we are going?

We want the cheapest admission for our trip. Refer to the calculations you made at the end of Lesson 2-1.

a. Find the price that a student would pay including the group discount for

each amusement park. _____

_____

b. Which is the best deal? _____

8. The Wares want to buy a new computer. The regular price is $1,049. The store is offering a 20% discount and a sales tax of 5.25% is added after the discount. What is the total cost? _____

Find the original price to the nearest cent.

9. calendar: discount, 75%;

sale price, $2.25 _____

10. telescope: discount, 30%;

sale price, $126 _____

11. (PS) **Use Math Tools** Compare and contrast tax and discount.

Tax   Discount

H.O.T. Problems Higher Order Thinking

12. (PS) **Model with Mathematics** Give an example of the sale price of an item and the total cost including sales tax if the tax rate is 5.75% and the item is 25% off. _____

_____

13. (PS) **Persevere with Problems** A store is having a sale in which all items are discounted 20%. Including tax, Colin paid $21 for a picture. If the sales tax rate is 5%, what was the original price of the picture? _____

14. (PS) **Reason Abstractly** Describe two methods for finding the sale price of an item that is discounted 30%. Which method do you prefer? Explain.

_____

_____

_____

_____

Extra Practice

Find the sale price to the nearest cent.

15. $119.50 skateboard;
20% off; 7% tax   *$102.29*

$0.20 \times \$119.50 = \$23.90$
$\$119.50 - \$23.90 = \$95.60$
$0.07 \times \$95.60 = \$6.69$
$\$95.60 + \$6.69 = \$102.29$

16. $40 sweater; 33% discount _____

17. $199 MP3 player; 15% discount _____

18. $12.25 pen set; 60% discount _____

19. Mrs. Robinson bought a novel at a bookstore on sale for 20% off its regular price of $29.99. Mr. Chang bought the same novel at a different bookstore for 10% off its regular price of $25. Which person received the better

discount? Explain. _____

_____

20. **Multiple Representations** An online store is having a sale on digital cameras. The table shows the regular price and the sale price for the cameras.

a. **Words** Write a rule that can be used to find the percent of decrease for any of the cameras.

_____

_____

Camera Model	Regular Price	Sale Price	Discount
A	$97.99	$83.30	
B	$102.50	$82.00	
C	$75.99	$65.35	
D	$150.50	$135.45	

b. **Table** Complete the table for the discount.

c. **Numbers** Which model has the greatest percent discount?

_____

21. An appliance store is having a 15% off sale during a holiday weekend. Which of the following could be deals offered by the store during the sale? Select all that apply.

    ☐ washing machine: regular price: $680, sale price: $578

    ☐ refrigerator: regular price: $1,120, sale price: $896

    ☐ dryer: regular price: $340, sale price: $289

    ☐ chest freezer: regular price: $250, sale price: $212.50

22. The table shows the regular prices and sale prices of items at 4 different stores. Select the correct percent of discount offered by each store.

Store	Price	Sale Price	Percent of Discount
A	$68.20	$51.15	
B	$125.40	$100.32	
C	$269.75	$215.80	
D	$38.60	$32.81	

15%	25%
20%	30%

Spiral Review

Find the percent of change. Round to the nearest whole percent if necessary. State whether the percent of change is an *increase* or *decrease*.

23. 35 birds to 45 birds

24. 60 inches to 38 inches

25. $2.75 to $1.80

26. Complete the table to express each number of months in years. Write in simplest form. The first one is done for you.

Number of Months	1	2	3	4	6
Time in Years	$\frac{1}{12}$				

Financial Literacy: Simple Interest

Vocabulary Start-Up

Principal is the amount of money deposited or borrowed. **Simple interest** is the amount paid or earned for the use of money.

The simple interest formula is shown below. Fill in the diagram using the correct words from the word bank.

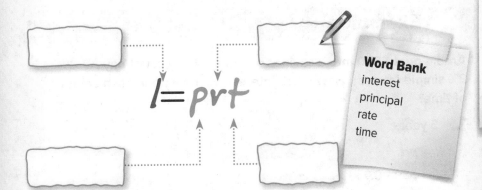

$$I = prt$$

Word Bank
interest
principal
rate
time

Essential Question

HOW can percent help you understand situations involving money?

Vocabulary

principal
simple interest

Indiana Academic Standards
7.C.6

PS Process Standards
1, 3, 4

Real-World Link

Mrs. Ramirez is investing $400 in a savings account at a simple interest rate of 2% to purchase a laptop computer. She plans on investing the money for 18 months.

Based on this real-world situation, fill in the blanks with the correct numbers. Write the rate as a decimal. Time is expressed in years.

principal = [ ]   rate = [ ]   time = [ ] years

Which **PS Process Standards** did you use?
Shade the circle(s) that applies.

① Persevere with Problems
② Reason Abstractly
③ Construct an Argument
④ Model with Mathematics

⑤ Use Math Tools
⑥ Attend to Precision
⑦ Make Use of Structure
⑧ Use Repeated Reasoning

Simple Interest Formula

Words   Simple interest I is the product of the principal p, the annual interest rate r, and the time t, expressed in years.

Symbols $I = prt$

Work Zone

If you have a savings account, the bank pays you interest for the use of your money. Use the formula $I = prt$ to find the amount of interest that will be earned.

Examples

Tutor

Arnold puts \$580 into a savings account. The account pays 3% simple interest. How much interest will he earn in each amount of time?

1. **5 years**

$I = prt$	Formula for simple interest
$I = 580 \cdot 0.03 \cdot 5$	Replace p with \$580, r with 0.03, and t with 5.
$I = 87$	Simplify.

So, Arnold will earn \$87 in interest in 5 years.

2. **6 months**

6 months $= \dfrac{6}{12}$ or 0.5 year	Write the time as years.
$I = prt$	Formula for simple interest
$I = 580 \cdot 0.03 \cdot 0.5$	$p = \$580, r = 0.03, t = 0.5$
$I = 8.7$	Simplify.

So, Arnold will earn \$8.70 in interest in 6 months.

Show your work.

Got it? Do these problems to find out.

a. _____

b. _____

a. Jenny puts \$1,560 into a savings account. The account pays 2.5% simple interest. How much interest will she earn in 3 years?

b. Marcos invests \$760 into a savings account. The account pays 4% simple interest. How much interest will he earn after 5 years?

Interest on Loans and Credit Cards

If you borrow money from a bank, you pay the bank interest for the use of their money. You also pay interest to a credit card company if you have an unpaid balance. Use the formula $I = prt$ to find the amount of interest owed.

Examples

 Tutor

3. **Rondell's parents borrow $6,300 from the bank for a new car. The interest rate is 6% per year. How much simple interest will they pay if they take 2 years to repay the loan?**

$I = prt$	Formula for simple interest
$I = 6,300 \cdot 0.06 \cdot 2$	Replace p with $6,300, r$ with 0.06, and t with 2.
$I = 756$	Simplify.

Rondell's parents will pay $756 in interest in 2 years.

STOP and Reflect

Explain in the space below how you would find the simple interest on a $500 loan at a 6% interest rate for 18 months.

4. **Derrick's dad bought new tires for $900 using a credit card. His card has an interest rate of 19%. If he has no other charges on his card and does not make a payment, how much money will he owe after one month?**

$I = prt$	Formula for simple interest
$I = 900 \cdot 0.19 \cdot \dfrac{1}{12}$	Replace p with $900, r$ with 0.19, and t with $\dfrac{1}{12}$.
$I = 14.25$	Simplify.

The interest owed after one month is $14.25.

So, the total amount owed would be $900 + $14.25 or $914.25.

Got it? Do these problems to find out.

 Show your work.

c. Mrs. Hanover borrows $1,400 at a rate of 5.5% per year. How much simple interest will she pay if it takes 8 months to repay the loan?

c. _____

d. An office manager charged $425 worth of office supplies on a credit card. The credit card has an interest rate of 9.9%. How much money will he owe at the end of one month if he makes no other charges on the card and does not make a payment?

d. _____

Tutor

5. Luis is taking out a car loan for $5,000. He plans on paying off the car loan in 2 years. At the end of 2 years, Luis will have paid $300 in interest. What is the simple interest rate on the car loan?

$I = prt$	Formula for simple interest
$300 = 5{,}000 \cdot r \cdot 2$	Replace I with 300, p with 5,000, and t with 2.
$300 = 10{,}000r$	Simplify.
$\dfrac{300}{10{,}000} = \dfrac{10{,}000r}{10{,}000}$	Divide each side by 10,000.
$0.03 = r$	

The simple interest rate is 0.03 or 3%.

Got it? Do this problem to find out.

e. _____

e. Maggie is taking out a student loan for $2,600. She plans on paying off the loan in 3 years. At the end of 3 years, Maggie will have paid $390 in interest. What is the simple interest rate on the student loan?

Guided Practice

Check

1. The Masters family financed a computer that cost $1,200. If the interest rate is 19%, how much will the family owe for the computer after one

month if no payments are made? (Examples 1–4) _____

2. Samantha received a loan from the bank for $4,500. She plans on paying off the loan in 4 years. At the end of 4 years, Samantha will have paid $900 in interest. What is the simple interest rate on the bank loan? (Example 5)

_____

3. **Building on the Essential Question** How can you use a formula to find simple interest?

_____

_____

_____

_____

Rate Yourself!

How confident are you about using the simple interest formula? Check the box that applies.

For more help, go online to access a Personal Tutor.

Tutor

Independent Practice

Go online for Step-by-Step Solutions

Find the simple interest earned to the nearest cent for each principal, interest rate, and time. (Examples 1 and 2)

1. $640, 3%, 2 years _____

2. $1,500, 4.25%, 4 years _____

3. $580, 2%, 6 months _____

4. $1,200, 3.9%, 8 months _____

Find the simple interest paid to the nearest cent for each loan amount, interest rate, and time. (Example 3)

5. $4,500, 9%, 3.5 years _____

6. $290, 12.5%, 6 months _____

7. Leon charged $75 at an interest rate of 12.5%. How much will Leon have to pay after one month if he makes no payments?
(Example 4)

8. Jamerra received a $3,000 car loan. She plans on paying off the loan in 2 years. At the end of 2 years, Jamerra will have paid $450 in interest. What is the simple interest rate on the car loan? (Example 5)

9. **PS** **Justify Conclusions** Pablo has $4,200 to invest for college.

a. If Pablo invests $4,200 for 3 years and earns $630, what is the simple

interest rate? _____

b. Pablo's goal is to have $5,000 after 4 years. Is this possible if he

invests with a rate of return of 6%? Explain. _____

_____

10. **Financial Literacy** The table shows interest owed for a home improvement loan based on how long it takes to pay off the loan.

a. How much more interest is owed on $900 for 9 months than for 6 months?

_____

_____

b. Does the interest rate increase at a constant

rate? _____

_____

Time	Rate
6 months	2.4%
9 months	2.9%
12 months	3.0%
18 months	3.1%

H.O.T. Problems Higher Order Thinking

11. **Justify Conclusions** Suppose you earn 3% on a $1,200 deposit for 5 years. Explain how the simple interest is affected if the rate is increased by 1%. What happens if the time is increased by 1 year?

_____

_____

_____

12. **PS Persevere with Problems** Dustin bought a $2,000 computer with a credit card. The minimum payment each month is $35. Each month 1% of the unpaid balance is added to the amount he owes.

a. If Dustin pays only $35 the first month, what will he owe the second

month? _____

b. If Dustin makes the minimum payment, what will he owe the third

month? _____

13. **PS Reason Inductively** Compare the two investments below. Which will have a greater account balance in the given time periods? Explain.

Investment A
Principal: $1,500
Interest Rate: 3%
Time: 30 years

Investment B
Principal: $1,500
Interest Rate: 4.5%
Time: 15 years

_____

_____

Extra Practice

Find the simple interest earned to the nearest cent for each principal, interest rate, and time.

14. $1,050, 4.6%, 2 years $96.60

$I = prt$

$I = \$1,050 \cdot 0.046 \cdot 2$

$I = 96.60$

15. $500, 3.75%, 4 months _____

16. $250, 2.85%, 3 years _____

17. $3,000, 5.5%, 9 months _____

Find the simple interest paid to the nearest cent for each loan amount, interest rate, and time.

18. $1,000, 7%, 2 years _____

19. $725, 6.25%, 1 year _____

20. $2,700, 8.2%, 3 months _____

21. $175.80, 12%, 8 months _____

22. Jake received a student loan for $12,000. He plans on paying off the loan in 5 years. At the end of 5 years, Jake will have paid $3,600 in interest. What is the simple interest rate on the student loan?

_____

23. Amy invests $3000 in a savings account that pays 2.35% simple annual interest. She makes no other deposits or withdrawals for 3.5 years. Determine if each statement is true or false.

a. Amy's account will earn $246.75 in interest. ☐ True ☐ False

b. Amy's account will be worth $2753.25 after 3.5 years. ☐ True ☐ False

c. Amy's account would earn $15.75 more in interest if the annual interest rate were raised to 2.5%. ☐ True ☐ False

24. Mr. Chen needs to borrow $12,000 to buy a car. The table shows the terms of 3 different loan options.

Loan Option	Annual Interest Rate	Time (years)
A	5.35%	5
B	4.75%	3
C	5.1%	4

Select the correct amounts for the interest paid and the monthly payments to complete the table.

Interest Paid	Loan Option	Monthly Payment
	A	
	B	
	C	

$253.50	$380.83	$2,448.00
$301.00	$1,710.00	$3,210.00

Which loan option would you recommend for Mr. Chen? Explain your reasoning.

Spiral Review

Label the number line below from 0 to 10. Then graph each number.

25. 2.5

26. $8\frac{1}{4}$

27. 5.9

28. $\frac{1}{1}$

Inquiry Lab

Spreadsheet: Compound Interest

Indiana Academic Standards
7.C.6

PS **Process Standards**
1, 3, 5

 HOW is compound interest different from simple interest?

Jin Li's parents deposit $2,000 in a college savings account. The account pays an interest rate of 4% compounded annually. Complete the Activity to find how much money will be in the account after 9 years.

Hands-On Activity

Compound interest is interest earned on the original principal and on interest earned in the past. At the end of each time period, the interest earned is added to the principal, which becomes the new principal for the next time period.

A computer spreadsheet is a useful tool for quickly performing calculations involving compound interest. To perform a calculation in a spreadsheet cell, first enter the equals sign. For example, enter =A4+B4 to find the sum of Cells A4 and B4.

Create a spreadsheet like the one shown.

Compound Interest

	A	B	C	D
1	Rate	0.04		
2				
3	Principal	Interest	New Principal	Time (YR)
4	$2000.00	$80.00	$2080.00	1
5	$2080.00	$83.20	$2163.20	2
6	$2163.20	$86.53	$2249.73	3
7	$2249.73	$89.99	$2339.72	4
8	$2339.72	$93.59	$2433.31	5
9	$2433.31	$97.33	$2530.64	6
10	$2530.64	$101.23	$2631.86	7
11	$2631.86	$105.27	$2737.14	8
12				

Sheet 1 / Sheet 2 / Sheet 3

The interest rate is entered as a decimal.

The interest is added to the principal every year. The spreadsheet evaluates the formula A4 + B4.

The spreadsheet evaluates the formula A4×B1.

What formula would the spreadsheet use to find the new principal at the end of Year 9? _____

So, the account will have a balance of _____ after 9 years.

Investigate

Work with a partner. Create spreadsheets for the situations below.

1. Lakeesha deposits $1,500 into a Young Savers account. The account receives 4% interest compounded annually. What is the balance in Lakeesha's account after 2 years? after 3 years?

   2 Years: _____ 3 Years: _____

2. Michael deposits $2,650 into an account. The interest rate on the account is 6% compounded annually. What is the balance in Michael's account after 2 years? after 3 years?

   2 Years: _____ 3 Years: _____

Analyze and Reflect

3. **PS Reason Inductively** Suppose Elijah deposited $1,000 into a bank account paying 4.75% interest compounded annually. At the same time, Lily deposits $1,000 in a separate account that pays 5% simple interest. Elijah and Lily withdraw the money from their accounts after 6 years. Predict who made more money. Explain.

   _____

   _____

   _____

Create

4. **PS Model with Mathematics** Write a real-world problem that involves compound interest. Then create a spreadsheet and solve your problem.

   _____

   _____

   _____

5. **Inquiry** HOW is compound interest different from simple interest?

   _____

   _____

   _____

   _____

21ST CENTURY CAREER
in Video Game Design

Video Game Designer

Are you passionate about computer gaming? You might want to explore a career in video game design. A video game designer is responsible for a game's concept, layout, character development, and game-play. Game designers use math and logic to compute how different parts of a game will work.

College & Career
READINESS

Is This the Career for You?

Are you interested in a career as a video game designer? Take some of the following courses in high school.

◆ 3-D Digital Animation
◆ Introduction to Computer Literacy
◆ Introduction to Game Development

Find out how math relates to a career in Video Game Design.

PS All Fun and Games

Use the information in the circle graph and the table to solve the problems below.

1. How many of the top 20 video games sold were sports games? _____

2. Out of the top 20 video games sold, how many more music games were there than racer games? _____

3. In Week 1, the total sales for a video game were $2,374,136. What percent of the total sales was from the United States?

   Round to the nearest whole percent. _____

4. Find the percent of change in sales of the video game from Week 1 to Week 3 in Japan. Round to the nearest whole percent. _____

5. Which country had a greater percent decrease in sales from Week 1 to Week 2: Japan or the United States? Explain.

   _____

   _____

   _____

Top 20 Video Games in United States

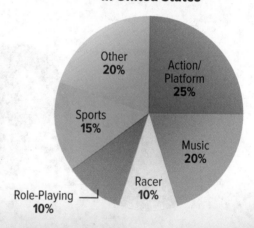

Video Game Sales History		
Week	Japan Sales ($)	U.S. Sales ($)
1	580,510	1,213,264
2	185,528	415,320
3	149,045	263,825

PS Career Project

It's time to update your career portfolio! Choose one of your favorite video games. Make a list of what you think are the best features of the game. Then describe any changes that you, as a video game designer, would make to the game.

_____

_____

_____

_____

_____

List the strengths you have that would help you succeed in this career.

• _____

• _____

• _____

• _____

Chapter Review

Vocabulary Check

Complete the crossword puzzle using the vocabulary list at the beginning of the chapter.

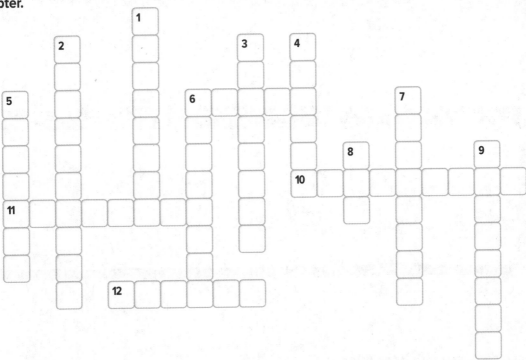

Down

1. type of percent when the final amount is greater than the original amount

2. statement that two ratios are equal

3. amount that the regular price is reduced

4. difference between what a store pays for an item and what a customer pays

5. price that a customer pays for an item

6. mathematical sentence stating that two expressions are equal

7. another term for the term in 3 down

8. gratuity

9. additional amount of money charged to items that people buy

Across

6. type of percent that compares the inaccuracy of an estimate to the actual amount

10. amount of money deposited or borrowed

11. amount paid or earned for the use of money

12. type of percent that compares the final and original amounts

Key Concept Check

Use Your FOLDABLES

Use your Foldable to help review the chapter.

Got it?

Match each sentence with its solution.

1. 15% of what number is 45?

2. What percent of 20 is 15?

3. What number is 30% of 60?

4. What percent of 600 is 750?

5. What number is 15% of 80?

6. 80% of what number is 20?

a. 125%

b. 12

c. 300

d. 18

e. 75%

f. 25

Power Up! Performance Task

DVD Deals

Anthony and Miguel go to the store to purchase some new DVDs. An advertisement in the window catches their attention.

Write your answers on another piece of paper. Show all of your work to receive full credit.

Part A
Does the information on the sign represent a proportional relationship? Explain how you know.

Part B
Miguel selects five DVDs to purchase. A few of the DVD cases appear to be damaged, so the manager gives Miguel a 20% discount on his entire purchase. Miguel tries to guess how much money will be deducted from the total cost. What is a reasonable estimate of the cost of the DVDs before tax is added? What is the actual cost before tax?

Part C
There is an 8% sales tax in the town where the store is located. What is Miguel's total cost after sales tax has been added?

Part D
Anthony decided to buy two DVDs that were not included in the deal. His price after tax was $21.60. What was the cost of the two DVDs before the sales tax was added?

Reflect

 Answering the Essential Question

Use what you learned about percent to complete the graphic organizer. For each situation, circle an arrow to show if the final amount would be greater or less than the original amount. Then write a real-world percent problem and an equation that models it.

Essential Question

HOW can percent help you understand situations involving money?

Sales Tax	Simple Interest	Discount
⬆ ⬇	⬆ ⬇	⬆ ⬇
Equation: _____	Equation: _____	Equation: _____

Answer the Essential Question. HOW can percent help you understand situations involving money?

_____

_____

UNIT PROJECT

Watch ▶ **Become a Travel Expert** Without proper planning, a family vacation could end up costing a fortune! In this project you will:

- **Collaborate** with your classmates as you research the cost of a family vacation.

- **Share** the results of your research in a creative way.

- **@ Reflect** on how you use mathematics to describe change and model real-world situations.

By the end of this project, you will be ready to plan a family vacation without breaking the bank.

Collaborate

⏻ **Go Online** Work with your group to research and complete each activity. You will use your results in the Share section on the following page.

1. Research the cost for a family of four to fly round trip to a destination of your choosing. Record the cost of a flight that is nonstop and one that has at least one extra stop. Make sure to include the cost of the tax.

2. Research two different rental cars that would be available at a local company. Compare the miles per gallon (mpg) that each car averages on the highway. How much gas would you use for each car if you were going to be traveling 450 miles on your trip?

3. If you are traveling out of the country you will need to know the current exchange rates. Record the exchange rate for three different countries. How much is $100 worth in those countries?

4. Choose a vacation spot that is a city in the United States. Find a popular restaurant for tourists in your city and look up their menu online. Calculate the cost for a dinner that feeds four people. Don't forget the tip.

5. Different states have different sales tax rates. Choose three different states. Research the sales tax rate for each of those states. Then, determine the total cost of buying jeans that cost $50 plus the sales tax.

With your group, decide on a way to share what you have learned about the cost of a family vacation. Some suggestions are listed below, but you can also think of other creative ways to present your information. Remember to show how you used mathematics in your project!

Financial Literacy Imagine that you are the director of tourism for your state. Write a script for a commercial that is trying to encourage tourists to visit. Your script should include:

- unique activities found in your state
- ways of traveling in your state

- Use your creative writing skills to write journal entries or blogs. Your writing should describe how you were able to save money while traveling on your vacations.
- Act as a travel agent to put together one domestic and one international travel package for a family of four. Create a digital brochure to explain each package.

Check out the note on the right to connect this project with other subjects.

6. **ⓔ Answer the Essential Question** How can you use mathematics to describe change and model real-world situations?

a. How did you use what you learned about ratios and proportional reasoning to describe change and model the real-world situations in this project?

_____

_____

_____

_____

b. How did you use what you learned about percents to describe change and model the real-world situations in this project?

_____

_____

_____

_____

UNIT 2
The Number System

Essential Question

HOW can mathematical ideas be represented?

Chapter 3
Integers

Negative integers can be used in everyday contexts that involve values below zero. In this chapter, you will add, subtract, multiply, and divide integers.

Chapter 4
Rational Numbers

Every quotient of integers (with non-zero divisor) is a rational number. In this chapter, you will solve multi-step real-life problems by performing operations on rational numbers.

Unit Project Preview

Watch

Explore the Ocean Depths Oceans are considered by many to be the last frontier on Earth. They are so huge that there is still a great deal that we have yet to discover about them. Think about the tallest thing on Earth. Whatever it is, it doesn't even come close to being as deep as the ocean. However, as new technologies advance, exploration continues deeper and deeper into the ocean allowing us to find many new sea creatures.

At the end of Chapter 4, you'll complete a project about the oceans. But for now, jot down four sea creatures in the table and list at what depth of the ocean you think they live.

Ocean Creatures	
Creature	Depth (m)

Chapter 3
Integers

Essential Question

WHAT happens when you add, subtract, multiply, and divide integers?

Indiana Academic Standards

7.C.1, 7.C.2, 7.C.3, 7.C.4, 7.C.8

PS Process Standards

1, 2, 3, 4, 5, 6, 7, 8

Math in the Real World

Penguins can stay under water up to 20 minutes at a time, sometimes diving to a depth of −275 feet. The number 20 is a positive integer; −275 is a negative integer.

On the graph below, graph a point at the maximum depth a penguin can dive.

FOLDABLES®
Study Organizer

 Cut out the Foldable on page FL7 of this book.

 Place your Foldable on page 254.

 Use the Foldable throughout this chapter to help you learn about integers.

Vocabulary

absolute value	integer	positive integer
additive inverse	negative integer	zero pair
graph	opposites	

Study Skill: Writing Math

Compare and Contrast When you *compare*, you notice how things are alike. When you *contrast*, you notice how they are different. Here are two cell phone plans.

Plan B
$34.99
300 anytime minutes
100 text messages
Free weekend minutes

Plan A
$34.99
200 anytime minutes
200 text messages
Free weekend minutes

Compare and contrast the monthly plans. Make a list of how they are alike and how they are different.

Alike/Compare	Different/Contrast

What Do You Already Know?

Place a checkmark below the face that expresses how much you know about each concept. Then scan the chapter to find a definition or example of it.

😞 I have no clue.   😐 I've heard of it.   🙂 I know it!

Integers

Concept	😞	😐	🙂	Definition or Example
absolute value				
adding integers				
comparing and ordering integers				
dividing integers				
multiplying integers				
subtracting integers				

When Will You Use This?

Here are a few examples of how integers are used in the real world.

Activity 1 Use the Internet or another media source to find an example of both positive and negative numbers used in the real world. Then explain the meaning of each number.

_____

_____

_____

Activity 2 Go online at **connectED.mcgraw-hill.com** to read the graphic novel *Homecoming Shirts*. Hannah asks Dario whether a certain task has been completed. What task is it?

_____

Are You Ready?

Try the Quick Check below.
Or, take the Online Readiness Quiz.

Quick Review

Example 1

Evaluate 48 ÷ (6 + 2)5.

Follow the order of operations.

$48 \div (6 + 2)5$

$= 48 \div 8 \cdot 5$ Add 6 and 2.

$= 6 \cdot 5$ Divide 48 by 8.

$= 30$ Multiply.

Example 2

Graph and label M(6, 3) on the coordinate plane.

Start from the origin. Point M is located 6 units to the right and 3 units up.

Draw a dot and label the point.

Quick Check

Order of Operations Evaluate each expression.

1. $54 \div (6 + 3) =$ _____

2. $(10 + 50) \div 5 =$ _____

3. $18 + 2(4 - 1) =$ _____

Coordinate Graphing Graph and label each point on the coordinate grid.

4. A(1, 1)

5. B(2, 8)

6. C(8, 1)

7. D(3, 4)

8. E(1, 5)

9. G(7, 6)

How Did You Do?

**Which problems did you answer correctly in the Quick Check?
Shade those exercise numbers below.**

Integers and Absolute Value

Vocabulary Start-Up

Numbers like 5 and −8 are called integers. An **integer** is any number from the set {..., −4, −3, −2, −1, 0, 1, 2, 3, 4, ...}, where ... means *continues without end*.

Complete the graphic organizer.

Describe It

Picture It

List Some Examples

List Some NonExamples

integer

Essential Question

WHAT happens when you add, subtract, multiply, and divide integers?

Vocabulary

integer
negative integer
positive integer
graph
absolute value

Indiana Academic Standards
7.C.1

PS **Process Standards**
1, 3, 4, 5

Real-World Link

- The bottom of a snowboarding halfpipe is 5 meters below the top. Circle the integer you would you use to represent this position?

    5   or   −5

- Describe another situation that uses negative

    integers. _____

    _____

Awesome halfpipe!

Which **PS** Process Standards did you use?
Shade the circle(s) that applies.

① Persevere with Problems

⑤ Use Math Tools

② Reason Abstractly

⑥ Attend to Precision

③ Construct an Argument

⑦ Make Use of Structure

④ Model with Mathematics

⑧ Use Repeated Reasoning

Identify and Graph Integers

Negative integers are integers less than zero. They are written with a − sign.

Positive integers are integers greater than zero. They can be written with a + sign.

−5 −4 −3 −2 −1   0 +1 +2 +3 +4 +5

Zero is neither negative nor positive.

Integers can be graphed on a number line. To **graph** an integer on the number line, draw a dot on the line at its location.

Examples

Tutor

Write an integer for each situation.

1. **an average temperature of 5 degrees below normal**

Because it represents *below* normal, the integer is −5.

2. **an average rainfall of 5 inches above normal**

Because it represents *above* normal, the integer is +5 or 5.

Got it? Do these problems to find out.

Write an integer for each situation.

a. 6 degrees above normal   **b.** 2 inches below normal

a. _____

b. _____

Example

Tutor

3. **Graph the set of integers {4, −6, 0} on a number line.**

Draw a number line. Then draw a dot at the location of each integer.

−10 −8 −6 −4 −2   0   2   4   6   8   10

Got it? **Do these problems to find out.**

Graph each set of integers on a number line.

c. $\{-2, 8, -7\}$

d. $\{-4, 10, -3, 7\}$

Show your work.

c. _____

d. _____

Absolute Value

Key Concept

Words	The absolute value of a number is the distance between the number and zero on a number line.

Examples	$|-5| = 5$	$|5| = 5$

On the number line in the Key Concept box, notice that -5 and 5 are each 5 units from 0, even though they are on opposite sides of 0. Numbers that are the same distance from zero on a number line have the same **absolute value**.

Examples

Tutor

Evaluate each expression.

4. $|-4|$

The graph of -4 is 4 units from 0.

So, $|-4| = 4$.

Order of Operations

The absolute value bars are considered to be a grouping symbol. When evaluating $|-5| - |2|$, evaluate the absolute values before subtracting.

5. $|-5| - |2|$

$|-5| - |2| = 5 - 2$ $|-5| = 5, |2| = 2$

So, $|-5| - |2| = 3$.

Show your work.

e. _____

Got it? **Do these problems to find out.**

e. $|8|$

f. $2 + |-3|$

g. $|-6| - 5$

f. _____

g. _____

Tutor

 Example

6. Nick climbs 30 feet up a rock wall and then climbs 22 feet down to a landing area. The number of feet Nick climbs can be represented using the expression $|30| + |-22|$. How many feet does Nick climb?

$$|30| + |-22| = 30 + |-22|$$ The absolute value of 30 is 30.

$$= 30 + 22 \text{ or } 52$$ The absolute value of -22 is 22. Simplify.

So, Nick climbs 52 feet.

Guided Practice

Check ✓

Write an integer for each situation. (Examples 1 and 2)

1. a deposit of $16 _____

2. a loss of 11 yards _____

3. 6°F below zero _____

Show your work.

Evaluate each expression. (Examples 4–6)

4. $|-9| =$ _____

5. $|18| - |-10| =$ _____

6. $|-11| - |-6| =$ _____

7. Graph the set of integers {11, −5, −8} on a number line. (Example 3)

-8 -6 -4 -2 0 2 4 6 8 10 12

8. Ⓔ **Building on the Essential Question** Why is the absolute value of a nonzero number positive? Explain your reasoning. _____

_____

_____

Rate Yourself!

☐ I understand integers and absolute value.

▶▶ Great! You're ready to move on!

☐ I still have some questions about integers and absolute value.

📖 No Problem! Go online to access a Personal Tutor.

Tutor

Independent Practice

Go online for Step-by-Step Solutions

Write an integer for each situation. (Examples 1 and 2)

1. a profit of $9 _____

Show your work.

2. a bank withdrawal of $50 _____

3. 53°C below zero _____

4. 7 inches more than normal _____

Graph each set of integers on a number line. (Example 3)

 5. {0, 1, −3}

6. {−5, −1, 10, −9}

Evaluate each expression. (Examples 4 and 5)

7. |10| = _____

8. |−7| − 5 = _____

9. 1 + |7| = _____

10. The number of yards a football team moves on the field can be represented using the expression |8| + |−4|. How many yards does the football team move? (Example 6)

_____

11. In golf, scores are often written in relationship to *par*, the average score for a round at a certain course. Write an integer to represent a score that is 7 under par. (Examples 1 and 2)

_____

_____

_____

12. A scuba diver descended 10 feet, 8 feet, and 11 feet. The total number of feet can be represented using the expression $|-10| + |-8| + |-11|$. What is the total number of feet the scuba diver descended?

13. (PS) **Use Math Tools** Mr. Chavez spent $199.99 for a new smart phone, $39.99 on a carrying case, and $59.99 on accessories. The expression $|-199.99| + |-39.99| + |-59.99|$ represents the total amount that Mr. Chavez spent. How much did Mr. Chavez spend altogether? Check your answer using estimation.

🔥 H.O.T. Problems Higher Order Thinking

14. (PS) **Reason Inductively** If $|x| = 3$, what is the value of x?

15. (PS) **Persevere with Problems** Two numbers A and B are graphed on a number line. Is it *always*, *sometimes*, or *never* true that $A - |B| \leq A + B$ and $A > |B|$? Explain.

16. (PS) **Which One Doesn't Belong?** Identify the expression that is not equal to the other three. Explain your reasoning.

$15 - |-5|$	$|-4| + 6$	$-|7 + 3|$	$|-10|$

17. (PS) **Persevere with Problems** Determine whether each statement is *always*, *sometimes*, or *never* true. Explain your reasoning.

a. $|x| = |-x|$

b. $|x| = -|x|$

c. $|-x| = -|x|$

Extra Practice

Write an integer for each situation.

18. 2 feet below flood level -2 _____

Homework
Help

Because it represents below flood level, the
integer is -2.

19. an elevator goes up 12 floors _____

PS **Model with Mathematics** Graph each set of integers on a number line.

20. {3, −7, 6}

−10 −8 −6 −4 −2   0   2   4   6   8   10

21. {−2, −4, −6, −8}

−10 −9 −8 −7 −6 −5 −4 −3 −2 −1   0

Evaluate each expression.

22. $|-12| = $ _____

23. $7 + |4| = $ _____

24. $|-9| + |-5| = $ _____

25. $|-10| \div 2 \times |5| = $ _____

26. $12 - |-8| + 7 = $ _____

27. $|27| \div 3 - |-4| = $ _____

28. Jasmine's pet guinea pig gained 8 ounces in one month.
Write an integer to describe the amount of weight her
pet gained.

_____

29. Determine if each statement is true or false.

a. A $100 check deposited in a bank can be represented by +100. ☐ True ☐ False

b. A loss of 15 yards in a football game can be represented by −15. ☐ True ☐ False

c. A temperature of 20 below zero can be represented by −20. ☐ True ☐ False

d. A submarine diving 300 feet below the surface can be represented by +300. ☐ True ☐ False

30. Rachel recorded the overnight low temperatures for one week in a table.

Low Temperatures							
Day	Sunday	Monday	Tuesday	Wednesday	Thursday	Friday	Saturday
Temperature (°F)	2	−6	4	−8	2	0	−1

Plot a point on the number line for each recorded temperature.

What is the distance on the number line between the points that represent the warmest and coldest temperatures? ☐

Spiral Review

Write the ordered pair corresponding to each point graphed at the right. Then state the quadrant or axis location of each point.

31. J _____

32. K _____

33. L _____

34. M _____

Graph and label each point on the coordinate plane.

35. A(2, 4)

36. B(−3, 1)

37. C(2, 0)

38. D(−3, −3)

Inquiry Lab
Add Integers

Indiana Academic Standards
7.C.1

PS **Process Standards**
1, 3, 7

 Inquiry **WHEN** is the sum of two integers a negative number?

In football, forward progress is represented by a positive integer. Losing yardage is represented by a negative integer. On the first play, a team lost 5 yards. On the second play, the team lost 2 yards. What was the team's total yardage on the two plays? Find out in Activity 1.

Hands-On Activity 1

Watch Tools

Use counters to find the total yardage.

Step 1 Use negative integers to represent the yards lost on each play.

$$\boxed{} + \boxed{}$$

a loss of 5 yards   a loss of 2 yards

Step 2 Combine a set of 5 negative counters and a set of 2 negative counters.

Step 3 There is a total of $\boxed{}$ negative counters. The model shows that adding a negative number to another negative number results in a negative sum.

So, $-5 + (-2) = \boxed{}$. The team lost a total of $\boxed{}$ yards on the first two plays.

The following two properties are important when modeling operations with integers.

- When one positive counter is paired with one negative counter, the result is called a **zero pair**. The value of a zero pair is 0.

- You can add or remove zero pairs from a mat because adding or removing zero does not change the value of the counters on the mat.

Hands-On Activity 2

Use counters to find −4 + 2.

Step 1　Combine ☐ negative counters with ☐ positive counters.

The addends have different signs.

Step 2　Remove all zero pairs.

There are more negative counters than positive counters.
4 > 2

Step 3　Find the number of counters remaining.

The model shows that the sum has the same sign as the greater number of counters.

There are ☐ negative counters remaining.

So, −4 + 2 = ☐.

How would the model and sum change if the addition expression was 4 + (−2)?

Investigate

Collaborate

Work with a partner. Find each sum. Show your work using drawings.

1. $5 + 6 =$ _____

Show your work.

2. $-3 + (-5) =$ _____

3. $-5 + (-4) =$ _____

4. $7 + 3 =$ _____

5. $-6 + 5 =$ _____

6. $-2 + 7 =$ _____

7. $8 + (-3) =$ _____

8. $3 + (-6) =$ _____

9. Study the exercises in which both addends are negative. What do you notice about the sum?

_____

10. Study the exercises in which one addend is negative and one is positive. What do you notice about the sum?

_____

Analyze and Reflect

Work with a partner to complete the table. The first one is done for you.

Addition Expression	Sum	Sign of Addend with Greater Absolute Value	Sign of Sum
5 + (−2)	3	positive	positive
11. −6 + 2			
12. 7 + (−12)			
13. −4 + 9			
14. −12 + 20			
15. 15 + (−18)			

Create

16. **PS Model with Mathematics** Write a rule you can use to find the sum of two negative integers without using counters.

_____

_____

_____

17. **PS Model with Mathematics** Write a rule you can use to find the sum of a positive integer and a negative integer without using counters.

_____

_____

_____

18. Write two addition sentences where the sum is zero. Describe the numbers.

_____

_____

_____

19. **Inquiry** WHEN is the sum of two integers a negative number?

_____

_____

Add Integers

 Essential Question

WHAT happens when you add, subtract, multiply, and divide integers?

Vocab
Vocabulary

opposites
additive inverse

🔵 **Indiana Academic Standards**
7.C.1

PS **Process Standards**
1, 3, 4, 7

Vocabulary Start-Up

Integers like 2 and −2 are called **opposites** because they are the same distance from 0, but on opposite sides. Complete the graphic organizer about opposites.

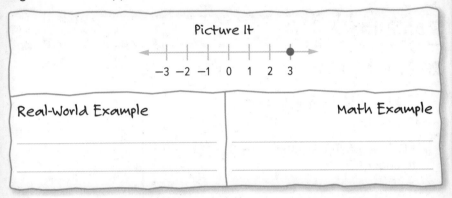

Picture It
−3 −2 −1 0 1 2 3

Real-World Example	Math Example

Two integers that are opposites are also called **additive inverses**. The Additive Inverse Property states that the sum of any number and its additive inverse is zero. You can show 2 + (−2) on a number line.

−4 −3 −2 −1 0 1 2 3 4

Start at zero.
Move 2 units to the right to show 2.
Then move 2 units to the left to show −2.

So, 2 + (−2) = ☐.

Real-World Link

The temperature outside is −5°. Name the temperature that would make the sum of the two temperatures 0°. ☐

Which PS Process Standards did you use?
Shade the circle(s) that applies.

① Persevere with Problems
② Reason Abstractly
③ Construct an Argument
④ Model with Mathematics

⑤ Use Math Tools
⑥ Attend to Precision
⑦ Make Use of Structure
⑧ Use Repeated Reasoning

Add Integers with the Same Sign

Words To add integers with the same sign, add their absolute values. The sum is:

- positive if both integers are positive.
- negative if both integers are negative.

Examples $7 + 4 = 11$ $\qquad\qquad$ $-7 + (-4) = -11$

Work Zone

Examples

Tutor

1. Find $-3 + (-2)$.

Start at 0. Move 3 units down to show -3.

From there, move 2 units down to show -2.

So, $-3 + (-2) = -5$.

2. Find $-26 + (-17)$.

$-26 + (-17) = -43$ $\qquad$ Both integers are negative, so the sum is negative.

Got it? Do these problems to find out.

a. $-5 + (-7)$ $\qquad$ **b.** $-10 + (-4)$ $\qquad$ **c.** $-14 + (-16)$

Show your work.

a. _____

b. _____

c. _____

Key Concept

Add Integers with Different Signs

Words To add integers with different signs, subtract their absolute values. The sum is:

- positive if the positive integer's absolute value is greater.
- negative if the negative integer's absolute value is greater.

Examples $9 + (-4) = 5$ $\qquad$ $-9 + 4 = -5$

When you add integers with different signs, start at zero. Move right for positive integers. Move left for negative integers. So, the sum of $p + q$ is located a distance $|q|$ from p.

Examples

Watch | **Tutor**

3. Find $5 + (-3)$.

So, $5 + (-3) = 2$.

4. Find $-3 + 2$.

So, $-3 + 2 = -1$.

Show your work.

Got it? Do these problems to find out.

d. $6 + (-7)$ **e.** $-15 + 19$

d. _____

e. _____

Examples

Tutor

5. Find $7 + (-7)$.

$7 + (-7) = 0$ Subtract absolute values; $7 - 7 = 0$. 7 and (-7) are opposites. The sum of any number and its opposite is always zero.

6. Find $-8 + 3$.

$-8 + 3 = -5$ Subtract absolute values; $8 - 3 = 5$. Since -8 has the greater absolute value, the sum is negative.

7. Find $2 + (-15) + (-2)$.

$$2 + (-15) + (-2) = 2 + (-2) + (-15)$$ Commutative Property (+)

$$= [2 + (-2)] + (-15)$$ Associative Property (+)

$$= 0 + (-15)$$ Additive Inverse Property

$$= -15$$ Additive Identity Property

Got it? Do these problems to find out.

f. $10 + (-12)$ **g.** $-13 + 18$ **h.** $(-14) + (-6) + 6$

f. _____

g. _____

h. _____

Commutative Properties

$a + b = b + a$

$a \cdot b = b \cdot a$

Associative Properties

$a + (b + c) = (a + b) + c$

$a \cdot (b \cdot c) = (a \cdot b) \cdot c$

Identity Properties

$a + 0 = a$

$a \cdot 1 = a$

Example

8. A roller coaster starts at point *A*. It goes up 20 feet, down 32 feet, and then up 16 feet to point *B*. Write an addition sentence to find the height at point *B* in relation to point *A*. Then find the sum and explain its meaning.

$$20 + (-32) + 16 = 20 + 16 + (-32)$$ Commutative Property (+)

$$= 36 + (-32)$$ $20 + 16 = 36$

$$= 4$$ Subtract absolute values.

Point *B* is 4 feet higher than point *A*.

Got it? Do this problem to find out.

Show your work.

i. The temperature is −3°. An hour later, it drops 6° and 2 hours later, it rises 4°. Write an addition expression to describe this situation. Then find the sum and explain its meaning.

i. _____

Guided Practice

Check ✓

Add. (Examples 1–7)

Show your work.

1. $-6 + (-8) =$ _____

2. $-3 + 10 =$ _____

3. $-8 + (-4) + 12 =$ _____

4. Sofia owes her brother $25. She gives her brother the $18 she earned dog-sitting. Write an addition expression to describe this situation. Then find the sum and explain its meaning. (Example 8) _____

5. **Building on the Essential Question** Explain how you know whether a sum is positive, negative, or zero without actually adding. _____

Rate Yourself!

How confident are you about adding integers? Check the box that applies.

For more help, go online to access a Personal Tutor.

Tutor

FOLDABLES Time to update your Foldable!

Independent Practice

Go online for Step-by-Step Solutions   eHelp

Add. (Examples 1–7)

1. $-22 + (-16) =$ _____

2. $-10 + (-15) =$ _____

3. $6 + 10 =$ _____

4. $21 + (-21) + (-4) =$ _____

5. $-17 + 20 + (-3) =$ _____

6. $-34 + 25 + (-25) =$ _____

7. $4 + 5 =$ _____

8. $-15 + 8 =$ _____

9. $7 + (-11) =$ _____

10. Financial Literacy Stephanie has $152 in the bank. She withdraws $20. Then she deposits $84. Write an addition expression to represent this situation. Then find the sum and explain its meaning. (Example 8)

_____

11. **PS** **Model with Mathematics** Find the total profit or loss for each color of T-shirt. _____

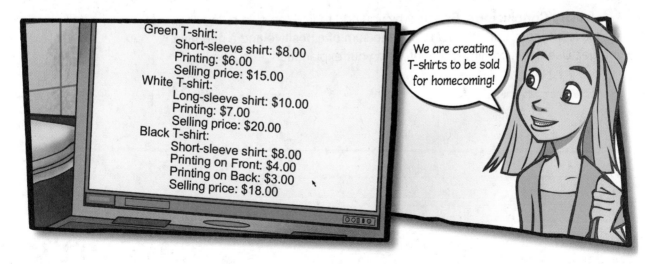

Green T-shirt:
   Short-sleeve shirt: $8.00
   Printing: $6.00
   Selling price: $15.00
White T-shirt:
   Long-sleeve shirt: $10.00
   Printing: $7.00
   Selling price: $20.00
Black T-shirt:
   Short-sleeve shirt: $8.00
   Printing on Front: $4.00
   Printing on Back: $3.00
   Selling price: $18.00

We are creating T-shirts to be sold for homecoming!

12. **⒫ Reason Abstractly** Lena deposits and withdraws money from a bank account. The table shows her transactions for March.

a. Write an addition expression to describe her transactions.

_____

b. Find the sum and explain its meaning.

_____

_____

March	
Week	Transaction
1	deposit $300
2	withdraw $50
3	withdraw $75
4	deposit $225

🔥 H.O.T. Problems Higher Order Thinking

13. **⒫ Model with Mathematics** Describe two situations in which opposite quantities combine to make zero.

_____

_____

_____

14. **⒫ Identify Structure** Name the property illustrated by the following.

a. $x + (-x) = 0$ _____

b. $x + (-y) = -y + x$ _____

⒫ Model with Mathematics Simplify.

15. $8 + (-8) + a$ _____

16. $x + (-5) + 1$ _____

17. $-9 + m + (-6)$ _____

18. **⒫ Justify Conclusions** Explain why you add to find the sum of two negative integers, but subtract to find the sum of a positive and a negative integer. Use a number line or counters in your explanation.

_____

_____

_____

_____

_____

Extra Practice

Add.

19. $18 + (-5) =$ __13__

$18 + (-5) = |18| - |-5|$

 Homework Help ➡

$= 18 - 5$

$= 13$

20. $-19 + 24 =$ __5__

$-19 + 24 = 24 + (-19)$

$= |24| - |-19|$

$= 24 - 19$

$= 5$

21. $13 + (-19) =$ _____

22. $14 + (-6) =$ _____

23. $15 + 9 + (-9) =$ _____

24. $-4 + 12 + (-9) =$ _____

25. $-16 + 16 + 22 =$ _____

26. $25 + 3 + (-25) =$ _____

27. $7 + (-19) + (-7) =$ _____

PS **Justify Conclusions** Write an addition expression to describe each situation. Then find each sum and explain its meaning.

28. Ronnie receives $40 for his birthday. Then he spends $15 at the movies.

_____

29. A quarterback is sacked for a loss of 5 yards. On the next play, his team loses 15 yards. Then the team gains 12 yards on the third play.

_____

_____

30. A pelican starts at 60 feet above sea level. It descends 60 feet to catch a fish.

_____

31. The number line at the right models an addition sentence. Determine if the situations below could be modeled by the addition sentence. Select yes or no.

-12 -11 -10 -9 -8 -7 -6 -5 -4 -3 -2 -1 0

   a. Alison spent 8 dollars on a movie ticket. Then she spent 3 dollars on a drink. ☐ Yes ☐ No

   b. A dolphin swims at a depth of 11 feet below sea level. The dolphin swims up 3 feet and then swims up another 8 feet. ☐ Yes ☐ No

   c. A football team lost 8 yards on their first play. On the second play, the team lost 3 yards. ☐ Yes ☐ No

32. At 8 A.M., the temperature was 3°F below zero. By 1 P.M., the temperature rose 14°F and by 10 P.M., dropped 12°F. Plot points and draw arrows on the number line below to model this situation.

-14 -12 -10 -8 -6 -4 -2 0 2 4 6 8 10 12 14

What was the temperature at 10 P.M.? Explain how the number line helped you find your answer.

Spiral Review

Write an integer for each situation.

33. a bank deposit of $75 _____

34. a loss of 8 pounds _____

35. 13° below zero _____

36. a gain of 4 yards _____

37. spending $12 _____

38. a gain of 5 hours _____

Inquiry Lab
Subtract Integers

Indiana Academic Standards
7.C.2

PS Process Standards
1, 2, 3, 7

 Inquiry HOW is the subtraction of integers related to the addition of integers?

A dolphin swims 6 meters below the surface of the ocean. Then it jumps to a height of 5 meters above the surface of the water. Determine the difference between the two distances.

Hands-On Activity 1

Watch | Tools

Use counters to find 5 − (−6), the difference between the distances.

| the number of positive counters placed on the mat | ┄┄> **5 − (−6)** <┄┄ | the number of negative counters that need removed from the mat |

Step 1 Place 5 positive counters on the mat. Remove 6 negative counters. However, there are 0 negative counters.

Step 2 Add ☐ zero pairs to the mat.

Step 3 Now you can remove ☐ negative counters. Count the remaining positive counters.

So, 5 − (−6) = ☐. The difference between the distances is ☐ meters.

The model shows that removing 6 negative counters yielded the same result as adding 6 positive counters.

Hands-On Activity 2

Use counters to find −6 − (−3).

the number of negative counters placed on the mat ······▸ **−6 − (−3)** ◂······ the number of negative counters removed from the mat

Step 1   Place 6 negative counters on the mat.

Step 2   Remove 3 negative counters.

There are [ ] negative counters remaining. So, −6 − (−3) = [ ].

Hands-On Activity 3

Use counters to find −5 − 1.

Step 1   Place [ ] negative counters on the mat.
You need to remove 1 positive counter.
However, there are 0 positive counters.

Step 2   Add 1 zero pair to the mat.

Step 3   Now you can remove 1 positive counter.
Find the remaining number of counters.

There are [ ] negative counters remaining.

So, −5 − 1 = [ ].

The model shows that removing 1 positive counter yielded the same result as adding 1 negative counter.

Check Find −5 + (−1). Is it the same as −5 − 1?

   −5 + (−1) = −6 ✓

Investigate

Work with a partner. Find each difference. Show your work using drawings.

1. $7 - 6 =$ _____

Show your work.

2. $5 - (-3) =$ _____

3. $6 - (-2) =$ _____

4. $5 - 8 =$ _____

5. $-7 - (-2) =$ _____

6. $-7 - 3 =$ _____

7. Refer to Exercises 2 and 3. How can you remove negative counters from a set of positive counters? What is the net effect? _____

8. Refer to Exercise 4. How can you remove a greater number of positive counters from a smaller set of positive counters? _____

Analyze and Reflect

Work with a partner. Circle an expression that is equivalent to the expression in the first column. The first one is done for you.

−3 − 1	−3 + 1	(−3 + (−1))	−3 − (−1)
9. −2 − 9	−2 − (−9)	−2 + 9	−2 + (−9)
10. −8 − 4	−8 + 4	−8 + (−4)	−8 − (−4)
11. 6 − (−2)	6 + 2	6 − 2	6 + (−2)
12. 5 − (−7)	5 − 7	5 + (−7)	5 + 7
13. −1 − (−3)	−1 − 3	−1 + 3	−1 + (−3)
14. −3 − (−8)	−3 + 8	−3 − 8	−3 + (−8)

15. **PS Model with Mathematics** Study the pattern in the table. Write a rule you can use to find the difference of two integers without using counters. Test your rule by finding 3 − (−2) two different ways using counters.

_____

_____

On Your Own

Create

16. **PS Identify Structure** Write a subtraction sentence where the difference is positive. Use a positive and a negative integer.

_____

17. Write a subtraction sentence where the difference is negative. Use a positive and a negative integer.

_____

18. **Inquiry** HOW is the subtraction of integers related to the addition of integers?

_____

_____

Subtract Integers

 Real-World Link

Diving The platform on a diving board is 3 meters high. The actions of a diver climbing up to the diving board platform and diving 1 meter below the water's surface are shown on the number line at the right.

The diver's actions can be represented by the subtraction equation $3 - 4 = -1$.

1. Write a related addition sentence for the subtraction sentence.

   _____

2. Use a number line to find $1 - 5$. Then write a related addition sentence for the subtraction sentence.

Difference: _____   Addition Sentence: _____

Essential Question

WHAT happens when you add, subtract, multiply, and divide integers?

Indiana Academic Standards
7.C.2

PS Process Standards
1, 2, 3, 4, 5, 6, 7

Which **PS Process Standards** did you use?
Shade the circle(s) that applies.

① Persevere with Problems   ⑤ Use Math Tools

② Reason Abstractly   ⑥ Attend to Precision

③ Construct an Argument   ⑦ Make Use of Structure

④ Model with Mathematics   ⑧ Use Repeated Reasoning

Subtract Integers

Work Zone

Words	To subtract an integer, add its additive inverse.
Symbols	$p - q = p + (-q)$
Examples	$4 - 9 = 4 + (-9) = -5$ $7 - (-10) = 7 + (10) = 17$

When you subtract 7, the result is the same as adding its additive inverse, -7.

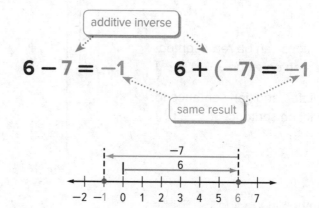

additive inverse

$$6 - 7 = -1 \qquad 6 + (-7) = -1$$

same result

Examples

Tutor

1. Find $8 - 13$.

$8 - 13 = 8 + (-13)$ To subtract 13, add -13.

$\quad\quad\quad = -5$ Simplify.

Check by adding $-5 + 13 \overset{?}{=} 8$

$\quad\quad\quad\quad\quad\quad 8 = 8 \checkmark$

2. Find $-10 - 7$.

$-10 - 7 = -10 + (-7)$ To subtract 7, add -7.

$\quad\quad\quad\quad = -17$ Simplify.

Show your work.

a. _____

Check by adding $-17 + 7 \overset{?}{=} -10$

$\quad\quad\quad\quad\quad -10 = -10 \checkmark$

b. _____

Got it? Do these problems to find out.

c. _____

a. $6 - 12$ b. $-20 - 15$ c. $-22 - 26$

Examples

Tutor

3. Find $1 - (-2)$.

$1 - (-2) = 1 + 2$ To subtract -2, add 2.

$\qquad\quad = 3$ Simplify.

---

4. Find $-10 - (-7)$.

$-10 - (-7) = -10 + 7$ To subtract -7, add 7.

$\qquad\qquad = -3$ Simplify.

> **Got it?** Do these problems to find out.
>
> **d.** $4 - (-12)$ **e.** $-15 - (-5)$ **f.** $18 - (-6)$

STOP and Reflect

Circle the integer below that will make this number sentence true.

$$-5 - (?) = -3$$

-8 -2 2

 Show your work.

d. _____

e. _____

f. _____

Examples

Tutor

5. Evaluate $x - y$ if $x = -6$ and $y = -5$.

$x - y = -6 - (-5)$ Replace x with -6 and y with -5.

$\qquad = -6 + 5$ To subtract -5, add 5.

$\qquad = -1$ Simplify.

---

6. Evaluate $m - n$ if $m = -15$ and $n = 8$.

$m - n = -15 - 8$ Replace m with -15 and n with 8.

$\qquad = -15 + (-8)$ To subtract 8, add -8.

$\qquad = -23$ Simplify.

> **Got it?** Do these problems to find out.
>
> Evaluate each expression if $a = 5$, $b = -8$, and $c = -9$.
>
> **g.** $b - 10$ **h.** $a - b$ **i.** $c - a$

g. _____

h. _____

i. _____

Tutor

Real World Example

7. The temperatures on the Moon vary from −173°C to 127°C. Find the difference between the maximum and minimum temperatures.

Subtract the lower temperature from the higher temperature.

Estimate $100 - (-200) = 300$

$127 - (-173) = 127 + 173$ To subtract −173, add 173.

$\qquad\qquad\quad = 300$ Simplify.

So, the difference between the temperatures is 300°C.

Got it? Do this problem to find out.

Show your work.

j. Brenda had a balance of −$52 in her account. The bank charged her a fee of $10 for having a negative balance. What is her new balance?

j. _____

Guided Practice

Check ✓

Subtract. (Examples 1–4)

1. $14 - 17 =$ _____

2. $14 - (-10) =$ _____

3. $12 - 26 =$ _____

4. Evaluate $q - r$ if $q = -14$ and $r = -6$. (Examples 5 and 6)

_____

5. **STEM** The sea surface temperatures range from −2°C to 31°C. Find the difference between the maximum and minimum temperatures. (Example 7) _____

6. **Building on the Essential Question** If x and y are positive integers, is $x - y$ always positive? Explain.

_____

_____

Rate Yourself!

How well do you understand subtracting integers? Circle the image that applies.

Clear   Somewhat Clear   Not So Clear

For more help, go online to access a Personal Tutor.

Tutor

FOLDABLES Time to update your Foldable!

Name _____   My Homework _____

Independent Practice

Subtract. (Examples 1–4)

1. $0 - 10 =$ _____

2. $-9 - 5 =$ _____

3 $-4 - 8 =$ _____

4. $31 - 48 =$ _____

5. $-25 - 5 =$ _____

6. $-44 - 41 =$ _____

7. $4 - (-19) =$ _____

8. $-11 - (-42) =$ _____

9. $52 - (-52) =$ _____

Evaluate each expression if $f = -6$, $g = 7$, and $h = 9$. (Examples 5 and 6)

10. $g - 7$ _____

11. $-h - (-9)$ _____

12. $f - g$ _____

13 **PS Use Math Tools** Use the information below. (Example 7)

State	Alabama	California	Florida	Louisiana	New Mexico
Lowest Elevation (ft)	0	−282	0	−8	2,842
Highest Elevation (ft)	2,407	14,494	345	535	13,161

a. What is the difference between the highest elevation in Alabama and the lowest elevation in Louisiana? _____

b. Find the difference between the lowest elevation in New Mexico and the lowest elevation in California. _____

c. Find the difference between the highest elevation in Florida and the lowest elevation in California. _____

d. What is the difference between the lowest elevation in Alabama and the lowest elevation in Louisiana? _____

Evaluate each expression if $h = -12$, $j = 4$, and $k = 15$.

14. $-j + h - k$ _____

15. $|h - j|$ _____

16. $k - j - h$ _____

H.O.T. Problems Higher Order Thinking

17. **PS Identify Structure** Write a subtraction sentence using integers. Then, write the equivalent addition sentence and explain how to find the sum.

_____

_____

18. **PS Identify Structure** Use the properties of operations.

 a. The Commutative Property is true for addition. For example, $7 + 2 = 2 + 7$. Does the Commutative Property apply to subtraction?

 Is $2 - 7$ equal to $7 - 2$? Explain. _____

 _____

 b. Using the Associative Property, $9 + (6 + 3) = (9 + 6) + 3$.

 Is $9 - (6 - 3)$ equal to $(9 - 6) - 3$? Explain. _____

 _____

19. **PS Find the Error** Hiroshi is finding $-15 - (-18)$. Find his mistake and correct it.

_____

_____

_____

_____

$$-15 - (-18) = -15 + (-18)$$
$$= -33$$

20. **PS Justify Conclusions** *True* or *false*? When n is a negative integer,

 $n - n = 0$. Justify your response. _____

_____

_____

21. **PS Model with Mathematics** Write a real-world problem in which two

 negative integers are subtracted. _____

_____

_____

Extra Practice

Subtract.

22. 13 − 17 = $\underline{-4}$

Homework
Help

$13 - 17 = 13 + (-17)$

$\qquad = -4$

23. 27 − (−8) = $\underline{35}$

$27 - (-8) = 27 + 8$

$\qquad = 35$

24. −8 − 9 = _____

25. −34 − (−20) = _____

26. 15 − (−14) = _____

27. −27 − (−33) = _____

Evaluate each expression if f = −6, g = 7, and h = 9.

28. f − 6 _____

29. h − f _____

30. g − h _____

31. 5 − f _____

32. 4 − (−g) _____

33. −8 − (−h) _____

34. **PS** **Be Precise** To find the percent error, you can use this equation.

$$\text{percent error} = \frac{\text{amount of error}}{\text{actual amount}} \times 100$$

Bryan estimates the cost of a vacation to be $730. The actual cost of the vacation is $850. Find the percent error. Round to the nearest whole percent if necessary. Is the percent positive or negative? Explain.

_____

_____

35. Determine if each statement below about integers is *always* true or *sometimes* true.

a. positive − positive = positive   ☐ Always True   ☐ Sometimes True

b. positive + positive = positive   ☐ Always True   ☐ Sometimes True

c. negative + negative = negative   ☐ Always True   ☐ Sometimes True

d. negative − negative = negative   ☐ Always True   ☐ Sometimes True

36. The table shows the record high and low temperatures recorded in different states. The *range* of temperatures in a state is the difference between the highest and lowest temperatures. Sort the range of temperatures for each state from least to greatest.

State	Alaska	Colorado	Florida	Nevada
Record High	100°F	118°F	109°F	125°F
Record Low	−80°F	−61°F	−2°F	−50°F

	State	Range
Least		
Greatest		

Spiral Review

Multiply.

37. 18(10) = _____

38. 15(13) = _____

39. 12(30) = _____

Evaluate each expression.

40. $|-12| =$ _____

41. $|-3| + |-5| =$ _____

42. $|-25| \div 5 - |-3| =$ _____

Inquiry Lab

Distance on a Number Line

 Inquiry **HOW is the distance between two rational numbers related to their difference?**

Indiana Academic Standards
7.C.2

PS **Process Standards**
1, 2, 3, 8

For a science project, Carmelo recorded the daily low and high temperatures for four days in January. His results are shown in the table below. Find the day that had the greatest difference in temperature readings.

	M	T	W	Th
Low Temperature (°F)	1	−3	−4	−3
High Temperature (°F)	5	0	2	−1

Hands-On Activity

Step 1 In the table below, a represents each daily low temperature, and b represents each daily high temperature. Find $a + b$ and $a - b$. Record your results in the table.

Day	a	b	$a + b$	$a - b$	Distance
M	1	5	6	−4	4 units
T	−3	0			
W	−4	2			
Th	−3	−1			

Step 2 Use a number line to find the distance between each rational number a and b. For example, the distance between 1 and 5 on the number line below is ☐ units.

Complete the last column in the table.

Step 3 Compare the distances.

So, the day with the greatest difference in temperature readings

was _____.

Work with a partner to find the distance between each pair of numbers without using a number line. Then use a number line to check your answer.

1. The distance between −9 and −3 is _____.

2. The distance between −2 and 5 _____.

Analyze and Reflect

Collaborate

PS Identify Repeated Reasoning Work with a partner to answer the following questions. Refer back to the table in Step 1 of the Activity.

3. Is there a relationship between the sum of each pair of integers and the distance between them? If so, explain.

_____

_____

4. Is there a relationship between the difference of the integers and the

distance between them? If so, explain. _____

_____

5. **PS Reason Inductively** For each pair of integers in the Activity, find $b - a$. How does $b - a$ compare to $a - b$? How does it compare to the distance between the points? Use the term *absolute value* in your answer.

_____

_____

Create

On Your Own

6. **Inquiry** HOW is the distance between two rational numbers related to their difference?

_____

_____

PS Problem-Solving Investigation
Look for a Pattern

Indiana Academic Standards
7.C.8
PS Process Standards
1, 4, 8

Case #1 Shooting Star

Laura wants to make the girls basketball team and knows that making free throws is a skill that impresses the coach. In practice, she makes about 3 out of every 5 free throws she attempts. In tryouts, she has to shoot the ball 30 times from the free throw line.

How many of these can she expect to make?

1 Understand *What are the facts?*
- Laura can make 3 out of 5 free throw attempts.
- In tryouts, she will have to shoot the ball 30 times from the free throw line.

2 Plan *What is your strategy to solve this problem?*
Make a table to extend the pattern and solve the problem.

3 Solve *How can you apply the strategy?*
Complete the table below.

+3 +3 +3 +3 +3

Free Throws	3	6	9	12	
Shots Attempted	5	10	15	20	

+5 +5 +5 +5 +5

If Laura attempts 30 shots, how many should she make? ☐

4 Check *Does the answer make sense?*
She makes free throws a little more than half the time. Since 18 is a little more than 15, the answer is reasonable.

Analyze the Strategy

PS Identify Repeated Reasoning How would the results have changed if

Laura could make 4 out of 5 free throw attempts? _____

_____

Case #2 Display Dilemma

Tomás looks through a window and sees the top 3 rows of a 7-row display of digital cameras. He sees 4, 6, and 8 cameras in these 3 rows.

How many cameras are there in the whole display?

Understand

Read the problem. What are you being asked to find?

I need to find _____.

Underline key words and values. What information do you know?

The display contains ☐ rows of digital cameras. The problem states that the top three rows have ☐ cameras, ☐ cameras, and ☐ cameras.

Is there any information that you do *not* need to know?

I do not need to know _____.

Plan

Choose a problem-solving strategy.

I will use the _____ strategy.

Solve

Describe the pattern in the table. Then extend it using your problem-solving strategy. _____

_____

Row	7	6	5			
Number of Cameras	4	6	8			

The total number of cameras is ☐.

So, _____.

Check

Use information from the problem to check your answer.

_____

Work with a small group to solve the following cases. Show your work on a separate piece of paper.

Case #3 Nature

A sunflower usually has two different spirals of seeds, one with 34 seeds and the other with 55 seeds. The numbers 34 and 55 are part of the Fibonacci sequence.

1, 1, 2, 3, 5, 8, 13, 21, 34, 55, ...

Find the pattern in the Fibonacci sequence and identify the next two terms.

Case #4 Financial Literacy

Peter is saving money to buy an MP3 player. After one month, he has $50. After 2 months, he has $85. After 3 months, he has $120. After 4 months, he has $155.

At this rate, how long will it take Peter to save enough money to buy an MP3 player that costs $295?

Case #5 Geometry

The pattern at the right is made from toothpicks.

How many toothpicks would be needed for the sixth term in the pattern?

First term   Second term   Third term

Case #6 Diving

A diver descends to −15 feet after 1 minute, −30 feet after 2 minutes, and −45 feet after 3 minutes.

If she keeps descending at this rate, find the diver's position after ten minutes.

Use any strategy!

Mid-Chapter Check

Vocabulary Check

1. Define *integer*. Give an example of a number that is an integer and a number that is not an integer. (Lesson 1)

_____

_____

2. Fill in the blank in the sentence below with the correct term. (Lesson 1)

The _____ of a number is the distance between the number and zero on a number line.

Skills Check and Problem Solving

Evaluate each expression. (Lessons 1, 2, and 3)

3. $|-6| =$ _____

Show your work.

4. $-4 + (-8) =$ _____

5. $3 + 4 + (-5) =$ _____

6. $-3 - 10 =$ _____

7. $8 - (-12) =$ _____

8. $|-5| - |-9| =$ _____

9. The melting point of mercury is $-36°$F and its boiling point is $672°$F. What is the difference between the boiling point and the melting point? (Lesson 3)

_____

10. **PS Persevere with Problems** Patrick starts hiking at an elevation of -418 feet. He ascends to an elevation of 387 feet and then descends to an elevation 94 feet higher than where he began. He descended 132 feet. What is the elevation of where he stops hiking? (Lesson 2)

_____

Inquiry Lab
Multiply Integers

Indiana Academic Standards
7.C.3

PS Process Standards
1, 3, 4

 Inquiry **WHEN** is the product of two integers a positive number?
WHEN is the product a negative number?

The number of students who bring their lunch to Phoenix Middle School has been decreasing at a rate of 4 students each month. What integer represents the total change in the number of students bringing their lunch after three months?

What do you know? _____

_____

What do you need to find? _____

_____

Hands-On Activity 1

 Tools

The integer ☐ represents a decrease of 4 students each month. After three months, the total change will be 3 × (−4).

$$3 \times (-4)$$

Add 3 sets...   ... of 4 negative counters.

Step 1 Add 3 sets of 4 negative counters to the mat.

Step 2 Count the number of negative counters.

There are ☐ negative counters.

So, 3 × (−4) = ☐ . After three months, the total change in the number of students bringing their lunch will be ☐ .

The model shows that *adding* sets of *negative* counters results in *negative* counters on the mat.

Hands-On Activity 2

Use counters to find −2 × 3.

If the first factor is negative, you need to *remove* counters from the mat.

-2×3

Remove 2 sets... ... of 3 positive counters

Step 1 There are no counters on the mat, so add 2 sets of 3 zero pairs on the mat. The value on the mat is zero.

Step 2 Remove 2 sets of 3 positive counters from the mat.

There are ☐ negative counters remaining.

So, −2 × 3 = ☐.

The model shows that *removing* sets of *positive* counters results in sets of *negative* counters that are left.

Hands-On Activity 3

Use counters to find −2 × (−4).

Both factors are negative. Remove ☐ sets of ☐ negative counters from the mat.

Step 1 There are no counters on the mat, so draw 2 sets of 4 zero pairs on the mat.

Step 2 Cross out 2 sets of 4 negative counters from the mat.

There are ☐ positive counters remaining.

So, −2 × (−4) = ☐.

The model shows that *removing* sets of *negative* counters results in sets of *positive* counters that are left.

Investigate

Work with a partner. Find each product. Show your work using drawings.

1. $2 \times (-3) =$ _____

2. $6 \times (-1) =$ _____

3. $-2 \times 4 =$ _____

4. $-1 \times 5 =$ _____

5. $-4 \times 2 =$ _____

6. $-2 \times (-4) =$ _____

7. $-3 \times (-1) =$ _____

8. $-6 \times (-2) =$ _____

9. What do your models show about removing sets of positive counters?

removing sets of negative counters? _____

_____

_____

Analyze and Reflect

Collaborate

Work with a partner to complete the table. Use counters if needed.
The first one is already done for you.

	Multiplication Expression	Same Signs or Different Signs?	Product	Positive or Negative?
	2 × 6	same signs	12	positive
10.	7 × (–2)			
11.	–3 × (–4)			
12.	5 × (–3)			
13.	2 × 8			
14.	–4 × (–1)			
15.	–3 × 6			
16.	–2 × 5			

17. **PS Reason Abstractly** Study the pattern in the table. Write a rule you can use to find the product of two integers without using counters. Test your rule by finding 3 × (−7) using counters.

_____

_____

_____

Create

On Your Own

18. **PS Model with Mathematics** Write a real-world problem that could be represented by the expression −5 × 4.

_____

_____

_____

19. **Inquiry** WHEN is the product of two integers a positive number? WHEN is the product a negative number?

_____

_____

_____

Lesson 4
Multiply Integers

 Real-World Link Watch ▶

Skydiving Once a parachute is deployed, a skydiver descends at a rate of about 5 meters per second. Where will the skydiver be in relation to where the parachute deployed after 4 seconds?

1. Descending is usually represented by a negative integer. What integer should you use to represent the position of the skydiver in relation to the parachute's deployment after 1 second? ☐

2. Complete the graphic below. What is the skydiver's position after 2, 3, and 4 seconds?

−5 meters ┼ 1 second

☐ meters ┼ 2 seconds

☐ meters ┼ 3 seconds

☐ meters ┼ 4 seconds

Look Mom, no hands!

3. Write a multiplication sentence to represent the skydiver's position after 5 seconds.

 Essential Question

WHAT happens when you add, subtract, multiply, and divide integers?

🇮 **Indiana Academic Standards**
7.C.3

PS **Process Standards**
1, 3, 4, 8

Which PS Process Standards did you use?
Shade the circle(s) that applies.

① Persevere with Problems

② Reason Abstractly

③ Construct an Argument

④ Model with Mathematics

⑤ Use Math Tools

⑥ Attend to Precision

⑦ Make Use of Structure

⑧ Use Repeated Reasoning

Multiply Integers with Different Signs

Words The product of two integers with different signs is negative.

Examples $6(-4) = -24$ $-5(7) = -35$

Remember that multiplication is the same as repeated addition.

$4(-3) = (-3) + (-3) + (-3) + (-3)$ −3 is used as an addend four times.

$\quad\quad = -12$

The Commutative Property of Multiplication states that you can multiply in any order. So, $4(-3) = -3(4)$.

Examples

1. Find $3(-5)$.

$3(-5) = -15$ The integers have different signs. The product is negative.

2. Find $-6(8)$.

$-6(8) = -48$ The integers have different signs. The product is negative.

Show your work.

Got it? Do these problems to find out.

a. $9(-2)$ **b.** $-7(4)$

a. _____

b. _____

Multiply Integers with the Same Signs

Words The product of two integers with the same sign is positive.

Examples $2(6) = 12$ $-10(-6) = 60$

The product of two positive integers is positive. You can use a pattern to find the sign of the product of two negative integers. Start with $(2)(-3) = -6$ and $(1)(-3) = -3$.

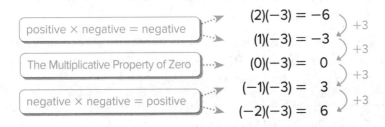

positive × negative = negative	$(2)(-3) = -6$
The Multiplicative Property of Zero	$(1)(-3) = -3$ +3
negative × negative = positive	$(0)(-3) = 0$ +3
	$(-1)(-3) = 3$ +3
	$(-2)(-3) = 6$ +3

Each product is 3 more than the previous product. This pattern can also be shown on a number line.

If you extend the pattern, the next two products are $(-3)(-3) = 9$ and $(-4)(-3) = 12$.

Examples

Tutor

3. Find $-11(-9)$.

$-11(-9) = 99$ The integers have the same sign. The product is positive.

4. Find $(-4)^2$.

$(-4)^2 = (-4)(-4)$ There are two factors of -4.

$= 16$ The product is positive.

5. Find $-3(-4)(-2)$.

$-3(-4)(-2) = [-3(-4)](-2)$ Associative Property

$= 12(-2)$ $-3(-4) = 12$

$= -24$ $12(-2) = -24$

Got it? Do these problems to find out.

c. $-12(-4)$ **d.** $(-5)^2$ **e.** $-7(-5)(-3)$

Show your work.

c. _____

d. _____

e. _____

Example

6. **A submersible is diving from the surface of the water at a rate of 90 feet per minute. What is the depth of the submersible after 7 minutes?**

The submersible descends 90 feet per minute. After 7 minutes, the vessel will be at 7(−90) or −630 feet. The submersible will descend to 630 feet below the surface.

Got it? **Do this problem to find out.**

f. **Financial Literacy** Mr. Simon's bank automatically deducts a $4 monthly maintenance fee from his savings account. Write a multiplication expression to represent the maintenance fees for one year. Then find the product and explain its meaning.

f. _____

Guided Practice

Multiply. (Examples 1–5)

1. $6(-10) =$ _____

2. $(-3)^3 =$ _____

3. $(-1)(-3)(-4) =$ _____

4. **Financial Literacy** Tamera owns 100 shares of a certain stock. Suppose the price of the stock drops by $3 per share. Write a multiplication expression to find the change in Tamera's investment. Explain your answer.

(Example 6)

_____

_____

_____

5. **ⓔ** **Building on the Essential Question** When is the product of two or more integers a positive number?

_____

_____

Rate Yourself!

Are you ready to move on?
Shade the section that applies.

I have a few questions. | I'm ready to move on.

I have a lot of questions.

For more help, go online to access a Personal Tutor.

FOLDABLES Time to update your Foldable!

Independent Practice

Go online for Step-by-Step Solutions

eHelp

Multiply. (Examples 1–5)

1. $8(-12) =$ _____

2. $-15(-4) =$ _____

3. $(-6)^2 =$ _____

Show your work.

4. $(-5)^3 =$ _____

5. $-4(-2)(-8) =$ _____

6. $-3(-2)(1) =$ _____

Write a multiplication expression to represent each situation. Then find each product and explain its meaning. (Example 6)

7. Ethan burns 650 Calories when he runs for 1 hour. Suppose he runs 5 hours in one week.

_____

_____

8. Wave erosion causes a certain coastline to recede at a rate of 3 centimeters each year. This occurs uninterrupted for a period of 8 years.

_____

_____

_____

9. **PS** **Model with Mathematics** Refer to the graphic novel frame below. How many black T-shirts would Hannah and Dario need to sell to make up the loss in profit?

_____

It looks like we spend $15 on every black T-shirt that is printed on both back and front. We should give one to the mascot for free.

We sell the black T-shirts for $18 each.

HOMECOMING

10. **PS Multiple Representations** When a movie is rented it has a due date. If the movie is not returned on time, a late fee is assessed. Kaitlyn is charged $5 each day for a movie that is 4 days late.

a. **Words** Explain why $4 \times (-5) = -20$ describes the situation. _____

_____

b. **Algebra** Write an expression to represent the fee when the movie is x days late. _____

11. **PS Identify Repeated Reasoning** When you multiply two positive integers, the product is a positive integer. Complete the graphic organizer to help you remember the other rules for multiplying integers. Describe any patterns in the products.

×	+	−
+		
−		

_____

_____

_____

 H.O.T. Problems Higher Order Thinking

12. **PS Model with Mathematics** Write a multiplication sentence with a product of −18.

_____

13. **PS Justify Conclusions** Explain how to evaluate $(-9)(-6)(15)(-7 + 7)$ as simply as possible.

_____

_____

14. **PS Persevere with Problems** Find values of a, b, and c that make each statement true. If no values exist, write *not possible*.

a. $a < b$ and $a + c < b + c$ _____

b. $a < b$ and $a + c > b + c$ _____

c. $a < b$ and $ac < bc$ _____

d. $a < b$ and $ac > bc$ _____

e. $a < b$ and $ac = bc$ _____

15. **PS Reason Inductively** The product of two integers is −21. The difference between the integers is −10. The sum of the two integers is 4. What are the two integers?

_____

Extra Practice

Multiply.

16. $-7(11) =$ _-77_

$-7(11) = -77$

 The integers have different signs. The product is negative.

17. $-20(-8) =$ _____

18. $25(-2) =$ _____

19. $(-4)^3 =$ _____

20. $(-9)^2 =$ _____

21. $-9(-1)(-5) =$ _____

Write a multiplication expression to represent each situation. Then find each product and explain its meaning.

22. The average person loses 50 to 80 hairs per day to make way for new growth. Suppose you lose 65 hairs per day for 15 days without growing any.

_____

_____

_____

23. **PS** **Financial Literacy** Lily has a $100 gift card to her favorite pastry shop. She spends $4 a day at the shop for the next 12 days.

_____

_____

_____

Copy and Solve Evaluate each expression if $a = -6$, $b = -4$, $c = 3$, and $d = 9$. **Show your work on a separate sheet of paper.**

24. $-5c =$

25. $b^2 =$

26. $2a =$

27. $bc =$

28. $abc =$

29. $abc^3 =$

30. $-3a^2 =$

31. $-cd^2 =$

32. $-2a + b =$

33. **PS** **Find the Error** Jamar is finding $(-2)(-3)(-4)$. Find his mistake and correct it. Explain your answer.

_____

_____

_____

_____

$(-2)(-3)(-4) = 24$

34. J.J. needed to withdraw money from his savings account to buy tickets to the zoo for himself and 7 of his friends. Each ticket costs $5. What multiplication expresssion represents this situation?

[   ]

Use the symbols to model the situation on the number line.

Write an integer to represent the total withdrawal. [   ]

35. Morgan drove from Los Angeles, at an elevation of 330 feet, to Death Valley, at an elevation of −282 feet. What is the difference in elevation between Los Angeles and Death Valley?

[   ]

Spiral Review

Fill in each ◯ with < or > to make a true sentence.

36. 0 ◯ −1

37. −9 ◯ 9

38. −84 ◯ 48

39. 32 ◯ −27

40. Laura's allowance balances over the last three months are shown in the table. Positive values indicate the number of dollars she had left over, and negative values indicate the number of dollars she overspent. Order the allowance balances from least to greatest.

Month	Allowance Balances ($)
May	−10
June	5
July	−2

_____

41. Graph 1, −4, 3, −2, 0, and 2 on the number line below.

Inquiry Lab
Use Properties to Multiply

 Inquiry HOW can properties be used to prove rules for multiplying integers?

Indiana Academic Standards
7.C.3

PS **Process Standards**
1, 3

Properties are used by scientists to classify elements into categories, such as metals. One property of a metal is that it is shiny.

Hands-On Activity

You have studied the mathematical properties listed in the table below. In mathematics, properties can be used to justify statements you make while verifying or proving another statement.

Properties of Mathematics	
Additive Inverse	Multiplicative Property of Zero
Distributive Property	Multiplicative Identity

For example, you have used models to show that $2(-1) = -2$.

You can *prove* $2(-1) = -2$ by using properties.

Write the correct property from the table above to provide the missing justifications. Use each property name once.

Statements	Properties
$0 = 2(0)$	_____
$0 = 2[1 + (-1)]$	_____
$0 = 2(1) + 2(-1)$	_____
$0 = 2 + 2(-1)$	_____

Conclusion In the last statement, $0 = 2 + 2(-1)$. In order for this to be true, $2(-1)$ must equal -2. Therefore, $2(-1) = \boxed{}$.

The sentence $(-2)(-1) = 2$ is an example of the rule that states the product of a negative integer and a negative integer is a positive integer.

Work with a partner to provide the missing information for the statements below.

1. Show that $(-2)(-1) = 2$.

Statements	Properties
$0 = -2(0)$	
$0 = -2[1 + (-1)]$	
$0 = -2(1) + (-2)(-1)$	
$0 = -2 + (-2)(-1)$	

Analyze and Reflect

Collaborate

Work with a partner.

2. **PS Justify Conclusions** Write a conclusion for Exercise 1.

_____

_____

Create

On Your Own

3. **PS Construct an Argument** When you prove a statement mathematically, you must show that the statement is true for all possible values. How could you prove the product of any two negative numbers is a positive number? Explain your reasoning to a classmate.

_____

_____

_____

4. **inquiry** HOW can properties be used to prove rules for multiplying integers?

_____

_____

Lesson 5
Divide Integers

Real-World Link

Sharks A Great White Shark has 3,000 teeth! It gains and loses teeth often in its lifetime. Suppose a Great White loses 3 teeth each day for 5 days without gaining any. The shark has lost 15 teeth in all.

1. Write a multiplication sentence for this situation.

_____

2. Division is related to multiplication. Write two division sentences related to the multiplication sentence you wrote for Exercise 1.

_____

_____

Collaborate

Work with a partner to complete the table. The first one is done for you.

Multiplication Sentence	Division Sentences	Same Signs or Different Signs?	Quotient	Positive or Negative?
2 × 6 = 12	12 ÷ 6 = 2	Same signs	2	Positive
	12 ÷ 2 = 6	Same signs	6	Positive
3. 2 × (−4) = −8				
4. −3 × 5 = −15				
5. −2 × (−5) = 10				

Which PS **Process Standards** did you use?
Shade the circle(s) that applies.

① Persevere with Problems
② Reason Abstractly
③ Construct an Argument
④ Model with Mathematics

⑤ Use Math Tools
⑥ Attend to Precision
⑦ Make Use of Structure
⑧ Use Repeated Reasoning

Essential Question

WHAT happens when you add, subtract, multiply, and divide integers?

Indiana Academic Standards
7.C.4

PS **Process Standards**
1, 3, 4, 5, 7

Divide Integers with Different Signs

Words The quotient of two integers with different signs is negative.

Examples $33 \div (-11) = -3$ $-64 \div 8 = -8$

Work Zone

You can divide integers provided that the divisor is not zero. Since multiplication and division sentences are related, you can use them to find the quotient of integers with different signs.

different signs

$2(-6) = -12$ → $-12 \div 2 = -6$
$-2(-6) = 12$ → $12 \div (-2) = -6$

negative quotient

Examples

Tutor

1. **Find $80 \div (-10)$.**   The integers have different signs.

$80 \div (-10) = -8$ The quotient is negative.

Dividing Integers

If p and q are integers and q does not equal 0,

then $-\frac{p}{q} = \frac{-p}{q} = \frac{p}{-q}$.

In Example 2, $\frac{-55}{11} = \frac{-55}{11}$
$= \frac{55}{-11}$.

2. **Find $\dfrac{-55}{11}$.**   The integers have different signs.

$\dfrac{-55}{11} = -5$ The quotient is negative.

3. **Use the table to find the constant rate of change in centimeters per hour.**

The height of the candle decreases by 2 centimeters each hour.

$\dfrac{\text{change in height}}{\text{change in hours}} = \dfrac{-2}{1}$

So, the constant rate of change is -2 centimeters per hour.

Show your work.

a. _____

b. _____

c. _____

Got it? Do these problems to find out.

a. $20 \div (-4)$ **b.** $\dfrac{-81}{9}$ **c.** $-45 \div 9$

Divide Integers with the Same Signs

Words The quotient of two integers with the same sign is positive.

Examples $15 \div 5 = 3$ $\qquad\qquad -64 \div (-8) = 8$

You can also use multiplication and division sentences to find the quotient of integers with the same sign.

same signs

$4(5) = 20 \longrightarrow 20 \div 4 = 5$

$-4(5) = -20 \longrightarrow -20 \div (-4) = 5$

positive quotient

Examples

4. **Find $-14 \div (-7)$.** The integers have the same sign.

$-14 \div (-7) = 2$ The quotient is positive.

5. **Find $\dfrac{-27}{-3}$.** The integers have the same sign.

$\dfrac{-27}{-3} = 9$ The quotient is positive.

Show your work.

6. **Evaluate $-16 \div x$ if $x = -4$.**

$-16 \div x = -16 \div (-4)$ Replace x with -4.

$\qquad\qquad = 4$ Divide. The quotient is positive.

d. _____

Got it? Do these problems to find out.

e. _____

d. $-24 \div (-4)$ **e.** $-9 \div (-3)$ **f.** $\dfrac{-28}{-7}$

f. _____

g. Evaluate $a \div b$ if $a = -33$ and $b = -3$.

g. _____

Example

Tutor

7. **STEM** One year, the estimated Australian koala population was 1,000,000. After 10 years, there were about 100,000 koalas. Find the average change in the koala population per year. Then explain its meaning.

$$\frac{N - P}{10} = \frac{100,000 - 1,000,000}{10}$$

N is the new population, 100,000. *P* is the previous population, 1,000,000.

$$= \frac{-900,000}{10} \text{ or } -90,000$$

Divide.

The koala population has changed by −90,000 per year.

Got it? Do this problem to find out.

Show your work.

h. **STEM** The average temperature in January for North Pole, Alaska, is −24°C. Use the expression $\frac{9C + 160}{5}$ to find this temperature in degrees Fahrenheit. Round to the nearest degree. Then explain its meaning.

h. _____

Guided Practice

Check ✓

Divide. (Examples 1, 2 , 4, and 5)

Show your work.

1. $-16 \div 2 =$ _____

2. $\frac{42}{-7} =$ _____

3. $-30 \div (-5) =$ _____

Evaluate each expression if $x = 8$ and $y = -5$. (Example 6)

4. $15 \div y$ _____

5. $xy \div (-10)$ _____

6. $(x + y) \div (-3)$ _____

7. The lowest recorded temperature in Wisconsin is −55°F on February 4, 1996. Use the expression $\frac{5(F - 32)}{9}$ to find this temperature in degrees Celsius. Round to the nearest tenth. Explain its meaning.
(Example 7)

_____

Rate Yourself!

How confident are you about dividing integers? Check the box that applies.

8. **ⓔ** **Building on the Essential Question** How is dividing integers similar to multiplying integers?

_____

_____

For more help, go online to access a Personal Tutor.

Tutor

FOLDABLES Time to update your Foldable!

Name _____ My Homework _____

Divide. (Examples 1, 2, 4, and 5)

1. $50 \div (-5) =$ _____

Show your work.

2. $-18 \div 9 =$ _____

3. $-15 \div (-3) =$ _____

4. $-100 \div (-10) =$ _____

5. $\dfrac{22}{-2} =$ _____

6. $\dfrac{84}{-12} =$ _____

7. $\dfrac{-26}{13} =$ _____

8. $\dfrac{-21}{-7} =$ _____

Evaluate each expression if $r = 12$, $s = -4$, and $t = -6$. (Example 6)

9. $r \div s$ _____

10. $rs \div 16$ _____

11. $\dfrac{t - r}{3}$ _____

12. $\dfrac{8 - r}{-2}$ _____

13. The distance remaining for a road trip over several hours is shown in the table. Use the information to find the constant rate of change in miles per hour. (Example 3)

_____

Time (h)	Distance Remaining (mi)
2	480
4	360
6	240
8	120

14. **PS** **Justify Conclusions** Last year, Mr. Engle's total income was $52,000, while his total expenses were $53,800. Use the expression $\dfrac{I - E}{12}$, where *I* represents total income and *E* represents total expenses, to find the average difference between his income and expenses each month. Then explain its meaning. (Example 7) _____

_____

Evaluate each expression if $d = -9$, $f = 36$, and $g = -6$.

15. $\dfrac{-f}{d}$ _____

16. $\dfrac{12 - (-f)}{-g}$ _____

17. $\dfrac{f^2}{d^2}$ _____

18. **STEM** The temperature on Mars ranges widely from $-207°F$ to $80°F$.

Find the average of the temperature extremes on Mars. _____

H.O.T. Problems Higher Order Thinking

19. **PS** **Construct an Argument** You know that multiplication is commutative because $9 \times 3 = 3 \times 9$. Is division commutative? Explain.

_____

_____

PS **Identify Structure** Use the graphs shown below to find the slope of each line.

20. _____

21. _____

22. **PS** **Identify Structure** Find values for x, y, and z so that all of the following statements are true.

- $y > x$, $z < y$, and $x < 0$
- $x \div z = -z$

- $z \div 2$ and $z \div 3$ are integers
- $x \div y = z$

$x =$ _____ $y =$ _____ $z =$ _____

23. **PS** **Reason Inductively** Addition, subtraction, and multiplication are said to be *closed* for integers. That is, when you add, subtract, or multiply integers, the result is also an integer. Is division closed for integers? Explain.

_____

_____

Extra Practice

Divide.

24. $56 \div (-8) =$ ___−7___

$56 \div (-8) = -7$

The integers have different signs. The quotient is negative.

25. $-36 \div (-4) =$ ___9___

$-36 \div (-4) = 9$

The integers have the same signs. The quotient is positive.

26. $32 \div (-8) =$ _____

27. $\dfrac{-16}{-4} =$ _____

28. $\dfrac{-27}{3} =$ _____

29. $\dfrac{-54}{-6} =$ _____

Evaluate each expression if $r = 12$, $s = -4$, and $t = -6$.

30. $-12 \div r$ _____

31. $72 \div t$ _____

32. $\dfrac{s + t}{5}$ _____

33. Divide -200 by -100. _____

34. Find the quotient of -65 and -13. _____

35. STEM The boiling point of water is affected by changes in elevation. Use the expression $\dfrac{-2A}{1,000}$, where A represents the altitude in feet, to find the number of degrees Fahrenheit at which the boiling point of water changes at an altitude of 5,000 feet. Then explain its meaning.

_____

36. PS **Use Math Tools** The change in altitude over time for several hot air balloons is shown. Find the rate of change in feet per minute for each balloon.

Balloon	Change in Altitude (ft)	Time (min)	Rate of Change (ft/min)
Midnight Express	−2,700	135	
Neon Lights	480	30	
Star Wonder	−1,500	60	

37. A hang glider flew to an altitude of 10,000 feet. Fifteen minutes later, its altitude was 7,000 feet. What was the average change in elevation per minute?

38. The table shows the number of points that each student lost on the first math test. Each question on the test was worth an equal number of points. Christopher answered 6 questions incorrectly. How many questions did Nythia, Raul, Tonya, and Michael answer incorrectly?

Student	Points Lost	Number Incorrect
Christopher	−24	6
Michael	−12	
Nythia	−16	
Raul	−4	
Tonya	−28	

Another student answered 9 questions incorrectly. How many points did that student lose?

Spiral Review

Write the opposite of each integer.

39. 8 _____

40. 9 _____

41. −7 _____

42. −5 _____

43. A display of cereal boxes has one box in the top row, two boxes in the second row, three boxes in the third row, and so on, as shown. How many rows of boxes will there be in a display of 45 boxes?

44. Name the quadrant in which the point (−4, −3) could be found on the coordinate plane. _____

21ST CENTURY CAREER
in Astronomy

Space Weather Forecaster

Did you know that space weather, or the conditions on the Sun and in space, can directly affect communication systems and power grids here on Earth? If you enjoy learning about the mysteries of space, then you should consider a career involving space weather. A space weather forecaster uses spacecraft, telescopes, radar, and supercomputers to monitor the sun, solar winds, and the space environment in order to forecast the weather in space.

Is This the Career for You?

Are you interested in a career as a space weather forecaster? Take some of the following courses in high school.

- Astronomy
- Calculus
- Chemistry
- Earth Science
- Physics

Find out how math relates to a career in Astronomy.

Predicting Space Storms!

Use the information in the table to solve each problem.

1. Graph the average temperatures for Earth, Jupiter, Mars, Mercury, Neptune, and Saturn on a number line. Label the points.

2. The temperatures on Mercury range from −279°F to 800°F. What is the difference between the highest and lowest temperatures? _____

3. How much greater is the average temperature on Earth than the average temperature on Jupiter? _____

4. One of Neptune's moons, Triton, has a surface temperature that is 61°F less than Neptune's average temperature. What is Triton's surface temperature? _____

5. The temperature on Mars can reach a low of −187°C. Find the value of the expression $\dfrac{9(-187) + 160}{5}$ to determine this temperature in degrees Fahrenheit. _____

Average Temperature of Planets			
Planet	Average Temperature (°F)	Planet	Average Temperature (°F)
Earth	59	Neptune	−330
Jupiter	−166	Saturn	−220
Mars	−85	Uranus	−320
Mercury	333	Venus	867

Career Project

It's time to update your career portfolio! Investigate the education and training requirements for a career as a space weather forecaster.

_____
_____
_____
_____
_____

List other careers that someone with an interest in astronomy could pursue.

- _____
- _____
- _____
- _____
- _____

Chapter Review

Vocabulary Check

Complete each sentence using the vocabulary list at the beginning of the chapter.

1. The sum of an integer and its _____ inverse is 0.

2. A(n) _____ integer is greater than 0.

3. The set of _____ contains all the whole numbers and their opposites.

4. The _____ value of a number is the distance it is from 0 on a number line.

5. 5 and −5 are _____ .

6. The result when one positive counter is paired with one negative counter is

   a _____ pair.

Reconstruct the vocabulary word and definition from the letters under the grid. The letters for each column are scrambled directly under that column.

Use Your FOLDABLES

Use your Foldable to help review the chapter.

Tape here

Operations with Integers

How do I add integers with different signs?

How do I subtract integers with different signs?

How do I multiply integers with different signs?

How do I divide integers with different signs?

Got it?

Find the Error The problems below may or may not contain an error. If the problem is correct, write a "✔" by the answer. If the problem is not correct, write an "X" over the answer and correct the problem.

1. $|-5| + |2| = \cancel{3}$

$|-5| + |2| = 5 + 2$ or 7

The first one is done for you.

2. $3|-6| = 18$

3. $-24 \div |-2| = 12$

Power Up! Performance Task

Weather Report

A weather service records the temperatures in degrees Fahrenheit each day and publishes the report in the newspaper at the end of the week. The graphic below shows a report from January.

Sunday	Monday	Tuesday	Wednesday	Thursday	Friday	Saturday
High 11	High 7	High 8	High 6	High	High 12	High 3
Low 2	Low −2	Low	Low −4	Low −1	Low	Low −8

Write your answers on another piece of paper. Show all your work to receive full credit.

Part A

David read the paper while eating breakfast and some of the information was smudged. Use the information below to find all of the missing high and low temperatures during the week.

- On Tuesday, the low temperature was 3 degrees colder than on Monday.
- On Thursday, the high temperature was 5 degrees warmer than the low temperature.
- On Friday, the low temperature was 11 degrees higher than the low temperature on Saturday.

Part B

Graph each of the high and low temperatures on a number line. What is the difference in the highest and lowest temperatures?

Part C

Find the average high and low temperature for the week.

Part D

Because of the cold temperatures, David decides to makes scarves to sell at a craft fair. It costs him $5 to make each scarf and he sells them for $12 each. He sells 28 scarves at the craft fair. What is David's total profit? Explain.

Reflect

 Answering the Essential Question

Use what you learned about integers to complete the graphic organizer.
Explain how to determine the sign of the result when performing each
operation.

Addition and Subtraction

Essential Question

WHAT happens when you
add, subtract, multiply,
and divide integers?

Multiply and Divide

Answer the Essential Question. WHAT happens when you add, subtract,
multiply, and divide integers?

Chapter 4
Rational Numbers

Essential Question

WHAT happens when you add, subtract, multiply, and divide fractions?

Indiana Academic Standards
7.NS.1, 7.NS.2, 7.NS.3, 7.C.2, 7.C.6, 7.C.7, 7.C.8

PS Process Standards
1, 3, 4, 5, 6, 7, 8

Math in the Real World

Tennis About 70,000 tennis balls are used at the U.S. Open tennis tournament each year. This is only a small fraction of the 300,000,000 tennis balls produced each year. Write a fraction in simplest form that compares the number of tennis balls used at the U.S. Open to the number produced per year.

FOLDABLES® Study Organizer

 1 Cut out the Foldable on page FL9 of this book.

 2 Place your Foldable on page 338.

 3 Use the Foldable throughout this chapter to help you learn about rational numbers.

Vocabulary

bar notation

common denominator

least common denominator

like fractions

rational numbers

repeating decimal

terminating decimal

unlike fractions

Review Vocabulary

An *improper fraction* is a fraction in which the numerator is greater than or equal to the denominator, such as $\frac{21}{4}$. A *mixed number* is a number composed of a whole number and a fraction, such as $5\frac{1}{4}$.

In the organizer below, write each mixed number as an improper fraction and each improper fraction as a mixed number. The first one in each column is done for you.

Mixed Numbers and Improper Fractions

Change Mixed Numbers	Change Improper Fractions
$3\frac{1}{2} = \frac{7}{2}$	$\frac{41}{4} = 10\frac{1}{4}$
$5\frac{1}{3} =$	$\frac{16}{3} =$
$8\frac{2}{5} =$	$\frac{23}{5} =$
$6\frac{4}{9} =$	$\frac{90}{11} =$
$10\frac{3}{8} =$	$\frac{66}{7} =$
$7\frac{3}{4} =$	$\frac{101}{2} =$
$15\frac{5}{6} =$	$\frac{87}{20} =$

What Do You Already Know?

List three things you already know about rational numbers in the first section. Then list three things you would like to learn about rational numbers in the second section.

Rational Numbers

What I know...

What I want to find out...

When Will You Use This?

Here are a few examples of how rational numbers are used in the real world.

Activity 1 Use a tape measure to find the width of a closet in your home. Do you think that a shelf that is $28\frac{3}{4}$ inches long would fit in the space that you measured? Is it too long or too short? What would you need to do to make the new shelf fit?

_____

_____

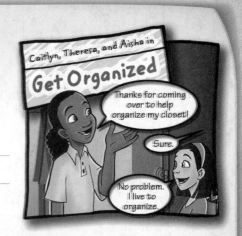

Caitlyn, Theresa, and Aisha in

Get Organized

Thanks for coming over to help organize my closet!

Sure.

No problem. I live to organize.

Activity 2 Go online at **connectED.mcgraw-hill.com** to read the graphic novel *Get Organized*. What are the dimensions of each storage cube?

_____

Are You Ready?

Try the Quick Check below.
Or, take the Online Readiness Quiz.

Quick Review

Example 1

Write $\frac{25}{100}$ in simplest form.

$$\frac{25}{100} = \frac{1}{4}$$

Divide the numerator and denominator by the GCF, 25.

Since the GCF of 1 and 4 is 1, the fraction $\frac{1}{4}$ is in simplest form.

Example 2

Graph $3\frac{2}{3}$ on a number line.

Find the two whole numbers between which $3\frac{2}{3}$ lies.

$3 < 3\frac{2}{3} < 4$

Since the denominator is 3, divide each space into 3 sections.

Draw a dot at $3\frac{2}{3}$.

Quick Check

Fractions Write each fraction in simplest form.

1. $\frac{24}{36} =$ _____

2. $\frac{45}{50} =$ _____

3. $\frac{88}{121} =$ _____

Graphing Graph each fraction or mixed number on the number line below.

4. $\frac{1}{2}$

5. $\frac{3}{4}$

6. $1\frac{1}{4}$

7. $2\frac{1}{2}$

How Did You Do?

Which problems did you answer correctly in the Quick Check?
Shade those exercise numbers below.

① ② ③ ④ ⑤ ⑥ ⑦

Inquiry Lab

Rational Numbers on the Number Line

 Inquiry HOW can you graph negative fractions on the number line?

Water evaporates from Earth at an average of about $-\frac{3}{4}$ inch per week.

Indiana Academic Standards
7.C.2

PS **Process Standards**
1, 3, 8

Hands-On Activity

Graph $-\frac{3}{4}$ on a number line.

Step 1 Use the fraction strip below that is divided in fourths above a number line.

Mark a 0 on the right side and a −1 on the left side.

Step 2 Starting from the right, shade three fourths. Label the number line with $-\frac{1}{4}$, $-\frac{2}{4}$, and $-\frac{3}{4}$.

Step 3 Draw the number line portion of the model in Step 2.

Place a dot on the number line to represent $-\frac{3}{4}$.

So, on a number line, $-\frac{3}{4}$ is between ⬚ and $\frac{⬚}{⬚}$ or $\frac{⬚}{⬚}$.

Investigate

PS Model with Mathematics Work with a partner. Graph each fraction on a number line. Use a fraction strip if needed.

1. $-\dfrac{3}{8}$

Show your work.

2. $-1\dfrac{2}{5}$

Analyze and Reflect

Work with a partner to complete each table. Use a number line if needed.

	< or >	
$\dfrac{7}{8}$	>	$\dfrac{3}{8}$
3. $\dfrac{9}{8}$		$\dfrac{5}{8}$
4. $\dfrac{13}{8}$		$\dfrac{3}{8}$
5. $\dfrac{15}{8}$		$\dfrac{13}{8}$

	< or >	
$-\dfrac{7}{8}$	<	$-\dfrac{3}{8}$
6. $-\dfrac{9}{8}$		$-\dfrac{5}{8}$
7. $-\dfrac{13}{8}$		$-\dfrac{3}{8}$
8. $-\dfrac{15}{8}$		$-\dfrac{13}{8}$

9. **PS Identify Repeated Reasoning** Compare and contrast the information in the tables.

_____

_____

Create

10. **PS Use Math Tools** Graph $-\dfrac{3}{4}$ and $\dfrac{3}{4}$ on a number line. Then use the graph to explain how the representations of the two fractions differ.

_____

_____

11. **Inquiry** HOW can you graph negative fractions on the number line?

_____

_____

Terminating and Repeating Decimals

Vocabulary Start-Up

 Vocab abc

Any fraction can be expressed as a decimal by dividing the numerator by the denominator.

The decimal form of a fraction is called a **repeating decimal**. Repeating decimals can be represented using **bar notation**. In bar notation, a bar is drawn only over the digit(s) that repeat.

$$0.3333... = 0.\overline{3} \qquad 0.1212... = 0.\overline{12} \qquad 11.38585... = 11.3\overline{85}$$

If the repeating digit is zero, the decimal is a **terminating decimal**. The terminating decimal $0.250\overline{0}$ is typically written as 0.25.

Match each repeating decimal to the correct bar notation.

0.1111...   0.61$\overline{1}$

0.61111...   0.$\overline{1}$

0.616161...   0.$\overline{61}$

Essential Question

WHAT happens when you add, subtract, multiply, and divide fractions?

 Vocab abc **Vocabulary**

repeating decimal
bar notation
terminating decimal

Indiana Academic Standards
7.C.8

PS **Process Standards**
1, 3, 4, 6, 7

Real-World Link

Jamie had two hits on her first nine times at bat. To find her batting "average," she divided 2 by 9.

$$2 \div 9 = 0.2222...$$

Write 0.2222... using bar notation. ⬚

Round 0.2222... to the nearest thousandth. ⬚

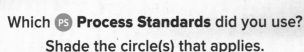

Which PS Process Standards did you use?
Shade the circle(s) that applies.

① Persevere with Problems   ⑤ Use Math Tools

② Reason Abstractly   ⑥ Attend to Precision

③ Construct an Argument   ⑦ Make Use of Structure

④ Model with Mathematics   ⑧ Use Repeated Reasoning

Write Fractions as Decimals

Our decimal system is based on powers of 10 such as 10, 100, and 1,000. If the denominator of a fraction is a power of 10, you can use place value to write the fraction as a decimal.

Complete the table below. Write fractions in simplest form.

Words	Fraction	Decimal
seven tenths	$\frac{7}{10}$	0.7
nineteen hundredths		
one-hundred five thousandths		

If the denominator of a fraction is a *factor* of 10, 100, 1,000, or any greater power of ten, you can use mental math and place value.

Examples

Tutor

Write each fraction or mixed number as a decimal.

1. $\frac{74}{100}$

Use place value to write the equivalent decimal.

$\frac{74}{100} = 0.74$ Read $\frac{74}{100}$ as *seventy-four hundredths*.

So, $\frac{74}{100} = 0.74$.

2. $\frac{7}{20}$

Think $\frac{7}{20} = \frac{35}{100}$

$\times 5$

So, $\frac{7}{20} = 0.35$.

3. $5\frac{3}{4}$

$5\frac{3}{4} = 5 + \frac{3}{4}$ Think of it as a sum.

$= 5 + 0.75$ You know that $\frac{3}{4} = 0.75$.

$= 5.75$ Add mentally.

So, $5\frac{3}{4} = 5.75$.

Got it? Do these problems to find out.

a. $\frac{3}{10}$ **b.** $\frac{3}{25}$ **c.** $-6\frac{1}{2}$

Show your work.

a. _____

b. _____

c. _____

Examples

4. Write $\frac{3}{8}$ as a decimal.

$$
\begin{array}{r}
0.375 \\
8\overline{)3.000} \\
-24 \\
\hline
60 \\
-56 \\
\hline
40 \\
-40 \\
\hline
0
\end{array}
$$

Divide 3 by 8.

Division ends when the remainder is 0.

So, $\frac{3}{8} = 0.375$.

5. Write $-\frac{1}{40}$ as a decimal.

$$
\begin{array}{r}
0.025 \\
40\overline{)1.000} \\
-80 \\
\hline
200 \\
-200 \\
\hline
0
\end{array}
$$

Divide 1 by 40.

So, $-\frac{1}{40} = -0.025$.

6. Write $\frac{7}{9}$ as a decimal.

$$
\begin{array}{r}
0.777... \\
9\overline{)7.000} \\
-63 \\
\hline
70 \\
-63 \\
\hline
70 \\
-63 \\
\hline
7
\end{array}
$$

Divide 7 by 9.

Notice that the division will never terminate in zero.

So, $\frac{7}{9} = 0.777...$ or $0.\overline{7}$.

Got it? Do these problems to find out.

Write each fraction or mixed number as a decimal. Use bar notation if needed.

d. $-\dfrac{7}{8}$

e. $2\dfrac{1}{8}$

f. $-\dfrac{3}{11}$

g. $8\dfrac{1}{3}$

Bar Notation

Remember that you can use bar notation to indicate a number pattern that repeats indefinitely. $0.333... = 0.\overline{3}$.

Show your work.

d. _____

e. _____

f. _____

g. _____

Write Decimals as Fractions

Every terminating decimal can be written as a fraction with a denominator of 10, 100, 1,000, or a greater power of ten. Use the place value of the final digit as the denominator.

Example

Watch | Tutor

7. **Find the fraction of the fish in the aquarium that are goldfish. Write in simplest form.**

$0.15 = \dfrac{15}{100}$ The digit 5 is in the hundredths place.

$= \dfrac{3}{20}$ Simplify.

So, $\dfrac{3}{20}$ of the fish are goldfish.

Fish	Amount
Angelfish	0.4
Goldfish	0.15
Guppy	0.25
Molly	0.2

Got it? Do these problems to find out.

Determine the fraction of the aquarium made up by each fish. Write the answer in simplest form.

h. molly   **i.** guppy   **j.** angelfish

STOP and Reflect

Suppose 0.6 of the fish are goldfish. Write this decimal as a fraction in the space below.

Show your work.

h. _____

i. _____

j. _____

Guided Practice

Check ✓

Write each fraction or mixed number as a decimal. Use bar notation if needed. (Examples 1–6)

Show your work.

1. $\dfrac{2}{5} =$ _____

2. $-\dfrac{9}{10} =$ _____

3. $\dfrac{5}{9} =$

4. During a hockey game, an ice resurfacer travels 0.75 mile. What fraction represents this distance? (Example 7)

_____

5. **Building on the Essential Question** How can you write a fraction as a decimal?

_____

_____

_____

Independent Practice

Go online for Step-by-Step Solutions eHelp

Write each fraction or mixed number as a decimal. Use bar notation if needed. (Examples 1–6)

1. $\frac{1}{2} =$ _____

 Show your work.

2. $-4\frac{4}{25} =$ _____

3. $\frac{1}{8} =$ _____

4. $\frac{3}{16} =$ _____

5. $-\frac{33}{50} =$ _____

6. $-\frac{17}{40} =$ _____

7. $5\frac{7}{8} =$ _____

8. $9\frac{3}{8} =$ _____

9. $-\frac{8}{9} =$ _____

10. $-\frac{1}{6} =$ _____

11. $-\frac{8}{11} =$ _____

12. $2\frac{6}{11} =$ _____

Write each decimal as a fraction or mixed number in simplest form. (Example 7)

13. $-0.2 =$ _____

14. $0.55 =$ _____

15. $5.96 =$ _____

16. The screen on Brianna's new phone is 2.85 centimeters long. What mixed number represents the length of the phone screen? (Example 7)

_____

17 **STEM** A praying mantis is an interesting insect that can rotate its head 180 degrees. Suppose the praying mantis at the right is 10.5 centimeters long. What mixed number represents this length? (Example 7)

_____

18. **PS Persevere with Problems** Suppose you buy a 1.25-pound package of ham at $5.20 per pound.

a. What fraction of a pound did you buy?

_____

b. How much money did you spend?

_____

H.O.T. Problems Higher Order Thinking

19. **PS Identify Structure** Write a fraction that is equivalent to a terminating decimal between 0.5 and 0.75.

_____

20. **PS Persevere with Problems** Fractions in simplest form that have denominators of 2, 4, 8, 16, and 32 produce terminating decimals. Fractions with denominators of 6, 12, 18, and 24 produce repeating decimals. What causes the difference? Explain.

_____

_____

_____

21. **PS Persevere with Problems** The value of pi (π) is 3.1415926... . The mathematician Archimedes believed that π was between $3\frac{1}{7}$ and $3\frac{10}{71}$. Was Archimedes correct? Explain your reasoning.

_____

_____

_____

22. **PS Reason Inductively** A *unit fraction* is a fraction that has 1 as its numerator. Write the four greatest unit fractions that are repeating decimals. Then write each fraction as a decimal.

_____

_____

23. **PS Model with Mathematics** Write a real-world scenario in which it would be appropriate to write a value in fractional form.

_____

_____

Extra Practice

Write each fraction or mixed number as a decimal. Use bar notation if needed.

24. $\frac{4}{5} =$ _0.8_

ework
Help →

$$\frac{4}{5} \overset{\times 2}{=} \frac{8}{10}$$
$$\overset{\times 2}{}$$

So, $\frac{4}{5} = 0.8$.

25. $-7\frac{1}{20} =$ _____

26. $-\frac{4}{9} =$ _____

27. $5\frac{1}{3} =$ _____

28. The fraction of a dime that is made up of copper is $\frac{12}{16}$. Write this fraction as a decimal.

_____

Write each decimal as a fraction or mixed number in simplest form.

29. $-0.9 =$ _____

30. $0.34 =$ _____

31. $2.66 =$ _____

Write each of the following as an improper fraction.

32. $-13 =$ _____

33. $7\frac{1}{3} =$ _____

34. $-3.2 =$ _____

35. **PS** **Be Precise** Nicolás practiced playing the cello for 2 hours and 18 minutes. Write the time Nicolás spent practicing as a decimal.

_____

Power Up! Test Practice

36. The table shows the lengths of four hiking trails. Select the appropriate decimal equivalent of each trail length.

1.2	1.25	1.3	1.$\overline{3}$
	1.6	1.$\overline{6}$	1.75

Hiking Trail	Trail Length	Decimal Equivalents
Lakeview	$1\frac{1}{4}$	
Forest Lane	$1\frac{1}{3}$	
Sparrow Stroll	$1\frac{3}{10}$	
Mountain Climb	$1\frac{2}{3}$	

37. Zoe went to lunch with a friend. After tax, her bill was $12.05. Which of the following rational numbers is equivalent to this amount? Select all that apply.

- ☐ $12\frac{1}{20}$
- ☐ $\frac{25}{2}$
- ☐ $\frac{241}{20}$
- ☐ $12\frac{5}{100}$

Spiral Review

Round each decimal to the tenths place.

38. $5.69 \approx$ _____

39. $0.05 \approx$ _____

40. $98.99 \approx$ _____

Graph and label each fraction on the number line below.

41. $\frac{1}{2}$

42. $\frac{3}{4}$

43. $\frac{2}{3}$

44. The table shows the discount on athletic shoes at two stores selling sporting equipment. Which store is offering the greater discount? Explain.

Store	Discount
Good Sports	$\frac{1}{5}$
Go Time	25%

_____

_____

Compare and Order Rational Numbers

Vocabulary Start-Up

A **rational number** is a number that can be expressed as a ratio of two integers written as a fraction, in which the denominator is not zero. The Venn diagram below shows that the number 2 can be called many things. It is a whole number, integer, and rational number. The number −1.4444... is only a rational number.

Common fractions, terminating and repeating decimals, percents, and integers are all rational numbers.

Write the numbers from the number bank on the diagram.

Number Bank

0.8
2.2̄
−1
1
1⅔

 Essential Question

WHAT happens when you add, subtract, multiply, and divide fractions?

 Vocabulary

rational number
common denominator
least common denominator

ⓙ **Indiana Academic Standards**
7.C.8

PS **Process Standards**
1, 3, 4

🌎 Real-World Link

Not all numbers are rational numbers. The Greek letter π (pi) represents the nonterminating and nonrepeating number whose first few digits are 3.14... . This number is an *irrational number*.

Use the Internet to search for the digits of pi. Describe

what you find. _____

_____

Yum, pi!

Which **PS** **Process Standards did you use?**
Shade the circle(s) that applies.

① Persevere with Problems   ⑤ Use Math Tools

② Reason Abstractly   ⑥ Attend to Precision

③ Construct an Argument   ⑦ Make Use of Structure

④ Model with Mathematics   ⑧ Use Repeated Reasoning

Compare Rational Numbers

A **common denominator** is a common multiple of the denominators of two or more fractions. The **least common denominator** or **LCD** is the LCM or least common multiple of the denominators. You can use the LCD to compare fractions. You can also use a number line.

Example

1. Fill in the ◯ with <, >, or = to make $-1\frac{5}{6}$ ◯ $-1\frac{1}{6}$ a true sentence.

Graph each rational number on a number line.
Mark off equal-size increments of $\frac{1}{6}$ between -2 and -1.

The number line shows that $-1\frac{5}{6} < -1\frac{1}{6}$.

Got it? Do this problem to find out.

a. Use the number line to compare $-5\frac{5}{9}$ and $-5\frac{1}{9}$.

a. _____

LCD

To find the least common denominator for $\frac{7}{12}$ and $\frac{8}{18}$, find the LCM of 12 and 18.

$12 = 2 \times 2 \times 3$
$18 = 2 \times 3 \times 3$
$LCM = 2 \times 2 \times 3 \times 3$
$= 36$

Example

2. Fill in the ◯ with <, >, or = to make $\frac{7}{12}$ ◯ $\frac{8}{18}$ a true sentence.

The LCD of the denominators 12 and 18 is 36.

$\frac{7}{12} = \frac{7 \times 3}{12 \times 3}$ $\frac{8}{18} = \frac{8 \times 2}{18 \times 2}$

$= \frac{21}{36}$ $= \frac{16}{36}$

Since $\frac{21}{36} > \frac{16}{36}, \frac{7}{12} > \frac{8}{18}$.

Got it? Do these problems to find out.

b. $\frac{5}{6}$ ◯ $\frac{7}{9}$ **c.** $\frac{1}{5}$ ◯ $\frac{7}{50}$ **d.** $-\frac{9}{16}$ ◯ $-\frac{7}{10}$

Example

Tutor

3. In Mr. Huang's class, 20% of students own roller shoes. In Mrs. Trevino's class, 5 out of 29 students own roller shoes. In which class does a greater fraction of students own roller shoes?

Express each number as a decimal and then compare.

$20\% = 0.2$ $\frac{5}{29} = 5 \div 29$ or about 0.1724

Since $0.2 > 0.1724$, $20\% > \frac{5}{29}$.

More students in Mr. Huang's class own roller shoes.

> **Got it?** Do this problem to find out.

Show your work.

e. In a second period class, 37.5% of students like to bowl. In a fifth period class, 12 out of 29 students like to bowl. In which class does a greater fraction of the students like to bowl?

e. _____

Order Rational Numbers

You can order rational numbers using place value.

Example

Tutor

4. Order the set $\{3.44, \pi, 3.14, 3.\overline{4}\}$ from least to greatest.

Line up the decimal points and compare using place value.

3.**140**	Annex a zero.	3.**440**	Annex a zero.
3.**1**415926...	$\pi \approx 3.1415926...$	3.**444**...	$3.\overline{4} = 3.444...$
Since $0 < 1$, $3.14 < \pi$.		Since $0 < 4$, $3.44 < 3.\overline{4}$.	

So, the order of the numbers from least to greatest is 3.14, π, 3.44, and $3.\overline{4}$.

> **Got it?** Do this problem to find out.

Show your work.

f. Order the set $\{23\%, 0.21, \frac{1}{4}, \frac{1}{5}\}$ from least to greatest.

f. _____

Tutor

5. Nolan is the quarterback on the football team. He completed 67% of his passes in the first game. He completed 0.64, $\frac{3}{5}$, and 69% of his passes in the next three games. List Nolan's completed passing numbers from least to greatest.

Express each number as a decimal and then compare.

67% = 0.67   0.64 $\frac{3}{5}$ = 0.6   69% = 0.69

Nolan's completed passing numbers from least to greatest are $\frac{3}{5}$, 0.64, 67%, and 69%.

Guided Practice

Check ✓

Fill in each ◯ with <, >, or = to make a true sentence. Use a number line if necessary. (Examples 1 and 2)

1. $-\frac{4}{5}$ ◯ $-\frac{1}{5}$

2. $1\frac{3}{4}$ ◯ $1\frac{5}{8}$

3. Elliot and Shanna are both soccer goalies. Elliot saves 3 goals out of 4. Shanna saves 7 goals out of 11. Who has the better average, Elliot or Shanna? Explain. (Example 3)

_____

_____

4. The lengths of four insects are 0.02 inch, $\frac{1}{8}$ inch, 0.1 inch, and $\frac{2}{3}$ inch. List the lengths in inches from least to greatest. (Examples 4 and 5)

_____

5. **Building on the Essential Question** How can you compare two fractions? _____

_____

_____

_____

Rate Yourself!

☐ I understand how to compare and order rational numbers.

▶▶ Great! You're ready to move on!

☐ I still have some questions about comparing and ordering rational numbers.

📖 Go online to access a Personal Tutor.

Tutor

Independent Practice

Go online for Step-by-Step Solutions

Fill in each ◯ **with <, >, or = to make a true sentence. Use a number line if necessary.** (Examples 1 and 2)

1. $-\dfrac{3}{5}$ ◯ $-\dfrac{4}{5}$

2. $-7\dfrac{5}{8}$ ◯ $-7\dfrac{1}{8}$

3. $6\dfrac{2}{3}$ ◯ $6\dfrac{1}{2}$

4. $-\dfrac{17}{24}$ ◯ $-\dfrac{11}{12}$

5 On her first quiz in social studies, Meg answered 92% of the questions correctly. On her second quiz, she answered 27 out of 30 questions correctly. On which quiz did Meg have the better score? (Example 3)

_____

Order each set of numbers from least to greatest. (Example 4)

6. $\{0.23, 19\%, \dfrac{1}{5}\}$

7. $\{-0.615, -\dfrac{5}{8}, -0.62\}$

8. Liberty Middle School is holding a fundraiser. The sixth-graders have raised 52% of their goal amount. The seventh- and eighth-graders have raised 0.57 and $\dfrac{2}{5}$ of their goal amounts, respectively. List the classes in order from least to greatest of their goal amounts. (Example 5)

_____

Fill in each ◯ **with <, >, or = to make a true sentence.**

9 $1\dfrac{7}{12}$ gallons ◯ $1\dfrac{5}{8}$ gallons

10. $2\dfrac{5}{6}$ hours ◯ 2.8 hours

11. **Model with Mathematics** Refer to the graphic novel frame below. If the closet organizer has a total width of $69\frac{1}{8}$ inches and the closet is $69\frac{3}{4}$ inches wide, will the organizer fit? Explain.

H.O.T. Problems Higher Order Thinking

12. **Justify Conclusions** Identify the ratio that does not have the same value as the other three. Explain your reasoning.

| 12 out of 15 | 0.08 | 80% | $\frac{4}{5}$ |

13. **Persevere with Problems** Explain how you know which number, $1\frac{15}{16}$, $\frac{17}{8}$, or $\frac{63}{32}$, is closest to 2.

14. **Reason Inductively** Are the fractions $\frac{5}{6}$, $\frac{5}{7}$, $\frac{5}{8}$, and $\frac{5}{9}$ arranged in order from least to greatest or from greatest to least? Explain.

15. **Model with Mathematics** Write a real-world problem in which you would compare and order rational numbers. Then solve the problem.

Extra Practice

Fill in each ◯ with <, >, or = to make a true sentence. Use a number line if necessary.

16. $-\frac{5}{7}$ ⓛ $-\frac{2}{7}$

Homework Help → Mark off equal-size increments of $\frac{1}{7}$ between −1 and 0.

17. $-3\frac{2}{3}$ ◯ $-3\frac{4}{6}$

18. $\frac{4}{7}$ ⓛ $\frac{5}{8}$

The LCD of the denominators 7 and 8 is 56.

$\frac{4}{7} = \frac{4 \times 8}{7 \times 8} = \frac{32}{56}$ and $\frac{5}{8} = \frac{5 \times 7}{8 \times 7} = \frac{35}{56}$

Since $\frac{32}{56} < \frac{35}{56}, \frac{4}{7} < \frac{5}{8}$.

19. $2\frac{3}{4}$ ◯ $2\frac{2}{3}$

20. Gracia and Jim were shooting free throws. Gracia made 4 out of 15 free throws. Jim *missed* 6 out of 16 free throws. Who made the free throw a greater fraction of the time? _____

Order each set of numbers from least to greatest.

21. $\{7.49, 7\frac{49}{50}, 7.5\%\}$

_____

22. $\{-1.4, -1\frac{1}{25}, -1.25\}$

_____

23. **STEM** Use the table that shows the lengths of small mammals.

   a. Which animal is the smallest mammal?

_____

   b. Which animal is smaller than the European Mole but larger than the Spiny Pocket Mouse?

_____

   c. Order the animals from greatest to least size.

_____

_____

Animal	Length (ft)
Eastern Chipmunk	$\frac{1}{3}$
European Mole	$\frac{5}{12}$
Masked Shrew	$\frac{1}{6}$
Spiny Pocket Mouse	0.25

24. The sales tax rates from 4 different counties are shown in the table. Convert each sales tax rate to a decimal. Then sort the counties from least to greatest tax rates.

County	Sales Tax Rate
Hamilton	$\frac{9}{160}$
Oakland	5.75%
Green	$5\frac{7}{8}$%
Campbell	$\frac{11}{200}$

	County	Sales Tax Rate (as a decimal)
Least		
Greatest		

Which county has the lowest sales tax rate? [_____]

25. The daily price changes for a stock are shown in the table. Determine if each statement is true or false.

Day	Price Change
Monday	−0.21
Tuesday	−1.05
Wednesday	−0.23
Thursday	+0.42
Friday	−1.15

  a. The price increased by the greatest amount on Thursday. ☐ True ☐ False

  b. The price decreased by the greatest amount on Tuesday. ☐ True ☐ False

  c. The price decreased by the least amount on Monday. ☐ True ☐ False

Spiral Review

Fill in each ◯ with < or > to make a true sentence.

26. −2 ◯ 2

27. −4 ◯ −5

28. −20 ◯ 20

29. −7 ◯ −8

30. −10 ◯ −1

31. 50 ◯ −100

32. Victoria, Cooper, and Diego are reading the same book for their language arts class. The table shows the fraction of the book each student has read. Which student has read the least amount? Explain your reasoning.

Student	Amount Read
Victoria	$\frac{2}{5}$
Cooper	$\frac{1}{5}$
Diego	$\frac{3}{5}$

_____

_____

_____

Inquiry Lab

Add and Subtract on the Number Line

 Inquiry HOW can you use a number line to add and subtract like fractions?

Indiana Academic Standards
7.C.2

PS Process Standards
1, 3, 5

In eight times at bat, Max hit 2 doubles, 5 singles, and struck out 1 time. Find the fraction of the times that Max hit either a single or a double.

Hands-On Activity 1

Step 1 Since there were 8 times at bat, create a vertical line that is divided into eighths.

Step 2 Graph the fraction of doubles, $\frac{2}{8}$, on the number line.

Step 3 From the $\frac{2}{8}$ point, count $\frac{5}{8}$ more on the number line.

So, $\frac{2}{8} + \frac{5}{8} = \dfrac{\boxed{}}{\boxed{}}$.

Max got a hit $\dfrac{\boxed{}}{\boxed{}}$ of the times he was at bat.

Hands-On Activity 2

Find $\frac{3}{6} - \frac{4}{6}$.

Step 1 Divide a number line into sixths. Since we do not know if our answer is negative or positive, include fractions to the left and to the right of zero.

Step 2 Graph $\frac{3}{6}$ on the number line.

Step 3 Move 4 units to the _____ to show taking away $\frac{4}{6}$.

So, $\frac{3}{6} - \frac{4}{6} = \dfrac{\boxed{}}{\boxed{}}$.

Hands-On Activity 3

Find $-\frac{4}{7} - \frac{2}{7}$. Fill in the missing numbers in the diagram below.

So, $-\frac{4}{7} - \frac{2}{7} = \dfrac{\boxed{}}{\boxed{}}$.

Investigate

Work with a partner. Use a number line to add or subtract. Write in simplest form.

1. $\dfrac{1}{5} + \dfrac{2}{5} =$ _____

2. $-\dfrac{3}{7} + \left(-\dfrac{1}{7}\right) =$ _____

3. $-\dfrac{3}{8} + \dfrac{5}{8} =$ _____

4. $\dfrac{8}{12} - \dfrac{4}{12} =$ _____

5. $-\dfrac{4}{9} + \dfrac{5}{9} =$ _____

6. $\dfrac{4}{7} - \dfrac{6}{7} =$ _____

Analyze and Reflect

PS Use Math Tools Work with a partner to complete the table. The first one is done for you.

Expression	Use only the Numerators	Use a number line to add or subtract the fractions.
$-\frac{5}{6} - \left(-\frac{1}{6}\right)$	$-5 - (-1) = -4$	
7. $-\frac{5}{6} - \frac{1}{6}$	$-5 - 1 = -6$	0
8. $\frac{5}{6} - \frac{1}{6}$	$5 - 1 = 4$	0
9. $-\frac{5}{6} + \frac{1}{6}$	$-5 + 1 = -4$	0

Create

10. **PS Reason Inductively** Refer to the table above. Compare your results for using only the numerators with your results for using a number line. Write a rule for adding and subtracting like fractions.

_____

_____

11. **Inquiry** HOW can you use a number line to add and subtract like fractions?

_____

_____

_____

Add and Subtract Like Fractions

 Real-World Link

Shoes Sean surveyed ten classmates to find which type of tennis shoe they like to wear.

Shoe Type	Number
Cross Trainer	5
Running	3
High Top	2

 Essential Question

WHAT happens when you add, subtract, multiply, and divide fractions?

 Vocabulary

like fractions

Indiana Academic Standards
7.C.7, 7.C.8

PS Process Standards
1, 3, 4, 7

1. What fraction of students liked to wear cross trainers?

Number of students that wear cross trainers. ⟶ ☐

Total number of students surveyed. ⟶ ☐

2. What fraction of students liked to wear high tops?

Number of students that wear high tops. ⟶ ☐

Total number of students surveyed. ⟶ ☐

3. What fraction of students liked to wear either cross trainers or high tops?

Fraction of students that wear cross trainers.   Fraction of students that wear high tops.

$$\frac{\Box}{\Box} \;+\; \frac{\Box}{\Box} \;=\; \frac{\Box}{\Box}$$

So, _____ of the students liked to wear either cross trainers or high tops.

4. Explain how to find $\frac{3}{10} + \frac{2}{10}$. Then find the sum.

_____

_____

Which PS Process Standards did you use?
Shade the circle(s) that applies.

① Persevere with Problems
② Reason Abstractly
③ Construct an Argument
④ Model with Mathematics

⑤ Use Math Tools
⑥ Attend to Precision
⑦ Make Use of Structure
⑧ Use Repeated Reasoning

Add and Subtract Like Fractions

Words To add or subtract like fractions, add or subtract the numerators and write the result over the denominator.

Examples

	Numbers	**Algebra**

$$\frac{5}{10} + \frac{2}{10} = \frac{5+2}{10} \text{ or } \frac{7}{10}$$ $\qquad \frac{a}{c} + \frac{b}{c} = \frac{a+b}{c}$, where $c \neq 0$

$$\frac{11}{12} - \frac{4}{12} = \frac{11-4}{12} \text{ or } \frac{7}{12}$$ $\qquad \frac{a}{c} - \frac{b}{c} = \frac{a-b}{c}$, where $c \neq 0$

Fractions that have the same denominators are called **like fractions**.

Examples

Add. Write in simplest form.

1. $\dfrac{5}{9} + \dfrac{2}{9}$

$$\frac{5}{9} + \frac{2}{9} = \frac{5+2}{9} \qquad \text{Add the numerators.}$$

$$= \frac{7}{9} \qquad \text{Simplify.}$$

2. $-\dfrac{3}{5} + \left(-\dfrac{1}{5}\right)$

$$-\frac{3}{5} + \left(-\frac{1}{5}\right) = -\frac{3}{5} + \left(\frac{-1}{5}\right)$$

$$= \frac{-3 + (-1)}{5} \qquad \text{Add the numerators.}$$

$$= \frac{-4}{5} \text{ or } -\frac{4}{5} \qquad \text{Use the rules for adding integers.}$$

Got it? Do these problems to find out.

a. $\dfrac{1}{3} + \dfrac{2}{3}$ **b.** $-\dfrac{3}{7} + \dfrac{1}{7}$

c. $-\dfrac{2}{5} + \left(-\dfrac{2}{5}\right)$ **d.** $-\dfrac{1}{4} + \dfrac{1}{4}$

Work Zone

Negative Fractions

Remember $\frac{1}{2} = \frac{-1}{2} = \frac{1}{-2}$.

Typically, the form $\frac{-1}{2}$ is used when performing computations.

Show your work.

a. _____

b. _____

c. _____

d. _____

Example

Tutor

3. Sofia ate $\frac{3}{5}$ of a cheese pizza. Jack ate $\frac{1}{5}$ of a cheese pizza and $\frac{2}{5}$ of a pepperoni pizza. How much pizza did Sofia and Jack eat altogether?

$$\frac{3}{5} + \left(\frac{1}{5} + \frac{2}{5}\right) = \frac{3}{5} + \left(\frac{2}{5} + \frac{1}{5}\right)$$ Commutative Property of Addition

$$= \left(\frac{3}{5} + \frac{2}{5}\right) + \frac{1}{5}$$ Associative Property of Addition

$$= 1 + \frac{1}{5} \text{ or } 1\frac{1}{5}$$ Simplify.

So, Sofia and Jack ate $1\frac{1}{5}$ pizzas altogether.

Got it? Do this problem to find out.

e. Eduardo used fabric to make three costumes. He used $\frac{1}{4}$ yard for the first, $\frac{2}{4}$ yard for the second, and $\frac{3}{4}$ yard for the third costume. How much fabric did Eduardo use altogether?

Show your work.

e. _____

Examples

Tutor

4. Find $-\frac{5}{8} - \frac{3}{8}$.

$$-\frac{5}{8} - \frac{3}{8} = -\frac{5}{8} + \left(-\frac{3}{8}\right)$$ Add $-\frac{3}{8}$.

$$= \frac{-5 + (-3)}{8}$$ Add the numerators.

$$= -\frac{8}{8} \text{ or } -1$$ Simplify.

Subtracting Integers

To subtract an integer, add its opposite.

$-9 - (-4) = -9 + 4$

$= -5$

5. Find $\frac{5}{8} - \frac{7}{8}$.

$$\frac{5}{8} - \frac{7}{8} = \frac{5 - 7}{8}$$ Subtract the numerators.

$$= -\frac{2}{8} \text{ or } -\frac{1}{4}$$ Simplify.

Got it? Do these problems to find out.

f. $\frac{5}{9} - \frac{2}{9}$ **g.** $-\frac{5}{9} - \frac{2}{9}$ **h.** $-\frac{11}{12} - \left(-\frac{5}{12}\right)$

f. _____

g. _____

h. _____

You can add or subtract like fractions to solve real-world problems.

 Example

6. About $\frac{6}{100}$ of the population of the United States lives in Florida. Another $\frac{4}{100}$ lives in Ohio. About what fraction more of the U.S. population lives in Florida than in Ohio?

$$\frac{6}{100} - \frac{4}{100} = \frac{6-4}{100} \qquad \text{Subtract the numerators.}$$

$$= \frac{2}{100} \text{ or } \frac{1}{50} \qquad \text{Simplify.}$$

About $\frac{1}{50}$ more of the U.S. population lives in Florida than in Ohio.

STOP and Reflect

In Example 6, what word or words indicate that you should subtract to solve the problem? Write your answer below.

Guided Practice

Add or subtract. Write in simplest form. (Examples 1–5)

1. $\frac{3}{5} + \frac{1}{5} =$ _____

2. $\frac{2}{7} + \frac{1}{7} =$ _____

3. $\left(\frac{5}{8} + \frac{1}{8}\right) + \frac{3}{8} =$ _____

4. $-\frac{4}{5} - \left(-\frac{1}{5}\right) =$ _____

5. $\frac{5}{14} - \left(-\frac{1}{14}\right) =$ _____

6. $\frac{2}{7} - \frac{6}{7} =$ _____

7. Of the 50 states in the United States, 14 have an Atlantic Ocean coastline and 5 have a Pacific Ocean coastline. What fraction of U.S. states have either an Atlantic Ocean or Pacific Ocean coastline? (Example 6)

_____

8. @ **Building on the Essential Question** What is a simple rule for adding and subtracting like fractions?

_____

_____

Rate Yourself!

How confident are you about adding and subtracting like fractions? Check the box that applies.

For more help, go online to access a Personal Tutor.

 Tutor

FOLDABLES Time to update your Foldable!

Name _____ My Homework _____

Add or subtract. Write in simplest form. (Examples 1, 2, 4, and, 5)

Show your work.

1. $\frac{5}{7} + \frac{6}{7} =$ _____

2. $\frac{3}{8} + \left(-\frac{7}{8}\right) =$ _____

3. $-\frac{1}{9} + \left(-\frac{5}{9}\right) =$ _____

4. $\frac{9}{10} - \frac{3}{10} =$ _____

5. $-\frac{3}{4} + \left(-\frac{3}{4}\right) =$ _____

6. $-\frac{5}{9} - \frac{2}{9} =$ _____

7. In Mr. Navarro's first period class, $\frac{17}{28}$ of the students got an A on their math test. In his second period class, $\frac{11}{28}$ of the students got an A. What fraction more of the students got an A in Mr. Navarro's first period class than in his second period class? Write in simplest form. (Example 6)

_____

8. To make a greeting card, Bryce used $\frac{1}{8}$ sheet of red paper, $\frac{3}{8}$ sheet of green paper, and $\frac{7}{8}$ sheet of white paper. How many sheets of paper did Bryce use? (Example 3)

_____

9. The table shows the Instant Messenger abbreviations students at Hillside Middle School use the most.

a. What fraction of these students uses LOL or CUL8R when using Instant Messenger? _____

b. What fraction of these students uses L8R or BRB when using Instant Messenger? _____

c. What fraction more of these students write L8R than CUL8R when using Instant Messenger? _____

Instant Messenger Abbreviations	
L8R (Later)	$\frac{48}{100}$
LOL (Laughing out loud)	$\frac{26}{100}$
BRB (Be right back)	$\frac{19}{100}$
CUL8R (See you later)	$\frac{7}{100}$

10. **(PS) Model with Mathematics** Cross out the expression that does not belong. Explain your reasoning.

_____

_____

_____

_____

$$\frac{2}{7} + \frac{3}{7} \quad \Big| \quad \frac{4}{7} - \left(-\frac{1}{7}\right)$$

$$\frac{8}{7} - \frac{3}{7} \quad \Big| \quad \frac{10}{7} + \left(-\frac{3}{7}\right)$$

H.O.T. Problems Higher Order Thinking

11. **(PS) Justify Conclusions** Select two like fractions with a difference of $\frac{1}{3}$ and with denominators that are *not* 3. Justify your selection.

_____

_____

12. **(PS) Persevere with Problems** Simplify the following expression.

$$\frac{14}{15} + \frac{13}{15} - \frac{12}{15} + \frac{11}{15} - \frac{10}{15} + \cdots - \frac{4}{15} + \frac{3}{15} - \frac{2}{15} + \frac{1}{15}$$

_____

13. **(PS) Justify Conclusions** Is the difference between a positive like fraction and a negative like fraction *always*, *sometimes*, or *never* positive? Justify your answer with an example.

_____

14. **(PS) Use Math Tools** Explain how you could use mental math to find the following sum. Then find the sum. Support your answer with a model.

$$1\frac{1}{4} + 2\frac{1}{3} + 3\frac{2}{3} + 4\frac{1}{2} + 5\frac{1}{2} + 6\frac{3}{4}$$

_____

_____

_____

15. **(PS) Persevere with Problems** A construction company is replacing a window in a house. The window is currently 3 feet wide by 4 feet tall. The homeowner wants to add $4\frac{1}{2}$ inches to each side of the window. What is the new perimeter of the window in feet? Justify your reasoning.

_____

_____

Extra Practice

Add or subtract. Write in simplest form.

16. $\frac{4}{5} + \frac{3}{5} = 1\frac{2}{5}$

$\qquad \frac{4}{5} + \frac{3}{5} = \frac{4+3}{5}$

$\qquad\qquad = \frac{7}{5}$ or $1\frac{2}{5}$

Homework Help

17. $-\frac{5}{6} + \left(-\frac{5}{6}\right) = $ _____

18. $-\frac{15}{16} + \left(-\frac{7}{16}\right) = $ _____

19. $\frac{5}{8} - \frac{3}{8} = $ _____

20. $\frac{7}{12} - \frac{2}{12} = $ _____

21. $\frac{15}{18} - \frac{13}{18} = $ _____

22. Two nails are $\frac{5}{16}$ inch and $\frac{13}{16}$ inch long. How much shorter is

the $\frac{5}{16}$-inch nail? _____

PS Identify Structure Add. Write in simplest form.

23. $\left(\frac{81}{100} + \frac{47}{100}\right) + \frac{19}{100} = $ _____

24. $\frac{\frac{1}{3}}{6} + \frac{\frac{2}{3}}{6} = $ _____

25. A recipe for Michigan blueberry pancakes calls for $\frac{3}{4}$ cup

flour, $\frac{1}{4}$ cup milk, and $\frac{1}{4}$ cup blueberries. How much more

flour is needed than milk? Write in simplest form.

_____

26. The graph shows the location of volcanic eruptions.

   a. What fraction represents the volcanic eruptions for
   both North and South America?

   _____

   b. How much larger is the section for Asia and South
   Pacific than for Europe? Write in simplest form.

   _____

Worldwide Volcano Eruptions

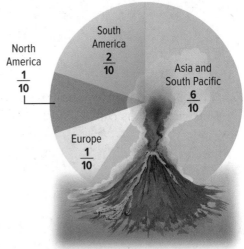

North America $\frac{1}{10}$

South America $\frac{2}{10}$

Asia and South Pacific $\frac{6}{10}$

Europe $\frac{1}{10}$

27. A group of friends bought two large pizzas and ate only part of each pizza. The picture shows how much was left. How many pizzas did they eat?

First Pizza   Second Pizza

28. The table shows the results of a survey on students' favorite kind of movie. Select the appropriate values to complete the model to find the fraction of students that prefer comedy or action movies.

Type of Movie	Number of Students
Action	29
Comedy	42
Drama	14
Horror	15

14	50
15	60
29	71
42	100

What fraction of the students who were surveyed prefers comedy or action movies?

Spiral Review

Fill in each ◯ with <, >, or = to make a true sentence.

29. $\frac{7}{8}$ ◯ $\frac{3}{4}$

30. $\frac{1}{3}$ ◯ $\frac{7}{9}$

31. $\frac{5}{7}$ ◯ $\frac{4}{5}$

32. $\frac{6}{11}$ ◯ $\frac{9}{14}$

Find the least common denominator for each pair of fractions.

33. $\frac{1}{2}$ and $\frac{1}{3}$ _____

34. $\frac{4}{7}$ and $\frac{3}{28}$ _____

35. $\frac{1}{5}$ and $\frac{7}{6}$ _____

36. $\frac{13}{15}$ and $\frac{7}{12}$ _____

37. The results of a survey about favorite lunch choices are shown. Which lunch was chosen most often?

_____

Favorite Lunch	
Food	Fraction of Students
Pizza	$\frac{39}{50}$
Hot Dogs	$\frac{3}{25}$
Grilled Cheese	$\frac{1}{10}$

Add and Subtract Unlike Fractions

Real-World Link

Time The table shows the fractions of one hour for certain minutes.

1. What fraction of one hour is equal to the sum of 15 minutes and 20 minutes?

15 minutes   20 minutes

$\dfrac{\boxed{}}{\boxed{}} + \dfrac{\boxed{}}{\boxed{}} = \dfrac{\boxed{}}{\boxed{}}$

Number of Minutes	Fraction of One Hour	Simplified Fraction
5	$\frac{5}{60}$	
10	$\frac{10}{60}$	
15	$\frac{15}{60}$	
20	$\frac{20}{60}$	
30	$\frac{30}{60}$	

2. Write each fraction of an hour in simplest form in the third column of the table.

3. Explain why $\frac{1}{6}$ hour $+ \frac{1}{3}$ hour $= \frac{1}{2}$ hour.

_____

_____

_____

_____

4. Explain why $\frac{1}{12}$ hour $+ \frac{1}{2}$ hour $= \frac{7}{12}$ hour.

_____

_____

_____

 Essential Question

WHAT happens when you add, subtract, multiply, and divide fractions?

Vocabulary

unlike fractions

Indiana Academic Standards
7.C.7, 7.C.8

PS Process Standards
1, 3, 4

Which **PS Process Standards** did you use?
Shade the circle(s) that applies.

1. Persevere with Problems
2. Reason Abstractly
3. Construct an Argument
4. Model with Mathematics
5. Use Math Tools
6. Attend to Precision
7. Make Use of Structure
8. Use Repeated Reasoning

Add or Subtract Unlike Fractions

To add or subtract fractions with different denominators,

- Rename the fractions using the least common denominator (LCD).
- Add or subtract as with like fractions.
- If necessary, simplify the sum or difference.

Before you can add two **unlike fractions**, or fractions with different denominators, rename one or both of the fractions so that they have a common denominator.

Example

1. Find $\frac{1}{2} + \frac{1}{4}$.

> **Method 1** Use a number line.

Divide the number line into fourths since the LCD is 4.

> **Method 2** Use the LCD.

The least common denominator of $\frac{1}{2}$ and $\frac{1}{4}$ is 4.

$$\frac{1}{2} + \frac{1}{4} = \frac{1 \times 2}{2 \times 2} + \frac{1 \times 1}{4 \times 1}$$ Rename using the LCD, 4.

$$= \frac{2}{4} + \frac{1}{4}$$ Add the fractions.

$$= \frac{3}{4}$$ Simplify.

Using either method, $\frac{1}{2} + \frac{1}{4} = \frac{3}{4}$.

Got it? Do these problems to find out.

Add. Write in simplest form.

a. $\frac{1}{6} + \frac{2}{3}$

b. $\frac{9}{10} + \left(-\frac{1}{2}\right)$

c. $\frac{1}{4} + \frac{3}{8}$

d. $-\frac{1}{3} + \left(-\frac{1}{4}\right)$

STOP and Reflect

Circle the pairs of fractions that are unlike fractions.

$\frac{1}{3}$ and $\frac{5}{3}$ $\frac{1}{7}$ and $\frac{1}{5}$ $\frac{5}{9}$ and $\frac{4}{11}$

Show your work.

a. _____

b. _____

c. _____

d. _____

Example

2. Find $\left(-\dfrac{3}{4} + \dfrac{5}{9}\right) + \dfrac{7}{4}$.

$\left(-\dfrac{3}{4} + \dfrac{5}{9}\right) + \dfrac{7}{4} = \left(\dfrac{5}{9} + \left(-\dfrac{3}{4}\right)\right) + \dfrac{7}{4}$ Commutative Property of Addition

$= \dfrac{5}{9} + \left(-\dfrac{3}{4} + \dfrac{7}{4}\right)$ Associative Property of Addition

$= \dfrac{5}{9} + 1$ or $1\dfrac{5}{9}$ Simplify.

Got it? Do these problems to find out.

e. $\dfrac{2}{5} + \left(\dfrac{4}{7} + \dfrac{3}{5}\right)$ **f.** $\left(-\dfrac{3}{10} + \dfrac{5}{8}\right) + \dfrac{23}{10}$

e. _____

f. _____

Example

3. Find $-\dfrac{2}{3} - \dfrac{1}{2}$.

Method 1   Use a number line.

Divide the number line into sixths since the LCD is 6.

Method 2   Use the LCD.

$-\dfrac{2}{3} - \dfrac{1}{2} = -\dfrac{2 \times 2}{3 \times 2} - \dfrac{1 \times 3}{2 \times 3}$ Rename using the LCD, 6.

$= -\dfrac{4}{6} - \dfrac{3}{6}$ Simplify.

$= \dfrac{-4}{6} - \dfrac{3}{6}$ Rewrite $-\dfrac{4}{6}$ as $\dfrac{-4}{6}$.

$= \dfrac{-4 - 3}{6}$ or $\dfrac{-7}{6}$ Subtract the numerators. Simplify.

Check by adding $-\dfrac{7}{6} + \dfrac{1}{2} = -\dfrac{7}{6} + \dfrac{3}{6} = -\dfrac{4}{6}$ or $-\dfrac{2}{3}$ ✓

Using either method, $-\dfrac{2}{3} - \dfrac{1}{2} = -\dfrac{7}{6}$ or $-1\dfrac{1}{6}$.

Check for Reasonableness

Estimate the difference.

$-\dfrac{2}{3} - \dfrac{1}{2} \approx -\dfrac{1}{2} - \dfrac{1}{2}$ or -1

Compare $-\dfrac{7}{6}$ to the estimate.

$-\dfrac{7}{6} \approx -1$. So, the answer is reasonable.

Got it? Do these problems to find out.

Subtract. Write in simplest form.

g. $\dfrac{5}{8} - \dfrac{1}{4}$ **h.** $\dfrac{3}{4} - \dfrac{1}{3}$ **i.** $\dfrac{1}{2} - \left(-\dfrac{2}{5}\right)$

g. _____

h. _____

i. _____

Choose an Operation

Add or subtract unlike fractions to solve real-world problems.

Example

Tutor

4. **STEM** Use the table to find the fraction of the total population that has type A or type B blood.

Blood Type Frequencies				
ABO Type	O	A	B	AB
Fraction	$\frac{11}{25}$	$\frac{21}{50}$	$\frac{1}{10}$	$\frac{1}{25}$

To find the fraction of the total population, add $\frac{21}{50}$ and $\frac{1}{10}$.

$$\frac{21}{50} + \frac{1}{10} = \frac{21 \times 1}{50 \times 1} + \frac{1 \times 5}{10 \times 5}$$ Rename using the LCD, 50.

$$= \frac{21}{50} + \frac{5}{50}$$ Add the fractions.

$$= \frac{26}{50} \text{ or } \frac{13}{25}$$ Simplify.

So, $\frac{13}{25}$ of the population has type A or type B blood.

Guided Practice

Check ✓

Add or subtract. Write in simplest form. (Examples 1–3)

Show your work.

1. $\frac{3}{5} + \frac{1}{10} =$ _____

2. $-\frac{5}{6} + \left(-\frac{4}{9}\right) =$ _____

3. $\left(\frac{7}{8} + \frac{3}{11}\right) + \frac{1}{8} =$ _____

4. $\frac{4}{5} - \frac{3}{10} =$ _____

5. $\frac{3}{8} - \left(-\frac{1}{4}\right) =$ _____

6. $\frac{3}{4} - \frac{1}{3} =$ _____

7. Cassandra cuts $\frac{5}{16}$ inch off the top of a photo and $\frac{3}{8}$ inch off the bottom. How much shorter is the total height of the photo now? Explain. (Example 4)

_____

_____

8. ⓔ **Building on the Essential Question** Compare adding unlike fractions and adding like fractions.

_____

_____

_____

Rate Yourself!

Are you ready to move on?
Shade the section that applies.

YES   ?   NO

For more help, go online to access a Personal Tutor.

Tutor

FOLDABLES Time to update your Foldable!

Independent Practice

Go online for Step-by-Step Solutions

Add or subtract. Write in simplest form. (Examples 1–3)

1. $\frac{1}{6} + \frac{3}{8} =$ _____

2. $-\frac{1}{15} + \left(-\frac{3}{5}\right) =$ _____

3. $\left(\frac{15}{8} + \frac{2}{5}\right) + \left(-\frac{7}{8}\right) =$

_____

4. $\left(-\frac{7}{10}\right) - \frac{2}{5} =$ _____

5. $\frac{7}{9} - \frac{1}{3} =$ _____

6. $-\frac{7}{12} + \frac{7}{10} =$ _____

7. $-\frac{4}{9} - \frac{2}{15} =$ _____

8. $\frac{5}{8} + \frac{11}{12} =$ _____

9. $\frac{7}{9} + \frac{5}{6} =$ _____

PS **Justify Conclusions** **Choose an operation to solve each problem. Explain your reasoning. Then solve the problem. Write in simplest form.** (Example 4)

10. Mrs. Escalante was riding a bicycle on a bike path. After riding $\frac{2}{3}$ of a mile, she discovered that she still needed to travel $\frac{3}{4}$ of a mile to reach the end of the path. How long is the bike path?

_____

_____

11. Four students were scheduled to give book reports in 1 hour. After the first report, $\frac{2}{3}$ hour remained. The next two reports took $\frac{1}{6}$ hour and $\frac{1}{4}$ hour. What fraction of the hour remained?

_____

_____

12. One hundred sixty cell phone owners were surveyed.

a. What fraction of owners prefers using their cell phone for text messaging or playing games? Explain.

_____

b. What fraction of owners prefers using their phone to take pictures or text message?

_____

13. Pepita and Francisco each spend an equal amount of time on homework. The table shows the fraction of time they spend on each subject. Complete the table by determining the missing fraction for each student.

Homework	Fraction of Time	
	Pepita	Francisco
Math		$\frac{1}{2}$
English	$\frac{2}{3}$	
Science	$\frac{1}{6}$	$\frac{3}{8}$

14. Chelsie saves $\frac{1}{5}$ of her allowance and spends $\frac{2}{3}$ of her allowance at the mall. What fraction of her allowance remains? Explain.

_____

H.O.T. Problems Higher Order Thinking

15. (PS) **Persevere with Problems** Fractions whose numerators are 1, such as $\frac{1}{2}$ or $\frac{1}{3}$, are called *unit fractions*. Describe a method you can use to add two unit fractions mentally. _____

_____

_____

16. (PS) **Use a Counterexample** Provide a counterexample to the following statement.

   The sum of three fractions with odd numerators is never $\frac{1}{2}$.

_____

17. (PS) **Reason Inductively** Suppose a bucket is placed under two faucets. If one faucet is turned on alone, the bucket will be filled in 6 minutes. If the other faucet is turned on alone, the bucket will be filled in 4 minutes. What fraction of the bucket will be filled in 1 minute if both faucets are turned on at the same time? Explain.

_____

_____

_____

Extra Practice

Add or subtract. Write in simplest form.

18. $\frac{5}{8} + \frac{1}{4} = \frac{7}{8}$ _____

Homework Help →

$$\frac{5}{8} + \frac{1}{4} = \frac{5}{8} + \frac{1 \times 2}{4 \times 2}$$

$$= \frac{5}{8} + \frac{2}{8}$$

$$= \frac{7}{8}$$

19. $\frac{4}{5} - \frac{1}{6} =$ _____

20. $\frac{5}{6} - \left(-\frac{2}{3}\right) =$ _____

21. $\frac{3}{10} - \left(-\frac{1}{4}\right) =$ _____

22. $-\frac{2}{3} + \left(\frac{3}{4} + \frac{5}{3}\right) =$ _____

23. $-\frac{7}{8} + \frac{1}{3} =$ _____

Choose an operation to solve each problem. Explain your reasoning. Then solve the problem. Write in simplest form.

24. Ebony is building a shelf to hold the two boxes shown. What is the least width she should make the shelf?

_____

_____

$\leftarrow \frac{4}{5}$ ft $\rightarrow$ $\leftarrow \frac{3}{4}$ ft $\rightarrow$

25. Makayla bought $\frac{1}{4}$ pound of ham and $\frac{5}{8}$ pound of turkey. How much more turkey did she buy? _____

_____

26. **PS** **Persevere with Problems** Find the sum of $\frac{3}{4}{8}$ and $\frac{1}{3}{4}$. Write in simplest form.

_____

27. **PS** **Find the Error** Theresa is finding $\frac{1}{4} + \frac{3}{5}$. Find her mistake and correct it. Explain your answer.

$$\frac{1}{4} + \frac{3}{5} = \frac{1+3}{4+5}$$

_____

_____

_____

_____

28. The table shows the number of hours Orlando spent at football practice last week. Select the appropriate numbers below to complete the model to find the number of hours Orlando spent practicing on Tuesday and Friday.

Day	Time (h)
Monday	$\frac{1}{2}$
Tuesday	$\frac{3}{4}$
Thursday	$\frac{1}{3}$
Friday	$\frac{5}{6}$

$$\frac{\square}{\square} + \frac{\square}{\square} = \frac{\square}{\square} + \frac{\square}{\square} = \frac{\square}{\square}$$

1	9
3	10
4	12
5	16
6	19

How many hours did Orlando spend practicing on Tuesday and Friday? [   ]

29. Brett has $\frac{5}{6}$ of his monthly income left to spend. He has budgeted $\frac{1}{8}$ of his income for a new video game and $\frac{1}{3}$ of his income for savings. Determine if each statement is true or false.

a. Brett will have $\frac{7}{8}$ of his income left if he only buys the video game.   ☐ True   ☐ False

b. Brett will have $\frac{1}{2}$ of his income left if he only puts money in savings.   ☐ True   ☐ False

c. Brett will have $\frac{3}{8}$ of his income left after buying the video game and putting money in savings.   ☐ True   ☐ False

Spiral Review

Write each improper fraction as a mixed number.

30. $\frac{7}{5} = $ _____

31. $\frac{14}{3} = $ _____

32. $\frac{101}{100} = $ _____

33. $\frac{22}{9} = $ _____

34. $\frac{77}{10} = $ _____

35. $\frac{23}{8} = $ _____

Add and Subtract Mixed Numbers

 ## Real-World Link

Hockey Junior and adult hockey sticks are shown below.

Junior

length $3\frac{2}{3}$ ft

Adult

length $4\frac{5}{6}$ ft

 Essential Question

WHAT happens when you add, subtract, multiply, and divide fractions?

Indiana Academic Standards
7.C.7, 7.C.8

PS Process Standards
1, 3, 4

1. Use the expression $4\frac{5}{6} - 3\frac{2}{3}$ to find how much longer the adult hockey stick is than the junior hockey stick.

Rename the fractions using the LCD, 6.

Subtract the fractions. Then subtract the whole numbers.

$$4\frac{5}{6} - \boxed{}\frac{\boxed{}}{\boxed{}} = \boxed{}\frac{\boxed{}}{\boxed{}}$$

2. Explain how to find $3\frac{7}{10} - 2\frac{2}{5}$. Then use your conjecture to find the difference.

_____

_____

_____

Which **PS** Process Standards did you use?
Shade the circle(s) that applies.

1 Persevere with Problems

2 Reason Abstractly

3 Construct an Argument

4 Model with Mathematics

5 Use Math Tools

6 Attend to Precision

7 Make Use of Structure

8 Use Repeated Reasoning

Add and Subtract Mixed Numbers

To add or subtract mixed numbers, first add or subtract the fractions. If necessary, rename them using the LCD. Then add or subtract the whole numbers and simplify if necessary.

Sometimes when you subtract mixed numbers, the fraction in the first mixed number is less than the fraction in the second mixed number. In this case, rename one or both fractions in order to subtract.

Tutor

Examples

1. Find $7\frac{4}{9} + 10\frac{2}{9}$. Write in simplest form.

Estimate $7 + 10 = 17$

$$7\frac{4}{9}$$
$$+\ 10\frac{2}{9}$$ Add the whole numbers and fractions separately.

$$\overline{17\frac{6}{9}\ \text{or}\ 17\frac{2}{3}}$$ Simplify.

Check for Reasonableness $17\frac{2}{3} \approx 17$ ✔

2. Find $8\frac{5}{6} - 2\frac{1}{3}$. Write in simplest form.

Estimate $9 - 2 = 7$

$$8\frac{5}{6} \quad \longrightarrow \quad 8\frac{5}{6}$$
$$-2\frac{1}{3} \quad \longrightarrow \quad -2\frac{2}{6}$$ Rename the fraction using the LCD. Then subtract.

$$\overline{6\frac{3}{6}\ \text{or}\ 6\frac{1}{2}}$$ Simplify.

Check for Reasonableness $6\frac{1}{2} \approx 7$ ✔

Got it? Do these problems to find out.

Add or subtract. Write in simplest form.

Show your work.

a. $6\frac{1}{8} + 2\frac{5}{8}$ b. $5\frac{1}{5} + 2\frac{3}{10}$ c. $1\frac{5}{9} + 4\frac{1}{6}$

d. $5\frac{4}{5} - 1\frac{3}{10}$ e. $13\frac{7}{8} - 9\frac{3}{4}$ f. $8\frac{2}{3} - 2\frac{1}{2}$

a. _____

b. _____

c. _____

d. _____

e. _____

f. _____

Example

3. Find $2\frac{1}{3} - 1\frac{2}{3}$.

Method 1 **Rename Mixed Numbers**

Estimate $2 - 1\frac{1}{2} = \frac{1}{2}$

Since $\frac{1}{3}$ is less than $\frac{2}{3}$, rename $2\frac{1}{3}$ before subtracting.

Change 1 to $\frac{3}{3}$.

$$2\frac{1}{3} \quad = \quad 1\frac{3}{3} + \frac{1}{3} \text{ or } 1\frac{4}{3}$$

$$
\begin{array}{ll}
2\frac{1}{3} \rightarrow 1\frac{4}{3} & \text{Rename } 2\frac{1}{3} \text{ as } 1\frac{4}{3}. \\
-1\frac{2}{3} \rightarrow -1\frac{2}{3} & \text{Subtract the whole numbers and then the fractions.} \\
\hline
\frac{2}{3}
\end{array}
$$

Check for Reasonableness $\frac{2}{3} \approx \frac{1}{2}$ ✓

Method 2 **Write as Improper Fractions**

$$
\begin{array}{ll}
2\frac{1}{3} \rightarrow \frac{7}{3} & \text{Write } 2\frac{1}{3} \text{ as } \frac{7}{3}. \\
-1\frac{2}{3} \rightarrow -\frac{5}{3} & \text{Write } 1\frac{2}{3} \text{ as } \frac{5}{3}. \\
\hline
\frac{2}{3} & \text{Simplify.}
\end{array}
$$

So, $2\frac{1}{3} - 1\frac{2}{3} = \frac{2}{3}$.

Using either method, the answer is $\frac{2}{3}$.

Got it? Do these problems to find out.

Subtract. Write in simplest form.

g. $7 - 1\frac{1}{2}$

h. $5\frac{3}{8} - 4\frac{11}{12}$

i. $11\frac{2}{5} - 2\frac{3}{5}$

j. $8 - 3\frac{3}{4}$

k. $3\frac{1}{4} - 1\frac{3}{4}$

l. $16 - 5\frac{5}{6}$

Fractions Greater Than One

An improper fraction has a numerator that is greater than or equal to the denominator. Examples of improper fractions are $\frac{5}{4}$ and $2\frac{6}{5}$.

Show your work.

g. _____

h. _____

i. _____

j. _____

k. _____

l. _____

Choose an Operation

Add or subtract unlike fractions to solve real-world problems.

 Example

4. An urban planner is designing a skateboard park. The length of the skateboard park is $120\frac{1}{2}$ feet. The length of the parking lot is $40\frac{1}{3}$ feet. What will be the length of the park and the parking lot combined?

$$120\frac{1}{2} + 40\frac{1}{3} = 120\frac{3}{6} + 40\frac{2}{6}$$ Rename $\frac{1}{2}$ as $\frac{3}{6}$ and $\frac{1}{3}$ as $\frac{2}{6}$.

$$= 160 + \frac{5}{6}$$ Add the whole numbers and fractions separately.

$$= 160\frac{5}{6}$$ Simplify.

The total length is $160\frac{5}{6}$ feet.

Guided Practice

Add or subtract. Write in simplest form. (Examples 1–3)

1. $8\frac{1}{2} + 3\frac{4}{5} =$ _____

2. $7\frac{5}{6} - 3\frac{1}{6} =$ _____

3. $11 - 6\frac{3}{8} =$ _____

4. A hybrid car's gas tank can hold $11\frac{9}{10}$ gallons of gasoline. It contains $8\frac{3}{4}$ gallons of gasoline. How much more gasoline is needed to fill the tank? (Example 4) _____

5. **Building on the Essential Question** How can you subtract mixed numbers when the fraction in the first mixed number is less than the fraction in the second mixed number? _____

_____

_____

_____

Rate Yourself!

How confident are you about adding and subtracting mixed numbers? Shade the ring on the target.

For more help, go online to access a Personal Tutor.

Independent Practice

Go online for Step-by-Step Solutions

eHelp

Add or subtract. Write in simplest form. (Examples 1–3)

1. $2\frac{1}{9} + 7\frac{4}{9} =$ _____

2. $8\frac{5}{12} + 11\frac{1}{4} =$ _____

3. $10\frac{4}{5} - 2\frac{1}{5} =$ _____

Show your work.

4. $9\frac{4}{5} - 2\frac{3}{10} =$ _____

5 $11\frac{3}{4} - 4\frac{1}{3} =$ _____

6. $9\frac{1}{5} - 2\frac{3}{5} =$ _____

7. $6\frac{3}{5} - 1\frac{2}{3} =$ _____

8. $14\frac{1}{6} - 7\frac{1}{3} =$ _____

9. $8 - 3\frac{2}{3} =$ _____

PS **Justify Conclusions For Exercises 10 and 11, choose an operation to solve. Explain your reasoning. Then solve the problem. Write your answer in simplest form.** (Example 4)

10. If Juliana and Brody hiked both of the trails listed in the table, how far did they hike?

_____

Trail	Length (mi)
Woodland Park	$3\frac{2}{3}$
Mill Creek Way	$2\frac{5}{6}$

11 The length of Kasey's garden is $4\frac{5}{8}$ feet. Find the width of Kasey's garden if it is $2\frac{7}{8}$ feet shorter than the length.

_____

12. Karen wakes up at 6:00 A.M. It takes her $1\frac{1}{4}$ hours to shower, get dressed, and comb her hair. It takes her $\frac{1}{2}$ hour to eat breakfast, brush her teeth, and make her bed. At what time will she be ready for school? _____

Add or subtract. Write in simplest form.

13. $-3\frac{1}{4} + \left(-1\frac{3}{4}\right) =$ _____

14. $\dfrac{3\frac{1}{2}}{5} + \dfrac{4\frac{2}{3}}{2} =$ _____

15. $6\frac{1}{3} + 1\frac{2}{3} + 5\frac{5}{9} =$ _____

16. $3\frac{1}{4} + 2\frac{5}{6} - 4\frac{1}{3} =$ _____

H.O.T. Problems Higher Order Thinking

17. **PS Model with Mathematics** Write a real-world problem that could be represented by the expression $5\frac{1}{2} - 3\frac{7}{8}$. Then solve your problem.

_____

_____

_____

_____

18. **PS Persevere with Problems** A string is cut in half. One of the halves is thrown away. One fifth of the remaining half is cut away and the piece left is 8 feet long. How long was the string initially? Justify your answer.

_____

_____

_____

19. **PS Model with Mathematics** Using three mixed numbers as side lengths, draw an equilateral triangle with a perimeter of $8\frac{1}{4}$ feet.

Extra Practice

Add or subtract. Write in simplest form.

20. $6\frac{1}{4} - 2\frac{3}{4} =$ ___$3\frac{1}{2}$___

$$6\frac{1}{4} - 2\frac{3}{4} = 5\frac{5}{4} - 2\frac{3}{4}$$
$$= 3\frac{2}{4}$$
$$= 3\frac{1}{2}$$

21. $8\frac{3}{8} + 10\frac{1}{3} =$ _____

22. $13 - 5\frac{5}{6} =$ _____

23. $3\frac{2}{7} + 4\frac{3}{7} =$ _____

24. $4\frac{3}{10} - 1\frac{3}{4} =$ _____

25. $12\frac{1}{2} - 6\frac{5}{8} =$ _____

PS **Justify Conclusions** Choose an operation to solve. Explain your reasoning. Then solve the problem. Write your answer in simplest form.

26. The length of Alana's hair was $9\frac{3}{4}$ inches. After her haircut, the length was $6\frac{1}{2}$ inches. How many inches did she have cut?

_____

_____

27. Emeril used a total of $7\frac{1}{4}$ cups of flour to make three pastries. He used $2\frac{1}{4}$ cups of flour for the first and $2\frac{1}{3}$ cups for the second. How much flour did Emeril use for the third pastry?

_____

_____

28. Margarite made the jewelry shown. If the necklace is $10\frac{5}{8}$ inches longer than the bracelet, how long is the necklace?

$7\frac{1}{4}$ in.

bracelet

necklace

_____

29. Find the perimeter of the figure. Write your answer in simplest form.

_____

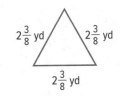

$2\frac{3}{8}$ yd $2\frac{3}{8}$ yd

$2\frac{3}{8}$ yd

30. Suppose you want to place a shelf that is $30\frac{1}{3}$ inches long in the center of a wall that is $45\frac{3}{4}$ inches wide. About how far from each edge of the wall should you place the shelf? _____

31. A recipe for snack mix calls for $4\frac{3}{4}$ cups of cereal. The amount of peanuts needed is $1\frac{2}{3}$ cups less than the amount of cereal needed. Complete each box below to make a true statement.

The recipe calls for ⬚ cups of peanuts. A total of

⬚ cups of peanuts and cereal are needed in all.

32. Maria practiced the piano for $2\frac{1}{2}$ hours last week and $1\frac{3}{4}$ hours this week. Use the bar diagram sections to construct a bar diagram that represents how many hours Maria practiced in the past 2 weeks.

⬚

▭

How many hours did Maria practice the piano in the past 2 weeks?

⬚

Spiral Review

Round each mixed number to its nearest whole number. Then estimate each product.

33. $5\frac{1}{4} \times 7\frac{2}{3} \approx \boxed{} \times \boxed{} \approx \boxed{}$

34. $1\frac{1}{11} \times 8\frac{14}{15} \approx \boxed{} \times \boxed{} \approx \boxed{}$

35. Zoe's average running speed is about $6\frac{4}{5}$ miles per hour. Suppose Zoe runs for $1\frac{3}{4}$ hours. About how far will she have run? Explain.

_____

_____

PS Problem-Solving Investigation
Draw a Diagram

Indiana Academic Standards
7.C.2

PS Process Standards
1, 4, 6

Case #1 Science Experiment

Casey drops a ball from a height of 12 feet. It hits the ground and bounces up half as high as it fell. This is true for each successive bounce.

What is the height the ball reaches after the fourth bounce?

Understand *What are the facts?*

Casey dropped the ball from a height of 12 feet. It bounces up half as high for each successive bounce.

Plan *What is your strategy to solve this problem?*

Draw a diagram to show the height of the ball after each bounce.

Solve *How can you apply the strategy?*

The ball reaches a height of _____ foot after the fourth bounce.

Check *Does the answer make sense?*

Use division to check. 12 ÷ 2 = 6, 6 ÷ 2 = 3, 3 ÷ 2 = 1.5, 1.5 ÷ 2 = 0.75.

Analyze the Strategy Watch ▶ Tutor 💬

PS **Be Precise** If the ball is dropped from 12 feet and bounces up $\frac{2}{3}$ as high on each successive bounce, what is the height of the fourth bounce?

Case #2 Travel

Mr. Garcia has driven 60 miles, which is $\frac{2}{3}$ of the way to his sister's house.

How much farther does he have to drive to get to his sister's house?

Understand

Read the problem. What are you being asked to find?

I need to find _____.

What information do you know?

Mr. Garcia has driven _____ of the way to his sister's house. This is

equal to _____.

Is there any information that you do *not* need to know?

I do not need to know _____.

Plan

Choose a problem-solving strategy.

I will use the _____ strategy.

Solve

Use your problem-solving strategy to solve the problem.

Use the bar diagram that represents the distance to his sister's house.

Fill in two of the sections to represent $\frac{2}{3}$.

|---------- 60 miles ----------|

☐ of the 3 parts = 60.

Each part is ☐ miles. The

distance to his sister's house

is 60 + ☐ = ☐.

So, Mr. Garcia has _____ miles left to drive.

Check

Use information from the problem to check your answer.

_____

Work with a small group to solve the following cases.
Show your work on a separate piece of paper.

Collaborate

Case #3 Fractions

Marta ate a quarter of a whole pie. Edwin ate $\frac{1}{4}$ of what was left.
Cristina then ate $\frac{1}{3}$ of what was left.

What fraction of the pie remains?

Case #4 Games

Eight members of a chess club are having a tournament. In the first round, every player will play a chess game against every other player.

How many games will be in the first round of the tournament?

Case #5 Distance

Alejandro and Pedro are riding their bikes to school. After 1 mile, they are $\frac{5}{8}$ of the way there.

How much farther do they have to go?

Case #6 Seats

The number of seats in the first row of a concert hall is 6. The second row has 9 seats, the third row has 12 seats, and the fourth row has 15 seats.

How many seats will be in the eighth row?

Use any strategy!

Mid-Chapter Check

Vocabulary Check

1. Define *rational number*. Give some examples of rational numbers written in different forms. (Lessons 3 and 4)

_____

_____

_____

2. Fill in the blank in the sentence below with the correct term. (Lesson 1)

Repeating decimals can be represented using _____.

Skills Check and Problem Solving

Add or subtract. Write in simplest form. (Lessons 3–5)

3. $\dfrac{5}{8} + \dfrac{3}{8} =$ _____

4. $-\dfrac{1}{9} + \dfrac{2}{9} =$ _____

5. $-\dfrac{11}{15} - \dfrac{1}{15} =$ _____

6. $2\dfrac{5}{9} + 1\dfrac{2}{3} =$ _____

7. $8\dfrac{3}{4} - 2\dfrac{5}{12} =$ _____

8. $5\dfrac{1}{6} - 1\dfrac{1}{3} =$ _____

9. The table at the right shows the fraction of each state that is water. Order the states from least to greatest fraction of water. (Lesson 2)

_____

What Part is Water?	
Alaska	$\dfrac{3}{41}$
Michigan	$\dfrac{40}{97}$
Wisconsin	$\dfrac{1}{6}$

10. The maximum height of an Asian elephant is 9.8 feet. What mixed number represents this height? (Lesson 1) _____

11. **PS** **Persevere with Problems** The table shows the weight of a newborn infant for its first year. During which three-month period was the infant's weight gain the greatest? (Lesson 5) _____

Month	Weight (lb)
0	$7\dfrac{1}{4}$
3	$12\dfrac{1}{2}$
6	$16\dfrac{5}{8}$
9	$19\dfrac{4}{5}$
12	$23\dfrac{3}{20}$

Real-World Link

Lunch There are 12 students at the lunch table. Two thirds of the students ordered a hamburger for lunch. One half of those students that ordered a hamburger put cheese on it.

Essential Question

WHAT happens when you add, subtract, multiply, and divide fractions?

Indiana Academic Standards
7.C.7, 7.C.8

PS Process Standards
1, 3, 4

Step 1 Draw an X through the students that did not order a hamburger.

Step 2 Draw a C on the students that ordered cheese on their hamburger.

1. What fraction of the students at the lunch table ordered a cheeseburger? Write in simplest form. _____

2. What is $\frac{1}{2}$ of $\frac{2}{3}$? Write in simplest form. _____

3. Write your own word problem that involves fractions that can be solved using a diagram like the one above.

_____

_____

_____

Didn't I order cheese with that?

Which **PS Process Standards** did you use?
Shade the circle(s) that applies.

① Persevere with Problems
② Reason Abstractly
③ Construct an Argument
④ Model with Mathematics
⑤ Use Math Tools
⑥ Attend to Precision
⑦ Make Use of Structure
⑧ Use Repeated Reasoning

Multiply Fractions

Words   To multiply fractions, multiply the numerators and multiply the denominators.

Examples   Numbers

$$\frac{1}{2} \times \frac{2}{3} = \frac{1 \times 2}{2 \times 3} \text{ or } \frac{2}{6}$$

Algebra

$$\frac{a}{b} \cdot \frac{c}{d} = \frac{a \cdot c}{b \cdot d} \text{ or } \frac{ac}{bd}, \text{ where } b, d \neq 0$$

When multiplying two fractions, write the product in simplest form. The numerator and denominator of either fraction may have common factors. If this is the case, you can simplify before multiplying.

Examples

Multiply. Write in simplest form.

1. $\frac{1}{2} \times \frac{1}{3}$

$$\frac{1}{2} \times \frac{1}{3} = \frac{1 \times 1}{2 \times 3} \qquad \begin{array}{l}\leftarrow \text{Multiply the numerators.} \\ \leftarrow \text{Multiply the denominators.}\end{array}$$

$$= \frac{1}{6} \qquad \text{Simplify.}$$

2. $2 \times \left(-\frac{3}{4}\right)$

$$2 \times \left(-\frac{3}{4}\right) = \frac{2}{1} \times \left(\frac{-3}{4}\right) \qquad \text{Write 2 as } \frac{2}{1} \text{ and } -\frac{3}{4} \text{ as } \frac{-3}{4}.$$

$$= \frac{2 \times (-3)}{1 \times 4} \qquad \begin{array}{l}\leftarrow \text{Multiply the numerators.} \\ \leftarrow \text{Multiply the denominators.}\end{array}$$

$$= \frac{-6}{4} \text{ or } -1\frac{1}{2} \qquad \text{Simplify.}$$

3. $\frac{2}{7} \times \left(-\frac{3}{8}\right)$

$$\frac{2}{7} \times \left(-\frac{3}{8}\right) = \frac{\overset{1}{\cancel{2}}}{7} \times \left(-\frac{3}{\underset{4}{\cancel{8}}}\right) \qquad \text{Divide 2 and 8 by their GCF, 2.}$$

$$= \frac{1 \times (-3)}{7 \times 4} \text{ or } -\frac{3}{28} \qquad \text{Multiply.}$$

> **Show your work.**

Got it? Do these problems to find out.

Multiply. Write in simplest form.

a. $\frac{3}{5} \times \frac{1}{2}$ b. $\frac{2}{3} \times (-4)$ c. $-\frac{1}{3} \times \left(-\frac{3}{7}\right)$

Work Zone

GCF

In Example 3, GCF stands for the greatest of the common factors of two or more numbers.

Example: The GCF of 8 and 2 is 2.

a. _____

b. _____

c. _____

Multiply Mixed Numbers

When multiplying by a mixed number, you can rename the mixed number as an improper fraction. You can also multiply mixed numbers using the Distributive Property and mental math.

Example

4. Find $\frac{1}{2} \times 4\frac{2}{5}$. **Write in simplest form.**

Estimate $\frac{1}{2} \times 4 = 2$

Method 1 Rename the mixed number.

$\frac{1}{2} \times 4\frac{2}{5} = \frac{1}{\overset{}{2}} \times \frac{\overset{11}{22}}{5}$ Rename $4\frac{2}{5}$ as an improper fraction, $\frac{22}{5}$.
Divide 2 and 22 by their GCF, 2.

$= \frac{1 \times 11}{1 \times 5}$ Multiply.

$= \frac{11}{5}$ Simplify.

$= 2\frac{1}{5}$ Simplify.

Method 2 Use mental math.

The mixed number $4\frac{2}{5}$ is equal to $4 + \frac{2}{5}$.

So, $\frac{1}{2} \times 4\frac{2}{5} = \frac{1}{2}\left(4 + \frac{2}{5}\right)$. Use the Distributive Property to multiply, then add mentally.

$\frac{1}{2}\left(4 + \frac{2}{5}\right) = 2 + \frac{1}{5}$ Think Half of 4 is 2 and half of 2 fifths is 1 fifth.

$= 2\frac{1}{5}$ Rewrite the sum as a mixed number.

Check for Reasonableness $2\frac{1}{5} \approx 2$ ✔

So, $\frac{1}{2} \times 4\frac{2}{5} = 2\frac{1}{5}$.

Using either method, the answer is $2\frac{1}{5}$.

> **Simplifying**
> If you forget to simplify before multiplying, you can always simplify the final answer. However, it is usually easier to simplify before multiplying.

Got it? Do these problems to find out.

Multiply. Write in simplest form.

d. $\frac{1}{4} \times 8\frac{4}{9}$ **e.** $5\frac{1}{3} \times 3$ **f.** $-1\frac{7}{8} \times \left(-2\frac{2}{5}\right)$

Show your work.

d. _____

e. _____

f. _____

Example

Tutor

5. Humans sleep about $\frac{1}{3}$ of each day. Let each year equal $365\frac{1}{4}$ days. Determine the number of days in a year the average human sleeps.

Find $\frac{1}{3} \times 365\frac{1}{4}$.

Estimate $\frac{1}{3} \times 360 = 120$

$\frac{1}{3} \times 365\frac{1}{4} = \frac{1}{3} \times \frac{1,461}{4}$ Rename the mixed number as an improper fraction.

$= \frac{1}{\overset{3}{\underset{1}{\cancel{3}}}} \times \frac{\overset{487}{\cancel{1,461}}}{4}$ Divide 3 and 1,461 by their GCF, 3.

$= \frac{487}{4}$ or $121\frac{3}{4}$ Multiply. Then rename as a mixed number.

Check for Reasonableness $121\frac{3}{4} \approx 120$ ✔

The average human sleeps $121\frac{3}{4}$ days each year.

Guided Practice

Check

Multiply. Write in simplest form. (Examples 1–4)

1. $\frac{2}{3} \times \frac{1}{3} =$ _____

2. $-\frac{1}{4} \times \left(-\frac{8}{9}\right) =$ _____

3. $2\frac{1}{4} \times \frac{2}{3} =$ _____

Show your work.

4. **STEM** The weight of an object on Mars is about $\frac{2}{5}$ its weight on Earth. How much would an $80\frac{1}{2}$-pound dog weigh on Mars? (Example 5) _____

5. **Building on the Essential Question** How is the process of multiplying fractions different from the process of adding fractions?

_____

_____

_____

_____

Meaning of Multiplication

Recall that one meaning of 3×4 is three groups with 4 in each group. In Example 5, there are $365\frac{1}{4}$ groups with $\frac{1}{3}$ in each group.

Rate Yourself!

How well do you understand multiplying fractions? Circle the image that applies.

Clear   Somewhat Clear   Not So Clear

For more help, go online to access a Personal Tutor.

Tutor

FOLDABLES Time to update your Foldable!

Independent Practice

Go online for Step-by-Step Solutions eHelp

Multiply. Write in simplest form. (Examples 1–4)

1. $\dfrac{3}{4} \times \dfrac{1}{8} =$ _____

2. $\dfrac{2}{5} \times \dfrac{2}{3} =$ _____

3. $-9 \times \dfrac{1}{2} =$ _____

 Show your work.

4. $-\dfrac{1}{5} \times \left(-\dfrac{5}{6}\right) =$ _____

5. $\dfrac{2}{3} \times \dfrac{1}{4} =$ _____

6. $-\dfrac{1}{12} \times \dfrac{2}{5} =$ _____

7 $\dfrac{2}{5} \times \dfrac{15}{16} =$ _____

8. $\dfrac{4}{7} \times \dfrac{7}{8} =$ _____

9. $\left(-1\dfrac{1}{2}\right) \times \dfrac{2}{3} =$ _____

10. The width of a vegetable garden is $\dfrac{1}{3}$ times its length. If the length of the garden is $7\dfrac{3}{4}$ feet, what is the width in simplest form? (Example 5)

_____

11 One evening, $\dfrac{2}{3}$ of the students in Rick's class watched television. Of those students, $\dfrac{3}{8}$ watched a reality show. Of the students that watched the show, $\dfrac{1}{4}$ of them recorded the show. What fraction of the students in Rick's class watched and recorded a reality TV show?

_____

Write each numerical expression. Then evaluate the expression.

12. one half of negative five eighths

_____

13. one third of eleven sixteenths

_____

14. **(PS) Model with Mathematics** Refer to the graphic novel frame below.

a. The height of the closet is 96 inches, and Aisha would like to have 4 rows of cube organizers. What is the most the height of each cube organizer can be?

_____

b. Aisha would like to stack 3 shoe boxes on top of each other at the bottom of the closet. The height of each shoe box is $4\frac{1}{2}$ inches. What is the total height of the 3 boxes?

_____

H.O.T. Problems Higher Order Thinking

15. **(PS) Model with Mathematics** Write a real-world problem that involves finding the product of $\frac{3}{4}$ and $\frac{1}{8}$. _____

_____

_____

16. **(PS) Persevere with Problems** Two positive improper fractions are multiplied. Is the product *sometimes, always,* or *never* less than 1? Explain.

_____

_____

17. **(PS) Reason Inductively** Find two fractions that satisify each of the following.
a. each greater than $\frac{2}{5}$ with a product less than $\frac{2}{5}$

_____

b. each greater than $\frac{1}{2}$ with a product greater than $\frac{1}{2}$

_____

Extra Practice

Multiply. Write in simplest form.

18. $\frac{4}{5} \times (-6) =$ _$-4\frac{4}{5}$_

$\frac{4}{5} \times (-6) = \frac{4}{5} \times \left(-\frac{6}{1}\right)$

$= \frac{4 \times (-6)}{5 \times 1}$

$= \frac{-24}{5} \text{ or } -4\frac{4}{5}$

Homework Help ➡

19. $-\frac{4}{9} \times \left(-\frac{1}{4}\right) =$ _____

20. $3\frac{1}{3} \times \left(-\frac{1}{5}\right) =$ _____

21. $\frac{1}{3} \times \frac{3}{4} =$ _____

22. $\frac{4}{9} \times \left(-\frac{1}{8}\right) =$ _____

23. $\frac{5}{6} \times 2\frac{3}{5} =$ _____

24. Each DVD storage case is about $\frac{1}{5}$ inch thick. What will be the height in simplest form of 12 cases sold together?

_____

25. Mark left $\frac{3}{8}$ of a pizza in the refrigerator. On Friday, he ate $\frac{1}{2}$ of what was left of the pizza. What fraction of the entire pizza did he eat on Friday?

_____

Multiply. Write in simplest form.

26. $\left(\frac{1}{4}\right)^2 =$ _____

27. $\left(-\frac{2}{3}\right)^3 =$ _____

28. $\frac{1\frac{1}{3}}{\frac{1}{4}} \times \frac{\frac{2}{5}}{\frac{1}{2}} =$ _____

29. **PS** **Justify Conclusions** Alano wants to make one and a half batches of the pasta salad recipe shown at the right. How much of each ingredient will Alano need? Explain how you solved the problem.

_____

_____

_____

Pasta Salad Recipe	
Ingredient	**Amount**
Broccoli	$1\frac{1}{4}$ c
Cooked pasta	$3\frac{3}{4}$ c
Salad dressing	$\frac{2}{3}$ c
Cheese	$1\frac{1}{3}$ c

30. Philip rode his bicycle at $9\frac{1}{2}$ miles per hour. If he rode for $\frac{3}{4}$ of an hour, how many miles in simplest form did he cover? _____

31. Of the dolls in Marjorie's doll collection, $\frac{2}{5}$ have red hair. Of these, $\frac{1}{4}$ have green eyes, $\frac{2}{3}$ have blue eyes, and $\frac{1}{12}$ have brown eyes. Determine if each statement is true or false.

a. $\frac{1}{10}$ of Marjorie's doll collection has red hair and green eyes. ☐ True ☐ False

b. $\frac{4}{15}$ of Marjorie's doll collection has red hair and blue eyes. ☐ True ☐ False

c. $\frac{29}{60}$ of Marjorie's doll collection has red hair and brown eyes. ☐ True ☐ False

32. The table shows the number of teaspoons of vanilla needed to make different batches of cookies.

Select one box from each row to describe how to find the number of teaspoons of vanilla needed to make n batches of cookies.

Batches	1	2	3	4	5	n
Vanilla (tsp)	$\frac{1}{4}$	$\frac{1}{2}$	$\frac{3}{4}$	1	$1\frac{1}{4}$	

Row 1 | Subtract | Add | Multiply | Divide

Row 2 | 4 | n | $\frac{1}{4}$

Row 3 | to | by | from

Row 4 | 4 | n | $\frac{1}{4}$

How many teaspoons of vanilla are needed to make $6\frac{1}{2}$ batches of cookies?

☐

Spiral Review

For each multiplication sentence, write two related division sentences.

33. $3 \times 4 = 12$

34. $\frac{1}{6} \times \frac{1}{3} = \frac{1}{18}$

35. $2\frac{2}{5} \times 4\frac{1}{2} = 10\frac{4}{5}$

36. $5\frac{5}{8} \times 1\frac{1}{5} = 6\frac{3}{4}$

Convert Between Systems

Real-World Link Watch

5K Race To raise money for a health organization, the Matthews family is participating in a 5K race. A 5K race is 5 kilometers.

1. How many meters long is the race?

   5 kilometers = [   ] meters

2. One mile is approximately 1.6 kilometers. About how many miles is the race?

   5 kilometers ≈ [   ] miles

3. A kilometer is a unit of length in the metric measurement system. A mile is a measure of length in the customary measurement system. Write the following units of length under the correct measurement system.

   centimeter, foot, inch, meter, millimeter, yard

Metric	Customary
kilometer	mile

Which PS **Process Standards** did you use?
Shade the circle(s) that applies.

① Persevere with Problems
② Reason Abstractly
③ Construct an Argument
④ Model with Mathematics

⑤ Use Math Tools
⑥ Attend to Precision
⑦ Make Use of Structure
⑧ Use Repeated Reasoning

Essential Question

HOW do you convert between measurement systems?

Indiana Academic Standards
7.C.6

PS **Process Standards**
1, 3, 4, 5, 6

Convert Between Measurement Systems

You can multiply by fractions to convert between customary and metric units. The table below lists common customary and metric relationships.

Customary and Metric Relationships			
Type of Measure	Customary	→	Metric
Length	1 inch (in.)	≈	2.54 centimeters (cm)
	1 foot (ft)	≈	0.30 meter (m)
	1 yard (yd)	≈	0.91 meter (m)
	1 mile (mi)	≈	1.61 kilometers (km)
Weight/Mass	1 pound (lb)	≈	453.6 grams (g)
	1 pound (lb)	≈	0.4536 kilogram (kg)
	1 ton (T)	≈	907.2 kilograms (kg)
Capacity	1 cup (c)	≈	236.59 milliliters (mL)
	1 pint (pt)	≈	473.18 milliliters (mL)
	1 quart (qt)	≈	946.35 milliliters (mL)
	1 gallon (gal)	≈	3.79 liters (L)

Examples

Tutor

1. **Convert 17.22 inches to centimeters. Round to the nearest hundredth if necessary.**

Since 2.54 centimeters ≈ 1 inch, multiply by $\frac{2.54 \text{ cm}}{1 \text{ in.}}$.

$17.22 ≈ 17.22 \text{ in.} \cdot \frac{2.54 \text{ cm}}{1 \text{ in.}}$ Multiply by $\frac{2.54 \text{ cm}}{1 \text{ in.}}$. Divide out common units.

$≈ 43.7388 \text{ cm}$ Simplify.

So, 17.22 inches is approximately 43.74 centimeters.

2. **Convert 5 kilometers to miles. Round to the nearest hundredth if necessary.**

Since 1 mile ≈ 1.61 kilometers, multiply by $\frac{1 \text{ mi}}{1.61 \text{ km}}$.

$5 \text{ km} ≈ 5 \text{ km} \cdot \frac{1 \text{ mi}}{1.61 \text{ km}}$ Multiply by $\frac{1 \text{ mi}}{1.61 \text{ km}}$. Divide out common units.

$≈ \frac{5 \text{ mi}}{1.61}$ or 3.11 mi   Simplify.

So, 5 kilometers is approximately 3.11 miles.

Got it? Do these problems to find out.

Complete. Round to the nearest hundredth if necessary.

    a. 6 yd ≈ ■ m   **b.** 1.6 cm ≈ ■ in.   **c.** 17 m ≈ ■ yd

STOP and Reflect

What metric unit of measure corresponds to miles? to pounds? Write your answers below.

a. _____

b. _____

c. _____

Show your work.

Examples

3. Convert 828.5 milliliters to cups. Round to the nearest hundredth if necessary.

Since 1 cup ≈ 236.59 milliliters, multiply by $\frac{1\,c}{236.59\,mL}$.

$828.5\,mL \approx 828.5\,mL \cdot \frac{1\,c}{236.59\,mL}$ 　Multiply by $\frac{1\,c}{236.59\,mL}$ and divide out common units.

$\approx \frac{828.5\,c}{236.59}$ or 3.50 c 　Simplify.

So, 828.5 milliliters is approximately 3.50 cups.

4. Convert 3.4 quarts to milliliters. Round to the nearest hundredth if necessary.

Since 946.35 milliliters ≈ 1 quart, multiply by $\frac{946.35\,mL}{1\,qt}$.

$3.4\,qt \approx 3.4\,qt \cdot \frac{946.35\,mL}{1\,qt}$ 　Multiply by $\frac{946.35}{1\,qt}$. Divide out common units.

$\approx 3,217.59\,mL$ 　Simplify.

So, 3.4 quarts is approximately 3,217.59 milliliters.

5. Convert 4.25 kilograms to pounds. Round to the nearest hundredth if necessary.

Since 1 pound ≈ 0.4536 kilogram, multiply by $\frac{1\,lb}{0.4536\,kg}$.

$4.25\,kg \approx 4.25\,kg \cdot \frac{1\,lb}{0.4536\,kg}$ 　Multiply by $\frac{1\,lb}{0.4536\,kg}$. Divide out common units.

$\approx \frac{4.25\,lb}{0.4536}$ or 9.37 lb 　Simplify.

So, 4.25 kilograms is approximately 9.37 pounds.

Got it? Do these problems to find out.

Complete. Round to the nearest hundredth if necessary.

d. 7.44 c ≈ ▇ mL

e. 22.09 lb ≈ ▇ kg

f. 35.85 L ≈ ▇ gal

Dimensional Analysis
Recall that dimensional analysis is the process of including units of measurement when you compute.

Show your work.

d. _____

e. _____

f. _____

6. **An Olympic-size swimming pool is 50 meters long. About how many feet long is the pool?**

Since 1 foot ≈ 0.30 meter, use the ratio $\frac{1\text{ ft}}{0.30\text{ m}}$.

$$50\text{ m} \approx 50\text{ m} \cdot \frac{1\text{ ft}}{0.30\text{ m}}$$ Multiply by $\frac{1\text{ ft}}{0.30\text{m}}$.

$$\approx 50\text{ m} \cdot \frac{1\text{ ft}}{0.30\text{ m}}$$ Divide out common units, leaving the desired unit, feet.

$$\approx \frac{50\text{ ft}}{0.30}\text{ or }166.67\text{ ft}$$ Divide.

An Olympic-size swimming pool is about 166.67 feet long.

Guided Practice

 Check

Complete. Round to the nearest hundredth if necessary. (Examples 1–5)

1. 3.7 yd ≈ _____ m

2. 11.07 pt ≈ _____ mL

3. 650 lb ≈ _____ kg

 Show your work.

4. About how many feet does a team of athletes run in a 1,600-meter relay race? (Example 6) _____

5. Raheem bought 3 pounds of bananas. About how many kilograms did he buy? (Example 6) _____

6. ⓔ **Building on the Essential Question** How can you use dimensional analysis to convert between measurement systems?

_____

_____

_____

_____

Rate Yourself!

Are you ready to move on? Shade the section that applies.

YES ? NO

For more help, go online to access a Personal Tutor. Tutor

Independent Practice

Go online for Step-by-Step Solutions

Complete. Round to the nearest hundredth if necessary. (Examples 1–5)

1. 5 in. ≈ _____ cm

2. 2 qt ≈ _____ mL

3. 58.14 kg ≈ _____ lb

4. 4 L ≈ _____ gal

5. 10 mL ≈ _____ c

6. 63.5 T ≈ _____ kg

7. 4.725 m ≈ _____ ft

8. 3 T ≈ _____ kg

9. 680.4 g ≈ _____ lb

10. A notebook computer has a mass of 2.25 kilograms. About how many pounds does the notebook weigh? (Example 6)

_____

11. A glass bottle holds 3.75 cups of water. About how many milliliters of water can the bottle hold? (Example 6)

_____

12. A Cabbage Palmetto has a height of 80 feet. What is the approximate height of the tree in meters? (Example 6)

_____

PS Persevere with Problems Determine the greater amount for each situation.

 13 Which box is greater, a 1.5-pound box of raisins or a 650-gram box of raisins?

14. Which is greater a 2.75-gallon container of juice or a 12-liter container of juice?

H.O.T. Problems Higher Order Thinking

15. PS Reason Inductively One gram of water has a volume of 1 milliliter. What is the volume of the water if it has a mass of 1 kilogram?

16. PS Persevere with Problems The distance from Earth to the Sun is approximately 93 million miles. About how many gigameters is this? Round to the nearest hundredth. *(Hint: In 1 gigameter there are about 621,118.01 miles.)*

PS Be Precise Order each set of measures from greatest to least.

17. 1.2 cm, 0.6 in., 0.031 m, 0.1 ft

18. 2 lb, 891 g, 1 kg, 0.02 T

19. $1\frac{1}{4}$ c, 0.4 L, 950 mL, 0.7 gal

20. 4.5 ft, 48 in., 1.3 m, 120 cm

21. PS Model with Mathematics Convert $2\frac{1}{8}$ inches and $2\frac{5}{8}$ inches to centimeters. Round to the nearest tenth. Then draw a segment whose length is between those two measures.

Extra Practice

Complete. Round to the nearest hundredth if necessary.

22. 15 cm ≈ _5.91_____ in.

23. 350 lb ≈ _158.76_ kg

24. 17 mi ≈ _____ km

Homework Help ➡

$15\ cm ≈ 15\ cm \cdot \dfrac{1\ in.}{2.54\ cm}$

$≈ 15\ cm \cdot \dfrac{1\ in.}{2.54\ cm}$

$≈ \dfrac{15\ in.}{2.54} ≈ 5.91\ in.$

$350\ lb ≈ 350\ lb \cdot \dfrac{0.4536\ kg}{1\ lb}$

$≈ 350\ lb \cdot \dfrac{0.4536\ kg}{1\ lb}$

$≈ 158.76\ kg$

25. 32 gal ≈ _____ L

26. 50 mL ≈ _____ fl oz

27. 19 kg ≈ _____ lb

28. The Willis Tower has a height of 1,451 feet. What is the estimated height of the building in meters? _____

29. Which is greater, a bottle containing 64 fluid ounces or a bottle containing 2 liters of water? _____

30. (PS) **Use Math Tools** A bakery uses 900 grams of peaches in a cobbler. About how many pounds of peaches does the bakery use in a cobbler?

_____

Determine which quantity is greater.

31. 3 gal, 10 L _____

32. 14 oz, 0.4 kg _____

33. 4 mi, 6.2 km _____

34. Velocity is a rate usually expressed in feet per second or meters per second. How can the units help you calculate velocity using the distance a car traveled and the time

recorded? _____

_____

35. The diagram shows the length of a fork from the cafeteria. Which measurements are approximately equal to the length of the fork? Select all that apply.

6 in.

☐ 15.2 cm   ☐ 0.152 m   ☐ 152 cm   ☐ 1.52 m

36. The masses of 4 different animals from a zoo are shown in the table. Convert each measure to pounds. Then sort the animals from least to greatest weight.

Animal	Mass (kg)
Brown Bear	272.16
Giraffe	1,134.0
Lion	226.8
Rhinoceros	1,587.6

	Animal	Weight (lb)
Least		
Greatest		

How many pounds greater is the heaviest animal than the lightest animal?

Explain how you can use units to be sure you are multiplying by the correct fraction when converting between measurement systems. Give an example.

Spiral Review

Convert. Round to the nearest tenth if necessary.

37. 17 ft = _____ yd

38. 82 in. = _____ ft

39. 3 mi = _____ ft

40. A skyscraper is 0.484 kilometer tall. What is the height of the skyscraper in meters? _____

Divide Fractions

 Real-World Link

Oranges Deandre has three oranges and each orange is divided evenly into fourths. Complete the steps below to find $3 \div \frac{1}{4}$.

Step 1 Draw three oranges. The first one is drawn for you.

Step 2 Imagine you cut each orange into fourths. Draw the slices for each orange.

So $3 \div \frac{1}{4} = 12$. Deandre will have ☐ orange slices.

1. Find $3 \div \frac{1}{2}$. Use a diagram. _____

2. What is true about $3 \div \frac{1}{2}$ and 3×2? _____

Essential Question

WHAT happens when you add, subtract, multiply, and divide fractions?

Ⓙ Indiana Academic Standards
7.C.7, 7.C.8

PS Process Standards
1, 3, 4, 5

Which **PS** **Process Standards** did you use?
Shade the circle(s) that applies.

① Persevere with Problems
② Reason Abstractly
③ Construct an Argument
④ Model with Mathematics

⑤ Use Math Tools
⑥ Attend to Precision
⑦ Make Use of Structure
⑧ Use Repeated Reasoning

Divide Fractions

Watch

Words To divide by a fraction, multiply by its multiplicative inverse, or reciprocal.

Examples Numbers

$$\frac{7}{8} \div \frac{3}{4} = \frac{7}{8} \cdot \frac{4}{3}$$

Algebra

$$\frac{a}{b} \div \frac{c}{d} = \frac{a}{b} \cdot \frac{d}{c}, \text{ where } b, c, d \neq 0$$

Work Zone

Dividing 3 by $\frac{1}{4}$ is the same as multiplying 3 by the reciprocal of $\frac{1}{4}$, which is 4.

reciprocals

$$3 \div \frac{1}{4} = 12 \qquad 3 \cdot 4 = 12$$

same result

Is this pattern true for any division expression?

Consider $\frac{7}{8} \div \frac{3}{4}$, which can be rewritten as $\dfrac{\frac{7}{8}}{\frac{3}{4}}$.

$$\frac{\frac{7}{8}}{\frac{3}{4}} = \frac{\frac{7}{8} \times \frac{4}{3}}{\frac{3}{4} \times \frac{4}{3}}$$

Multiply the numerator and denominator by the reciprocal of $\frac{3}{4}$, which is $\frac{4}{3}$.

$$= \frac{\frac{7}{8} \times \frac{4}{3}}{1} \qquad \frac{3}{4} \times \frac{4}{3} = 1$$

$$= \frac{7}{8} \times \frac{4}{3}$$

So, $\frac{7}{8} \div \frac{3}{4} = \frac{7}{8} \times \frac{4}{3}$. The pattern is true in this case.

STOP and Reflect

What is the reciprocal of $\frac{2}{3}$? of 15? of $-\frac{4}{9}$? Write your answers below.

Examples

Tutor

1. Find $\frac{1}{3} \div 5$.

$$\frac{1}{3} \div 5 = \frac{1}{3} \div \frac{5}{1}$$ A whole number can be written as a fraction over 1.

$$= \frac{1}{3} \times \frac{1}{5}$$ Multiply by the reciprocal of $\frac{5}{1}$, which is $\frac{1}{5}$.

$$= \frac{1}{15}$$ Multiply.

2. Find $\frac{3}{4} \div \left(-\frac{1}{2}\right)$. **Write in simplest form.**

Estimate $1 \div \left(-\frac{1}{2}\right) = \boxed{}$

$\frac{3}{4} \div \left(-\frac{1}{2}\right) = \frac{3}{4} \cdot \left(-\frac{2}{1}\right)$ Multiply by the reciprocal of $-\frac{1}{2}$, which is $-\frac{2}{1}$.

$= \frac{3}{\overset{2}{\cancel{4}}} \cdot \left(-\frac{\overset{1}{\cancel{2}}}{1}\right)$ Divide 4 and 2 by their GCF, 2.

$= -\frac{3}{2}$ or $-1\frac{1}{2}$ Multiply.

Check for Reasonableness $-1\frac{1}{2} \approx -2$ ✓

> **Got it?** Do these problems to find out.

Divide. Write in simplest form.

a. $\frac{3}{4} \div \frac{1}{4}$ b. $-\frac{4}{5} \div \frac{8}{9}$ c. $-\frac{5}{6} \div \left(-\frac{2}{3}\right)$

Show your work.

a. _____

b. _____

c. _____

Divide Mixed Numbers

To divide by a mixed number, first rename the mixed number as a fraction greater than one. Then multiply the first fraction by the reciprocal, or multiplicative inverse, of the second fraction.

Example

Tutor

3. Find $\frac{2}{3} \div 3\frac{1}{3}$. **Write in simplest form.**

$\frac{2}{3} \div 3\frac{1}{3} = \frac{2}{3} \div \frac{10}{3}$ Rename $3\frac{1}{3}$ a fraction greater than one.

$= \frac{2}{3} \cdot \frac{3}{10}$ Multiply by the reciprocal of $\frac{10}{3}$, which is $\frac{3}{10}$.

$= \frac{\overset{1}{\cancel{2}}}{\underset{1}{\cancel{3}}} \cdot \frac{\overset{1}{\cancel{3}}}{\underset{5}{\cancel{10}}}$ Divide out common factors.

$= \frac{1}{5}$ Multiply.

> **Got it?** Do these problems to find out.

Divide. Write in simplest form.

d. $5 \div 1\frac{1}{3}$ e. $-\frac{3}{4} \div 1\frac{1}{2}$ f. $2\frac{1}{3} \div 5$

d. _____

e. _____

f. _____

Example

Watch Tutor

4. The side pieces of a butterfly house are $8\frac{1}{4}$ inches long. How many side pieces can be cut from a board measuring $49\frac{1}{2}$ inches long?

To find how many side pieces can be cut, divide $49\frac{1}{2}$ by $8\frac{1}{4}$.

Estimate Use compatible numbers. $48 \div 8 = 6$

$49\frac{1}{2} \div 8\frac{1}{4} = \frac{99}{2} \div \frac{33}{4}$ Rename the mixed numbers as fractions greater than one.

$= \frac{99}{2} \cdot \frac{4}{33}$ Multiply by the reciprocal of $\frac{33}{4}$, which is $\frac{4}{33}$.

$= \frac{\overset{3}{\cancel{99}}}{\underset{1}{\cancel{2}}} \cdot \frac{\overset{2}{\cancel{4}}}{\underset{1}{\cancel{33}}}$ Divide out common factors.

$= \frac{6}{1}$ or 6 Multiply.

So, 6 side pieces can be cut.

Check for Reasonableness Compare to the estimate. $6 = 6$ ✓

Guided Practice

Check ✓

Divide. Write in simplest form. (Examples 1–3)

1. $\frac{1}{8} \div \frac{1}{3} =$ _____

2. $-3 \div \left(-\frac{6}{7}\right) =$ _____

3. $-\frac{7}{8} \div \frac{3}{4} =$ _____

Show your work.

4. On Saturday, Lindsay walked $3\frac{1}{2}$ miles in $1\frac{2}{5}$ hours. What was her walking pace in miles per hour? Write in simplest form. (Example 4) _____

5. **Bulding on the Essential Question** How is dividing fractions related to multiplying? _____

_____

_____

Rate Yourself!

Are you ready to move on? Shade the section that applies.

- I have a few questions.
- I'm ready to move on.
- I have a lot of questions.

For more help, go online to access a Personal Tutor.

Tutor

FOLDABLES Time to update your Foldable!

Independent Practice

Go online for Step-by-Step Solutions

eHelp

Divide. Write in simplest form. (Examples 1 – 3)

1. $\frac{3}{8} \div \frac{6}{7} =$ _____

2. $-\frac{2}{3} \div \left(-\frac{1}{2}\right) =$ _____

3. $\frac{1}{2} \div 7\frac{1}{2} =$ _____

4. $6 \div \left(-\frac{1}{2}\right) =$ _____

5. $-\frac{4}{9} \div (-2) =$ _____

6. $\frac{2}{3} \div 2\frac{1}{2} =$ _____

7. Cheryl is organizing her movie collection. If each movie case is $\frac{3}{4}$ inch wide, how many movies can fit on a shelf $5\frac{1}{4}$ feet wide? (Example 4)

_____

8. Use the table to solve. Write your answers in simplest form.

   a. How many times as heavy is the Golden Eagle as the Red-Tailed Hawk? _____

   b. How many times as heavy is the Golden Eagle as the Northern Bald Eagle? _____

Bird	Maximun Weight (lb)
Golden Eagle	$13\frac{9}{10}$
Northern Bald Eagle	$9\frac{9}{10}$
Red-Tailed Hawk	$3\frac{1}{2}$

9. **PS** **Model with Mathematics** Draw a model of the verbal expression below and then evaluate the expression. Explain how the model shows the division process.

        one half divided by two fifths _____

Show your work.

_____

_____

_____

_____

Copy and Solve For Exercises 10 and 11, show your work on a separate piece of paper.

10. **Multiple Representations** Jorge recorded the distance that five of his friends live from his house in the table shown.

   a. **Numbers** Tye lives about how many times farther away than Jamal?

   b. **Algebra** The mean is the sum of the data divided by the number of items in the data set. Write and solve an equation to find the mean number of miles that Jorge's friends live from his house. Write your answer in simplest form.

   c. **Model** Draw a bar diagram that can be used to find how many more miles Lon travels than Lucia to get to Jorge's house.

Student	Miles
Lucia	$5\frac{1}{2}$
Lon	$8\frac{2}{3}$
Sam	$12\frac{5}{6}$
Jamal	$2\frac{7}{9}$
Tye	$17\frac{13}{18}$

11. Tara bought a dozen folders. She took $\frac{1}{3}$ of the dozen and then divided the remaining folders equally among her four friends. What fraction of the dozen did each of her four friends receive? How many folders was this per person?

H.O.T. Problems

12. **PS Find the Error** Blake is finding $\frac{4}{5} \div \frac{6}{7}$. Find his mistake and correct it.

$$\frac{4}{5} \div \frac{6}{7} = \frac{5}{4} \cdot \frac{6}{7}$$

$$= \frac{30}{28} \text{ or } 1\frac{1}{14}$$

13. **PS Persevere with Problems** If $\frac{5}{6}$ is divided by a certain fraction $\frac{a}{b}$, the result is $\frac{1}{4}$. What is the fraction $\frac{a}{b}$? _____

14. **PS Reason Inductively** So far, the Rabun family has traveled 30 miles in $\frac{1}{2}$ hour. If it is currently 3:00 P.M. and their destination is 75 miles away from them, at what time will the Rabun family reach their destination? Explain how you solved the problem

Extra Practice

Divide. Write in simplest form.

15. $\frac{5}{9} \div \frac{5}{6} = \frac{2}{3}$

$\frac{5}{9} \div \frac{5}{6} = \frac{5}{9} \times \frac{6}{5}$

$= \frac{\overset{1}{\cancel{5}}}{\underset{3}{\cancel{9}}} \times \frac{\overset{2}{\cancel{6}}}{\underset{1}{\cancel{5}}}$

$= \frac{1 \times 2}{3 \times 1}$

$= \frac{2}{3}$

Homework Help

16. $-5\frac{2}{7} \div \left(-2\frac{1}{7}\right) =$ _____

17. $-5\frac{1}{5} \div \frac{2}{3} =$ _____

18. Vinh bought $4\frac{1}{2}$ gallons of ice cream to serve. If a pint is $\frac{1}{8}$ of a gallon, how many pint-sized servings can be made? _____

19. William has $8\frac{1}{4}$ cups of fruit juice. If he divides the juice into $\frac{3}{4}$-cup servings, how many servings will he have? _____

20. (PS) **Justify Conclusions** So far, a storm has traveled 35 miles in $\frac{1}{2}$ hour. If it is currently 5:00 P.M. and the storm is 105 miles away from you, at what time will the storm reach you? Explain how you solved the problem.

_____

_____

_____

21. Find $\dfrac{1\frac{2}{3}}{9} \div \dfrac{1\frac{1}{9}}{3}$. Write in simplest form. _____

22. (PS) **Use Math Tools** Write the letter of each statement below in the section of any operation to which the statement applies.

A Use a common denominator.

B Multiply by the multiplicative inverse.

C Write the result in simplest form.

23. Tracy has $94\frac{1}{4}$ inches of string that she uses for making bracelets. She uses $7\frac{1}{4}$ inches of string to make each bracelet. How many bracelets can Tracy make?

24. A grocery store offers 4 different size boxes of peanuts as shown below.

Large
$6\frac{3}{4}$ lb

Medium
$2\frac{1}{4}$ lb

Small
$1\frac{1}{8}$ lb

Write large, medium, or small in each box to make a true statement.

The [   ] box is 3 times larger than the [   ] box.

The [   ] box is 6 times larger than the [   ] box.

The [   ] box is 2 times larger than the [   ] box.

Spiral Review

Add or subtract. Write in simplest form.

25. $\frac{1}{5} + \frac{1}{4} =$ _____

26. $\frac{1}{3} - \frac{1}{6} =$ _____

27. $\frac{4}{9} + \frac{2}{7} =$ _____

28. $\frac{11}{15} - \frac{3}{20} =$ _____

29. The cheerleaders made spirit buttons for the basketball team. They used blue and red ribbons. How much total ribbon did they use?

Ribbon	
Blue	Red
$\frac{3}{8}$ ft	$\frac{3}{8}$ ft

30. How much longer is a $2\frac{1}{2}$-inch-long piece of string than a $\frac{2}{5}$-inch-long piece of string? _____

Prime Factorization

Vocabulary Start-Up

Every composite number can be expressed as a product of prime numbers, called the **prime factorization**. A *factor tree* can be used to find the prime factorization of a number.

Complete the factor tree to show two ways to find the prime factorization of 36.

Is there another way to find the prime factorization of 36? Explain.

_____

_____

If you use different factors, does the prime factorization change? Explain.

_____

_____

 Essential Question

WHAT strategies can be used to multiply whole numbers?

Indiana Academic Standards
7.NS.1

PS Process Standards
1, 2, 3, 8

Real-World Link

The test of a hybrid car resulted in 4,840 miles driven using 88 gallons of gas. Find the prime factorization of 88.

Which PS Process Standards did you use?
Shade the circle(s) that applies.

1 Persevere with Problems
2 Reason Abstractly
3 Construct an Argument
4 Model with Mathematics
5 Use Math Tools
6 Attend to Precision
7 Makes Use of Structure
8 Use Repeated Reasoning

Powers and Exponents

A product of repeated factors can be expressed as a **power**, that is, using an exponent and a base.

The **base** is the common factor.

$$\overbrace{2 \cdot 2 \cdot 2 \cdot 2}^{\text{4 factors}} = 2^4$$

The **exponent** tells how many times the base is used as a factor.

Powers are read in a certain way.

Read and Write Powers		
Power	**Words**	**Factors**
3^1	3 to the first power	3
3^2	3 to the second power or 3 squared	$3 \cdot 3$
3^3	3 to the third power or 3 cubed	$3 \cdot 3 \cdot 3$
3^4	3 to the fourth power or 3 to the fourth	$3 \cdot 3 \cdot 3 \cdot 3$
⋮	⋮	⋮
3^n	3 to the nth power or 3 to the nth	$\underbrace{3 \cdot 3 \cdot 3 \cdot \ldots \cdot 3}_{n \text{ factors}}$

Examples

Tutor

1. **Write $4 \times 4 \times 4 \times 4 \times 4$ using an exponent.**

The base is 4. The base is used as a factor 5 times, so the exponent is 5.

$4 \times 4 \times 4 \times 4 \times 4 = 4^5$

2. **Write $2 \times 2 \times 2 \times 5 \times 5$ using exponents.**

The base 2 is used as a factor 3 times. The base 5 is used as a factor 2 times.

$2 \times 2 \times 2 \times 5 \times 5 = 2^3 \times 5^2$

Show your work.

a. _____

b. _____

c. _____

Got it? Do these problems to find out.

Write each expression using exponents.

    a. $6 \times 6 \times 6 \times 6$ **b.** $8 \times 8 \times 8 \times 3 \times 3$ **c.** $7 \times 7 \times 9 \times 9 \times 9 \times 9$

Prime Factorization Using Exponents

You can use a factor tree to find the prime factorization of any composite number. Write repeated factors using exponents.

Examples

3. **Find the prime factorization of 24. Write the result using exponents.**

Choose any pair of whole number factors of 24, such as 3 and 8.

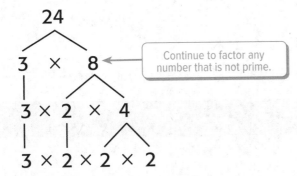

Continue to factor any number that is not prime.

The prime factorization of 24 is $2 \times 2 \times 2 \times 3$, or $2^3 \times 3$.

4. **Find the prime factorization of 120. Write the result using exponents.**

The prime factorization of 120 is $2 \times 2 \times 2 \times 3 \times 5$, or $2^3 \times 3 \times 5$.

Got it? Do these problems to find out.

Find the prime factorization of each number. Write the result using exponents.

 d. 54   **e.** 125   **f.** 441

Show your work.

d. _____

e. _____

f. _____

Example

5. A county in Indiana has 32 covered bridges. Find the prime factorization of 32. Write the result using exponents.

The prime factorization of 32 is $2 \times 2 \times 2 \times 2 \times 2$, or 2^5.

Guided Practice

Check ✓

Write each expression using exponents. (Examples 1 and 2)

1. $2 \times 2 \times 2 \times 2$ _____

2. $5 \times 5 \times 5$ _____

3. $6 \times 6 \times 7 \times 7 \times 7$ _____

Find the prime factorization of each number. Write the result using exponents. (Examples 3 and 4)

4. $44 =$ _____

5. $108 =$ _____

6. 147 _____

7. A housecat can hear sounds as high as 64 kHz (kilohertz), while humans can only hear sounds as high as 20 kHz. Find the prime factorization of 64. Write the result using exponents. (Example 5)

_____

8. **Building on the Essential Question** How can I write repeated multiplication using powers?

_____

_____

_____

Rate Yourself!

Are you ready to move on? Shade the section that applies.

- I have a few questions.
- I'm ready to move on.
- I have a lot of questions.

For more help, go online to access a Personal Tutor.

Tutor 💬

FOLDABLES Time to update your Foldable!

Independent Practice

Go online for Step-by-Step Solutions

eHelp

Write each expression using exponents. (Examples 1 and 2)

1. $3 \times 3 \times 3$ _____

2. $11 \times 11 \times 11 \times 11$ _____

3. $4 \times 4 \times 4 \times 4 \times 4 \times 4$ _____

4. $2 \times 2 \times 5 \times 5$ _____

5. $3 \times 7 \times 7 \times 7$ _____

6. $9 \times 9 \times 9 \times 5 \times 5$ _____

Find the prime factorization of each number. Write the result using exponents. (Examples 3 and 4)

7. 88 _____

8. 100 _____

9. 363 _____

10. 117 _____

11. 216 _____

12. 245 _____

13. Puppies have 28 teeth and most adult dogs have 42 teeth. Find the prime factorization of each number. Write the result using exponents. (Example 5)

_____

14. The average weight of a panther is 120 pounds. Find the prime factorization of 120. Write the result using exponents. (Example 5)

_____

15. In the United States, nearly 8×10^9 text messages are sent every month. About how many text messages is this? Find the prime factorization of this number and write the result using exponents.

_____

16. Interstate 70 stretches almost $2^3 \times 5^2 \times 11$ miles across the United States. About how many miles long is Interstate 70?

_____

For Exercises 17–20, refer to the table that shows the average weights of popular dog breeds.

Breed	Weight (lb)	Breed	Weight (lb)
Cocker Spaniel	20	Siberian Husky	50
German Shepherd	81	Boxer	60
Labrador Retriever	67	Rottweiler	112
Beagle	25	Dalmatian	55
Golden Retriever	70	Poodle	57

17. Which dog breed has an average weight with a prime factorization of 2×5^2?

_____

18. Which dog breed has an average weight with a prime factorization of $2^2 \times 3 \times 5$?

_____

19. Which dog breeds have average weights with prime factorizations that have the number 3 as a factor?

_____

20. Which dog breed(s) have average weights with prime factorizations that have a single factor used the most number of times? Explain.

_____

_____

H.O.T. Problems Higher Order Thinking

21. **PS** **Reason Quantitatively** Which is greater: 3^5 or 5^3? Explain.

_____

_____

22. **PS** **Identify Structure** The volume of a rectangular prism can be found by multiplying the length, width, and height of the prism. The length of a certain prism is twice its width, and the height is 3 feet. Find the prime factorization of the volume, in cubic feet, of the prism, if the width is three times the height.

_____

23. **PS** **Persevere with Problems** Write an expression for a prime factorization of a number that meets the following criteria.

- The number is between 1 and 500.
- There are three distinct prime factors.
- Two of the factors are each used only once.
- The third factor is used more than two times.
- Each prime factor is less than 13.

_____

Extra Practice

Write each expression using exponents.

24. $7 \times 7 \times 7 \times 7$

7^4

The base is 7. The base is
used as a factor 4 times,
so the exponent is 4.

Homework ➡ $7 \times 7 \times 7 \times 7 = 7^4$
Help

25. $13 \times 13 \times 13$

_____

26. $3 \times 3 \times 3 \times 3 \times 3 \times 3 \times 3$

_____

27. $8 \times 8 \times 8 \times 9 \times 9$

_____

28. $5 \times 5 \times 5 \times 5 \times 7$

_____

29. $11 \times 11 \times 11 \times 11 \times 2 \times 2$

_____

Find the prime factorization of each number. Write the result using exponents.

30. 140 _____

31. 88 _____

32. 845 _____

33. 432 _____

34. 1,000 _____

35. 567 _____

For Exercises 36–38, refer to the table that shows the average resting heart rates, in beats per minute of several animals.

36. Which animal has an average resting heart rate with a prime factorization of $2^4 \times 3 \times 5$?

_____

37. Which animal has an average resting heart rate with a prime factorization that has the greatest prime factor? What is that prime factor?

_____

Animal	Average Resting Heart Rate (bpm)
Blue Whale	6
Horse	38
Human	72
Cat	140
Rabbit	205
Guinea Pig	240
Mouse	670

38. **PS Persevere with Problems** A canary's heart beats 17 times per second, on average. Find the prime factorization of a canary's heart rate, in beats per minute. Write the result using exponents.

_____

39. Hard drive storage capacity is measured in bytes. The table shows some common units of storage capacity. Select the correct prime factorization for the number of bytes for each unit.

Unit	Number of Bytes
megabyte	1,000,000
terabyte	1,000,000,000,000
gigabyte	1,000,000,000

Unit	Prime Factorization
megabyte	
terabyte	
gigabyte	

| $2^3 \times 5^3$ | $2^6 \times 5^6$ | $2^9 \times 5^9$ | $2^{12} \times 5^{12}$ | $2^{15} \times 5^{15}$ |

40. A cube has the dimensions shown.

6 in.

What is the prime factorization of the volume, in cubic inches, of the cube?

Spiral Review

Add or subtract. Write in simplest form.

41. $\frac{2}{5} + \frac{7}{10}$ _____

42. $-\frac{3}{4} + \frac{5}{8}$ _____

43. $\frac{2}{3} - \left(-\frac{4}{9}\right)$ _____

44. $-12 + (-19)$ _____

45. $-8 + (-11)$ _____

46. $-5 + 6$ _____

Vocabulary Start-Up

A **square root** of a number is one of its two equal factors. Numbers such as 1, 4, 9, 16, and 25 are called **perfect squares** because they are squares of integers.

Complete the graphic organizer.

I think this word means...

How does this word fit with other words and concepts I know?

square root

Are there parts of the word that I recognize?

What makes this an important word for me to know?

What is the relationship between squaring a number and finding the square root? _____

 Real-World Link   Watch

The square base of the Great Pyramid of Giza covers almost 562,500 square feet. How could you determine the length of each side of the base?

_____

 Which **PS** **Process Standards** did you use?
Shade the circle(s) that applies.

① Persevere with Problems
② Reason Abstractly
③ Construct an Argument
④ Model with Mathematics

⑤ Use Math Tools
⑥ Attend to Precision
⑦ Make Use of Structure
⑧ Use Repeated Reasoning

 Essential Question

WHY is it helpful to write numbers in different ways?

Vocabulary

square root
perfect square
radical sign
cube root
perfect cube

Indiana Academic Standards
7.NS.2

PS **Process Standards**
1, 3, 4

Square Root

Watch

Words   A square root of a number is one of its two equal factors.

Symbols   If $x^2 = y$, then x is a square root of y.

Example $5^2 = 25$ so 5 is a square root of 25.

Every positive number has *both* a positive and negative square root. In most real-world situations, only the positive or *principal* square root is considered. A **radical sign**, $\sqrt{}$, is used to indicate the principal square root. If $n^2 = a$, then $n = \pm\sqrt{a}$.

Examples

Tutor

Find each square root.

1. $\sqrt{64}$

     $\sqrt{64} = 8$ Find the positive square root of 64; $8^2 = 64$.

2. $\pm\sqrt{1.21}$

     $\pm\sqrt{1.21} = \pm 1.1$ Find both square roots of 1.21; $1.1^2 = 1.21$.

Show your work.

3. $-\sqrt{\dfrac{25}{36}}$

     $-\sqrt{\dfrac{25}{36}} = -\dfrac{5}{6}$ Find the negative square root of $\dfrac{25}{36}$; $\left(\dfrac{5}{6}\right)^2 = \dfrac{25}{36}$.

4. $\sqrt{-16}$

     There is no real square root because no number times itself is equal to -16.

Got it? Do these problems to find out.

   a. $\sqrt{\dfrac{9}{16}}$ **b.** $\pm\sqrt{0.81}$ **c.** $-\sqrt{49}$ **d.** $\sqrt{-100}$

Example

Tutor

5. Solve $t^2 = 169$. Check your solution(s).

   $t^2 = 169$ Write the equation.

   $t = \pm\sqrt{169}$ Definition of square root

   $t = 13$ and -13 **Check** $13 \cdot 13 = 169$ and $(-13)(-13) = 169$ ✓

Got it? Do these problems to find out.

   e. $289 = a^2$ **f.** $m^2 = 0.09$ **g.** $y^2 = \dfrac{4}{25}$

Work Zone

a. _____

b. _____

c. _____

d. _____

e. _____

f. _____

g. _____

Cube Roots

Words A **cube root** of a number is one of its three equal factors.

Symbols If $x^3 = y$, then x is the cube root of y.

Numbers such as 8, 27, and 64 are **perfect cubes** because they are the cubes of integers.

$8 = 2 \cdot 2 \cdot 2$ or 2^3 $27 = 3 \cdot 3 \cdot 3$ or 3^3 $64 = 4 \cdot 4 \cdot 4$ or 4^3

The symbol $\sqrt[3]{}$ is used to indicate a cube root of a number.

If $n^3 = a$, then $n = \sqrt[3]{a}$. You can use this relationship to solve equations that involve cubes.

Examples

Tutor

Cube Roots
While $\sqrt{-16}$ is not a real number, $\sqrt[3]{-27}$ is a real number. $-3 \cdot -3 \cdot -3 = -27$

Find each cube root.

6. $\sqrt[3]{125}$

$\sqrt[3]{125} = 5$ $5^3 = 5 \cdot 5 \cdot 5$ or 125

7. $\sqrt[3]{-27}$

$\sqrt[3]{-27} = -3$ $(-3)^3 = (-3) \cdot (-3) \cdot (-3)$ or -27

Show your work.

Got it? Do these problems to find out.

h. $\sqrt[3]{729}$ i. $\sqrt[3]{-64}$ j. $\sqrt[3]{1,000}$

h. _____

i. _____

j. _____

Real World Example

Tutor

8. Dylan has a planter in the shape of a cube that holds 8 cubic feet of potting soil. Solve the equation $8 = s^3$ to find the side length s of the container.

$8 = s^3$ Write the equation.

$\sqrt[3]{8} = s$ Take the cube root of each side.

$2 = s$ Definition of cube root

So, each side of the container is 2 feet.

Check $(2)^3 = 8$ ✓

k. _____

k. An aquarium in the shape of a cube that will hold 25 gallons of water has a volume of 3.375 cubic feet. Solve $s^3 = 3.375$ to find the length of one side of the aquarium.

Guided Practice

Find each square root. (Examples 1–4)

1. $-\sqrt{1.69} =$ _____

2. $\pm\sqrt{\dfrac{49}{144}} =$ _____

3. $\sqrt{-1.44} =$ _____

Solve each equation. Check your solution(s). (Example 5)

4. $p^2 = 36$ _____

5. $t^2 = \dfrac{1}{9}$ _____

6. $6.25 = r^2$ _____

Find each cube root. (Examples 6 and 7)

7. $\sqrt[3]{216} =$ _____

8. $\sqrt[3]{-125} =$ _____

9. $\sqrt[3]{-8} =$ _____

10. A cube-shaped packing box can hold 729 cubic inches of packing material. Solve $729 = s^3$ to find the length of one side of the box. (Example 8) _____

11. **Building on the Essential Question** Why would I need to use square roots and cube roots?

_____

_____

_____

_____

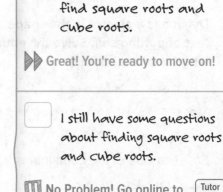

Rate Yourself!

☐ I understand how to find square roots and cube roots.

▶▶ Great! You're ready to move on!

☐ I still have some questions about finding square roots and cube roots.

 No Problem! Go online to access a Personal Tutor.

Name _____ My Homework _____

Find each square root. (Examples 1–4)

Show your work.

1. $\sqrt{16} =$ _____

2. $-\sqrt{484} =$ _____

3. $\sqrt{-36} =$ _____

4. $\pm\sqrt{\dfrac{9}{49}} =$ _____

5 $-\sqrt{2.56} =$ _____

6. $\sqrt{-0.25} =$ _____

Solve each equation. Check your solution(s). (Example 5)

7. $v^2 = 81$ _____

8. $w^2 = \dfrac{36}{100}$ _____

9. $0.0169 = c^2$ _____

Find each cube root. (Examples 6 and 7)

10. $\sqrt[3]{1{,}728} =$ _____

11. $\sqrt[3]{-0.125} =$ _____

12. $\sqrt[3]{\dfrac{27}{125}} =$ _____

13 A group of 169 students needs to be seated in a square formation for a yearbook photo. Solve the equation $169 = s^2$ to find how many students should be in each row. (Example 8) _____

14. Chloe wants to build a storage container in the shape of a cube to hold 15.625 cubic meters of hay for her horse. Solve the equation $15.625 = s^3$ to find the length of one side of the container. (Example 8)

_____

PS Persevere with Problems Given the area of each square, find the perimeter.

15.

Area = 121 square inches

_____

16.

Area = 25 square feet

_____

17.

Area = 36 square meters

_____

H.O.T. Problems Higher Order Thinking

PS Persevere with Problems Find each value.

18. $\left(\sqrt{36}\right)^2 =$ _____

19. $\left(\sqrt{\frac{25}{81}}\right)^2 =$ _____

20. $\left(\sqrt{199}\right)^2 =$ _____

21. $(\sqrt{x})^2 =$ _____

22. **PS Reason Abstractly** Based on your solutions to Exercises 18–21, write a rule that could be used to simplify the square of any square root of a number.

_____

_____

23. **PS Reason Inductively** Explain why $\sqrt{-4}$ is not a real number, but $\sqrt[3]{-8}$ is.

_____

_____

24. **PS Reason Inductively** Describe the difference between an exact value and an approximation when finding square roots of numbers that are not perfect squares. Give an example of each.

_____

_____

_____

Extra Practice

Find each square root.

25. $-\sqrt{81} =$ _−9_

omework
Help

$9 \cdot 9 = 81$

So, $-\sqrt{81} = -9$.

26. $-\sqrt{\dfrac{64}{225}} =$ _____

27. $-\sqrt{\dfrac{16}{25}} =$ _____

28. $\pm\sqrt{1.44} =$ _____

Find each cube root.

29. $\sqrt[3]{-216} =$ _____

30. $\sqrt[3]{-512} =$ _____

31. $\sqrt[3]{-1,000} =$ _____

32. $\sqrt[3]{-343} =$ _____

Solve each equation. Check your solution(s).

33. $b^2 = 100$

34. $\dfrac{9}{64} = c^2$

35. $a^2 = 1.21$

36. $\dfrac{1}{8} = z^3$

37. $1.331 = c^3$

38. $m^3 = 8,000$

39. $\sqrt{x} = 5$

40. $\sqrt{y} = 20$

41. $\sqrt{z} = 10.5$

42. **PS** **Persevere with Problems** A concert crew needs to set up some chairs on the floor level. The chairs are to be placed in a square pattern consisting of four square sections. If one of the square sections holds 900 chairs, how many chairs will there be along each length of the larger square? _____

43. Mr. Freeman has a square cornfield. Which of the following could be the area of the cornfield if the sides are measured in whole numbers? Select all that apply.

☐ 164,000 ft² ☐ 156,816 ft² ☐ 174,724 ft² ☐ 215,908 ft²

44. The area of each square in the figures below is 81 square units. Select the perimeter of each figure.

88 units	99 units
90 units	108 units
94 units	117 units

☐☐☐ ☐☐☐ ☐☐☐

Do any of the figures have the same perimeter? If so, explain why.

☐

Spiral Review

Evaluate each expression.

45. $13^3 =$ _____

46. $25^2 =$ _____

47. $15^3 =$ _____

48. $34^2 =$ _____

49. $5 \cdot \sqrt{121} =$ _____

50. $-6 \cdot \sqrt{36} =$ _____

51. $10 \cdot \sqrt[3]{8} =$ _____

52. $-4 \cdot \sqrt{144} =$ _____

Express the volume of each cube as a monomial.

53. _____

$4r^3s$

54. _____

$9m^2n^4$

Compare Real Numbers

Real-World Link

Sports Major League baseball has rules for the dimensions of the baseball diamond. A model of the diamond is shown.

2 in.

$\sqrt{8}$ in.

1.3 in.

1. On the model, the distance from the pitching mound to home plate is 1.3 inches. Is 1.3 a rational number? Explain.

_____

2. On the model, the distance from first base to second base is 2 inches. Is 2 a rational number? Explain.

_____

3. The distance from home plate to second base is $\sqrt{8}$ inches. Using a calculator, find $\sqrt{8}$. Does it appear to terminate or repeat?

_____

_____

4. To determine if the number terminates, on your calculator, multiply your answer to $\sqrt{8}$ by itself. Do not use the x^2 button.

   Is the answer 8? _____

5. Based on your results, can you classify $\sqrt{8}$ as a rational number? Explain.

_____

_____

_____

Essential Question

WHY is it helpful to write numbers in different ways?

Vocab

Vocabulary

irrational number
real number

Indiana Academic Standards
7.NS.3

PS Process Standards
1, 3, 4, 6

Which **PS** **Process Standards** did you use?

Shade the circle(s) that applies.

① Persevere with Problems

⑤ Use Math Tools

② Reason Abstractly

⑥ Attend to Precision

③ Construct an Argument

⑦ Make Use of Structure

④ Model with Mathematics

⑧ Use Repeated Reasoning

Real Numbers

Words	Rational Number	Irrational Number
	A rational number is a number that can be expressed as the ratio $\frac{a}{b}$, where a and b are integers and $b \neq 0$.	An **irrational number** is a number that *cannot* be expressed as the ratio $\frac{a}{b}$, where a and b are integers and $b \neq 0$.
Examples	$-2, 5, 3.\overline{76}, -12\frac{7}{8}$	$\sqrt{2} \approx 1.414213562...$

Numbers that are not rational are called irrational numbers. The square root of any number that is not a perfect square number is irrational. The set of rational numbers and the set of irrational numbers together make up the set of **real numbers**. Study the Venn diagram below.

Real Numbers

Examples

Tutor

Name all sets of numbers to which each real number belongs.

1. 0.2525...   The decimal ends in a repeating pattern. It is a rational number because it is equivalent to $\frac{25}{99}$.

2. $\sqrt{36}$ Since $\sqrt{36} = 6$, it is a natural number, a whole number, an integer, and a rational number.

Show your work.

a. _____

3. $-\sqrt{7}$ $-\sqrt{7} \approx -2.645751311...$ The decimal does not terminate nor repeat, so it is an irrational number.

b. _____

Got it? Do these problems to find out.

c. _____

a. $\sqrt{10}$ b. $-2\frac{2}{5}$ c. $\sqrt{100}$

Compare and Order Real Numbers

You can compare and order real numbers by writing them in the same notation. Write the numbers in decimal notation before comparing or ordering them.

Examples

Tutor

Fill in each $\bigcirc$ with <, >, or = to make a true statement.

4. $\sqrt{7} \bigcirc 2\frac{2}{3}$

$\sqrt{7} \approx 2.645751311...$

$2\frac{2}{3} = 2.666666666...$

Since 2.645751311... is less than 2.66666666..., $\sqrt{7} < 2\frac{2}{3}$.

5. **15.7%** $\bigcirc$ **$\sqrt{0.02}$**

$15.7\% = 0.157$

$\sqrt{0.02} \approx 0.141$

Since 0.157 is greater than 0.141, $15.7\% > \sqrt{0.02}$.

6. Order the set $\left\{\sqrt{30}, 6, 5\frac{4}{5}, 5.3\overline{6}\right\}$ from least to greatest. Verify your answer by graphing on a number line.

Write each number as a decimal. Then order the decimals.

$\sqrt{30} \approx 5.48$

$6 = 6.00$

$5\frac{4}{5} = 5.80$

$5.3\overline{6} \approx 5.37$

From least to greatest, the order is $5.3\overline{6}$, $\sqrt{30}$, $5\frac{4}{5}$, and 6.

Got it? Do these problems to find out.

Show your work.

d. $\sqrt{11} \bigcirc 3\frac{1}{3}$ **e.** $\sqrt{17} \bigcirc 4.03$ **f.** $\sqrt{6.25} \bigcirc 250\%$

g. Order the set $\left\{-7, -\sqrt{60}, -7\frac{7}{10}, -\frac{66}{9}\right\}$ from least to greatest. Verify your answer by graphing on the number line below.

g. _____

Example

Watch | Tutor

7. On a clear day, the number of miles a person can see to the horizon is about 1.23 times the square root of his or her distance from the ground in feet. Suppose Frida is at the Empire State Building observation deck at 1,250 feet and Kia is at the Freedom Tower observation deck at 1,362 feet. How much farther can Kia see than Frida?

Use a calculator to approximate the distance each person can see.

Frida: $1.23 \cdot \sqrt{1,250} \approx 43.49$ Kia: $1.23 \cdot \sqrt{1,362} \approx 45.39$

Kia can see $45.39 - 43.49$ or 1.90 miles farther than Frida.

Guided Practice

Name all sets of numbers to which each real number belongs. (Examples 1–3)

1. 0.050505... _____

2. $-\sqrt{64}$ _____

3. $\sqrt{17}$ _____

Fill in each $\bigcirc$ **with <, >, or = to make a true statement.** (Examples 4 and 5)

4. $\sqrt{15}$ $\bigcirc$ 3.5

5. $\sqrt{2.25}$ $\bigcirc$ 150%

6. $\sqrt{6.2}$ $\bigcirc$ $2.\overline{4}$

7. Order the set $\left\{\sqrt{5}, 220\%, 2.25, 2.\overline{2}\right\}$ from least to greatest. Verify your answer by graphing on a number line. (Example 6)

_____

2.19 2.2 2.21 2.22 2.23 2.24 2.25 2.26 2.27 2.28 2.29 2.3

8. The formula $A = \sqrt{s(s-a)(s-b)(s-c)}$ can be used to find the area A of a triangle. The variables a, b, and c are the side measures and s is one half the perimeter. Use the formula to find the area of a triangle with side lengths of 7 centimeters, 9 centimeters, and

10 centimeters. (Example 7) _____

9. **Building on the Essential Question** How are real numbers different from irrational numbers?

_____

_____

_____

Rate Yourself!

How well do you understand real numbers? Circle the image that applies.

Clear   Somewhat Clear   Not So Clear

For more help, go online to access a Personal Tutor.

Name _____   My Homework _____

Independent Practice

Go online for Step-by-Step Solutions

Name all sets of numbers to which each real number belongs. (Examples 1–3)

 Show your work.

1. $\frac{2}{3}$ _____

2. $-\sqrt{20}$ _____

3. $7.\overline{2}$ _____

4. $\frac{12}{4}$ _____

Fill in each ◯ **with <, >, or = to make a true statement.** (Examples 4 and 5)

5. $\sqrt{10}$ ◯ 3.2

6. $5\frac{1}{6}$ ◯ $5.\overline{16}$

 7 $2.\overline{21}$ ◯ $\sqrt{5.2}$

Order each set of numbers from least to greatest. Verify your answer by graphing on a number line. (Example 6)

8. $\left\{-415\%, -\sqrt{17}, -4.\overline{1}, -4.08\right\}$

9 $\left\{\sqrt{5}, \sqrt{6}, 2.5, 2.55, \frac{7}{3}\right\}$

−4.18 −4.16 −4.14 −4.12 −4.1 −4.08

_____

2.1   2.2   2.3   2.4   2.5   2.6   2.7

_____

10. The equation $s = \sqrt{30fd}$ can be used to find a car's speed s in miles per hour given the length d in feet of a skid mark and the friction factor f of the road. Police measured a skid mark of 90 feet on a dry concrete road. If the speed limit is 35 mph, was the car speeding? Explain. (Example 7)

Friction Factor		
Road	**Concrete**	**Tar**
Wet	0.4	0.5
Dry	0.8	1.0

_____

11. The surface area in square meters of the human body can be found using the expression $\sqrt{\dfrac{hm}{3,600}}$ where h is the height in centimeters and m is the mass in kilograms. Find the surface area of a 15-year-old boy with a height of 183 centimeters and a mass of 74 kilograms. (Example 7)

_____

_____

12. (PS) **Be Precise** Write a brief description and give an example of each type of number in the graphic organizer shown.

natural	whole	integer	rational	irrational

Use estimation to fill in each ◯ **with <, >, or = to make a true statement.**

13. 3π ◯ $\sqrt{78}$

14. π^2 ◯ $3 \cdot \sqrt{15}$

15. $\sqrt{980}$ ◯ $4\pi^2$

H.O.T. Problems Higher Order Thinking

16. (PS) **Use a Counterexample** Give a counterexample for the statement *All square roots are irrational numbers.* Explain your reasoning.

_____

(PS) **Persevere with Problems** Tell whether the following statements are *always*, *sometimes*, or *never* true. If a statement is not always true, explain.

17. Integers are rational numbers. _____

_____

18. Rational numbers are integers. _____

_____

19. The product of a non-zero rational number and an irrational number is

irrational. _____

_____

20. (PS) **Model with Mathematics** Identify two numbers, one rational number and one irrational number, that are between 1.4 and 1.6. Include the decimal approximation of the irrational number to the nearest hundredth.

_____

Extra Practice

21. Name all sets of real numbers to which $\sqrt{10}$ belongs. ___irrational___

$\sqrt{10} \approx 3.16227766...$ Since the decimal does not terminate nor repeat, it is an irrational number.

22. Fill in ◯ with <, >, or = to make $5.1\overline{5}$ ⃝> $\sqrt{26}$ a true statement.

Write each number as a decimal.
$5.1\overline{5} = 5.155555...$
$\sqrt{26} \approx 5.099019...$
Since $5.155555...$ is greater than $5.099019...$,
$5.1\overline{5} > \sqrt{26}$.

Name all sets of numbers to which each real number belongs.

23. 14

_____

24. $-\sqrt{16}$

_____

25. $-\sqrt[3]{90}$

_____

Fill in each ◯ with <, >, or = to make a true statement.

26. $\sqrt{12}$ ◯ 3.5

27. $6\frac{1}{3}$ ◯ $\sqrt[3]{240}$

28. 240% ◯ $\sqrt{5.76}$

29. About how much greater is the perimeter of a square with area 250 square meters than a square with an area of 125 square meters?

_____

30. **Persevere with Problems** In the sequence 4, 12, ■, 108, 324, the missing number can be found by simplifying $\sqrt{ab}$ where a and b are the numbers on either side of the missing number. Find the missing number.

_____

Fill in each ◯ with <, >, or = to make a true statement.

31. $3 + \sqrt{7}$ ◯ 6

32. $4 - \sqrt{10}$ ◯ $\sqrt{2}$

33. 13 ◯ $8 + \sqrt{20}$

34. Mr. Rodgers gave his students a test that was worth 100 points. Erika earned an 84%, Joe earned $\frac{5}{6}$ of the total points, Malcolm earned $\sqrt{7225}$ points, and Stephanie earned $\frac{83}{100}$ points. Plot points on the number line to represent each students' score.

Number of Points

Which student earned the most points?

☐

35. The diagonal of a rectangular room is $\sqrt{289}$ feet long. To which sets of numbers does $\sqrt{289}$ belong? Select all that apply.

☐ real ☐ rational ☐ whole

☐ integer ☐ irrational ☐ natural

Spiral Review

36. Order the set $\{7, \sqrt{53}, \sqrt{32}, 6\}$ from least to greatest.

_____

Solve each equation.

37. $t^2 = 25$ _____

38. $y^2 = \frac{1}{49}$ _____

39. $0.64 = a^2$ _____

Evaluate each expression. Express the result in scientific notation.

40. $(7.2 \times 10^4)(1.1 \times 10^{-6}) =$ _____

41. $(3.6 \times 10^3) + (5.7 \times 10^5) =$ _____

42. The table shows the approximate population of several countries. Order the countries from the greatest population to the least population.

_____

Country	Population
China	1.3×10^9
India	1.2×10^9
Indonesia	2.3×10^8
United States	3.1×10^8

21ST CENTURY CAREER
in Fashion Design

Fashion Designer

Do you enjoy reading fashion magazines, keeping up with the latest trends, and creating your own unique sense of style? You might want to consider a career in fashion design. Fashion designers create new designs for clothing, accessories, and shoes. In addition to being creative and knowledgeable about current fashion trends, fashion designers need to be able to take accurate measurements and calculate fit by adding, subtracting, and dividing measurements.

College & Career
READINESS

Is This the Career for You?

Are you interested in a career as a fashion designer? Take some of the following courses in high school.

◆ Algebra
◆ Art
◆ Digital Design
◆ Geometry

Find out how math relates to a career in Fashion Design.

Ⓟ A Flair for Fashion!

Use the information in the table to solve each problem. Write in simplest form.

1. For size 8, does Dress Style A or B require more fabric? Explain. _____

2. How many yards of fabric are needed to make Style A in sizes 8 and 14? _____

3. Estimate how many yards of fabric are needed to make Style B in each of the sizes shown. Then find the actual amount of fabric. _____

4. For Style B, how much more fabric is required for size 14 than for size 12? _____

5. A designer has half the amount of fabric needed to make Style A in size 10. How much fabric does she have? _____

6. A bolt has $12\frac{1}{8}$ yards of fabric left on it. How many dresses in Style B size 12 could be made? How much fabric is left over?

Amount of Fabric Needed (yards)				
Dress Style	Size 8	Size 10	Size 12	Size 14
A	$3\frac{3}{8}$	$3\frac{1}{2}$	$3\frac{3}{4}$	$3\frac{7}{8}$
B	$3\frac{1}{4}$	$3\frac{1}{2}$	$3\frac{7}{8}$	4

Ⓟ Career Project

It's time to update your career portfolio! Use blogs and webpages of fashion designers to answer some of these questions: Where did they go to school? What was their first job? What do they say is the most difficult part about being a fashion designer? What inspires them to create their designs? What advice do they have for new designers?

Suppose you are an employer hiring a fashion designer. What questions would you ask a potential employee?

- _____
- _____

Chapter Review

Vocabulary Check

Unscramble each of the clue words. After unscrambling each of the terms, use the numbered letters to find a vocabulary term that relates to all of the other terms.

RAB TONNOTIA

☐☐☐ ☐☐☐☐☐☐☐☐☐
   1   7

TAMTINRINGE

☐☐☐☐☐☐☐☐☐☐☐
         3

GIEPEATNR

☐☐☐☐☐☐☐☐☐
       4

KIEL STAFCOIRN

☐☐☐☐ ☐☐☐☐☐☐☐☐☐
              5

LUKIEN

☐☐☐☐☐☐
  6 8

NOMMOC NIOAREOMNDT

☐☐☐☐☐☐☐ ☐☐☐☐☐☐☐☐☐☐☐☐☐☐
                         2

☐☐☐☐☐☐☐☐
1 2 3 4 5 6 7 8

Complete each sentence using one of the unscrambled words above.

1. The process of using a line over the repeating digits of a decimal is called _____.

2. Fractions with different denominators are called _____ fractions.

3. The least common multiple of the denominators is called the least _____.

4. The decimal form of a fraction is a(n) _____ decimal.

5. A _____ decimal is a decimal in which the repeating digit is zero.

6. Fractions with the same denominator are called _____.

Use Your FOLDABLES

Use your Foldable to help review the chapter.

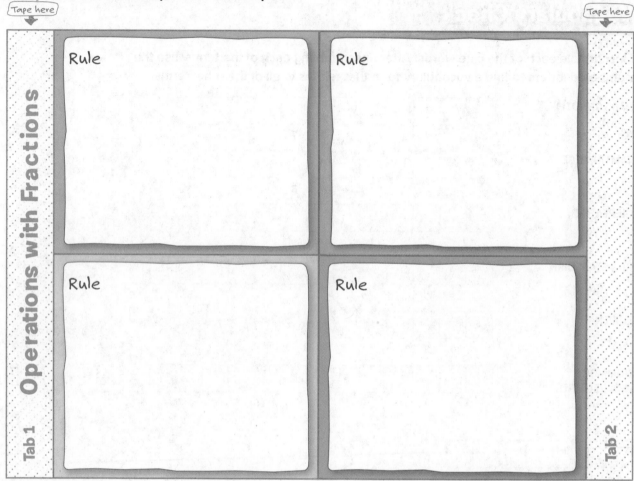

Tape here

Tape here

Operations with Fractions

Tab 1

Tab 2

Rule

Rule

Rule

Rule

Got it?

Circle the correct term or number to complete each sentence.

1. $\frac{1}{5}$ and $\left(\frac{1}{3}, \frac{3}{5}\right)$ are like fractions.

2. To add like fractions, add the (numerators, denominators).

3. To add unlike fractions, rename the fractions using the least common (numerator, denominator).

4. The reciprocal of $\frac{1}{3}$ is (−3, 3).

5. To divide by a fraction, (multiply, divide) by its reciprocal.

6. The least common denominator of $\frac{1}{5}$ and $\frac{1}{10}$ is (10, 50).

Power Up! Performance Task

Managing Money

Tamiko has recently started managing her own finances. She tracks her debts and income, as well as any gifts that she receives from her family members. Some of her recent transactions are listed below.

Transaction	Amount ($)
Borrowed money from a friend	43.75
Received a gift from Dad	50.00
Spent money on lunches	62.50
Received allowance	20.00

Write your answers on another piece of paper. Show all of your work to receive full credit.

Part A

What rational number represents the net result of the transactions shown in the table? Explain what your answer represents.

Part B

The following week, Tamiko receives a check for $109.60 for working at a local fast food restaurant and a small bonus check for $34.15. Determine the net result of her transactions using the result from Part A. She wants to save $\frac{3}{5}$ of this amount. How much will she save?

Part C

The next month, Tamiko develops a budget for her income. One-fourth of her income is budgeted for car insurance, $\frac{1}{10}$ of her income is budgeted for gasoline, $\frac{2}{5}$ of her income is budgeted for savings, and the remainder is budgeted for spending money. She earns $234.80 for working at the fast food restaurant, $64 for baby sitting, and $20 in allowance. According to her budget, how much of her total monthly income is allotted for spending money?

Reflect

 Answering the Essential Question

Use what you learned about operations with rational numbers to complete the graphic organizer. Describe a process to perform each operation.

Add	Subtract

Essential Question

WHAT happens when you add, subtract, multiply, and divide fractions?

Multiply	Divide

Answer the Essential Question. WHAT happens when you add, subtract, multipy, and divide fractions?

_____

_____

UNIT PROJECT

Explore the Ocean Depths For this project, imagine that your dream job is to become an oceanographer. In this project you will:

- **Collaborate** with your classmates as you research information about the ocean.
- **Share** the results of your research in a creative way.
- **Reflect** on how mathematical ideas can be represented.

Collaborate

Go Online Work with your group to research and complete each activity. You will use your results in the Share section on the following page.

1. About $\frac{2}{3}$ of Earth is covered by ocean. Research the five oceans of the world and create a table that shows about what fraction each ocean is of that $\frac{2}{3}$.

2. What is the greatest ocean depth? Find out and then display it on a vertical number line along with other facts about what you can find at different ocean depths.

3. Coral reefs are the home of many ocean creatures. Look up some facts about the state of coral reefs in the world today and display them in a creative way.

4. Choose three different types of whales that live in the ocean. Compare things like their size, the amount of food they eat, or the climate in which they live. Organize the information in a table or graph.

5. Research one of the larger icebergs in the Arctic Ocean. Sketch an image of the iceberg next to a vertical number line that shows the approximate top and bottom of the iceberg. Remember, about $\frac{7}{8}$ of an iceberg is under water.

With your group, decide on a way to share what you have learned about ocean depths. Some suggestions are listed below, but you could also think of other creative ways to present your information. Remember to show how you used mathematics in your project!

- Use presentation software to organize what you have learned in this project. Share your presentation with the class.
- Imagine you need to apply for funds to go on a deep sea exploration. Write a persuasive letter or speech that highlights the importance of studying ocean depths.

Check out the note on the right to connect this project with other subjects.

connect with Science

Environmental Literacy Research an animal that lives in the ocean that is on the endangered species list. Give a presentation to your class that answers the following questions:

- What are some of the causes for the animals being on the endangered species list?
- What efforts are currently being made to protect the animal you chose?

Reflect

On Your Own

6. **Answer the Essential Question** How can mathematical ideas be represented?

   a. How were mathematical ideas involving integers represented in the information you discovered about oceans?

   _____

   _____

   _____

   _____

   b. How were mathematical ideas involving rational numbers represented in the information you discovered about oceans?

   _____

   _____

   _____

   _____

Glossary/Glosario

The eGlossary contains words and definitions in the following 13 languages:

Arabic	Cantonese	Hmong	Spanish	Urdu
Bengali	English	Korean	Tagalog	Vietnamese
Brazilian Portuguese	Haitian Creole	Russian		

English	**Español**

absolute value   The distance the number is from zero on a number line.

valor absoluto   Distancia a la que se encuentra un número de cero en la recta numérica.

acute angle   An angle with a measure greater than 0° and less than 90°.

ángulo agudo   Ángulo que mide más de 0° y menos de 90°.

acute triangle   A triangle having three acute angles.

triángulo acutángulo   Triángulo con tres ángulos agudos.

Addition Property of Equality   If you add the same number to each side of an equation, the two sides remain equal.

propiedad de adición de la igualdad   Si sumas el mismo número a ambos lados de una ecuación, los dos lados permanecen iguales.

Addition Property of Inequality   If you add the same number to each side of an inequality, the inequality remains true.

propiedad de desigualdad en la suma   Si se suma el mismo número a cada lado de una desigualdad, la desigualdad sigue siendo verdadera.

Additive Identity Property   The sum of any number and zero is the number.

propiedad de identidad de la suma   La suma de cualquier número y cero es el mismo número.

additive inverse   Two integers that are opposites. The sum of an integer and its additive inverse is zero.

inverso aditivo   Dos enteros opuestos.

adjacent angles   Angles that have the same vertex, share a common side, and do not overlap.

ángulos adyacentes   Ángulos que comparten el mismo vértice y un común lado, pero no se sobreponen.

algebra   A branch of mathematics that involves expressions with variables.

álgebra   Rama de las matemáticas que trata de las expresiones con variables.

algebraic expression   A combination of variables, numbers, and at least one operation.

expresión algebraica   Combinación de variables, números y por lo menos una operación.

alternate exterior angles Angles that are on opposite sides of the transversal and outside the parallel lines.

ángulos alternos externos Ángulos en lados opuestos de la trasversal y afuera de las rectas paralelas.

alternate interior angles Angles that are on opposite sides of the transversal and inside the parallel lines.

ángulos alternos internos Ángulos en lados opuestos de la trasversal y dentro de las rectas paralelas.

angle Two rays with a common endpoint form an angle. The rays and vertex are used to name the angle.

∠ABC, ∠CBA, or ∠B

ángulo Dos rayos con un extremo común forman un ángulo. Los rayos y el vértice se usan para nombrar el ángulo.

∠ABC, ∠CBA o ∠B

arithmetic sequence A sequence in which the difference between any two consecutive terms is the same.

sucesión aritmética Sucesión en la cual la diferencia entre dos términos consecutivos es constante.

Associative Property The way in which numbers are grouped does not change their sum or product.

propiedad asociativa La forma en que se agrupan números al sumarlos o multiplicarlos no altera su suma o producto.

Bb

bar notation In repeating decimals, the line or bar placed over the digits that repeat. For example, $2.\overline{63}$ indicates that the digits 63 repeat.

notación de barra Línea o barra que se coloca sobre los dígitos que se repiten en decimales periódicos. Por ejemplo, $2.\overline{63}$ indica que los dígitos 63 se repiten.

base In a power, the number used as a factor. In 10^3, the base is 10. That is, $10^3 = 10 \times 10 \times 10$.

base En una potencia, el número usado como factor. En 10^3, la base es 10. Es decir, $10^3 = 10 \times 10 \times 10$.

base One of the two parallel congruent faces of a prism.

base Una de las dos caras paralelas congruentes de un prisma.

biased sample   A sample drawn in such a way that one or more parts of the population are favored over others.

muestra sesgada   Muestra en que se favorece una o más partes de una población.

box plot   A method of visually displaying a distribution of data values by using the median, quartiles, and extremes of the data set. A box shows the middle 50% of the data.

diagrama de caja   Un método de mostrar visualmente una distribución de valores usando la mediana, cuartiles y extremos del conjunto de datos. Una caja muestra el 50% del medio de los datos.

center   The point from which all points on circle are the same distance.

centro   El punto desde el cual todos los puntos en una circunferencia están a la misma distancia.

circle   The set of all points in a plane that are the same distance from a given point called the center.

círculo   Conjunto de todos los puntos de un plano que están a la misma distancia de un punto dado denominado "centro".

circle graph   A graph that shows data as parts of a whole. In a circle graph, the percents add up to 100.

gráfica circular   Gráfica que muestra los datos como partes de un todo. En una gráfica circular los porcentajes suman 100.

Area of Oceans

Atlantic 22.9%
Pacific 46.4%
Indian 20.4%
Southern 6.1%
Arctic 4.2%

Área de superficie de los océanos

Atlántico 22.9%
Pacífico 46.4%
Índico 20.4%
Mar del Sur 6.1%
Ártico 4.2%

circumference   The distance around a circle.

circunferencia   Distancia en torno a un círculo.

circumference

circunferencia

coefficient   The numerical factor of a term that contains a variable.

coeficiente   El factor numérico de un término que contiene una variable.

common denominator   A common multiple of the denominators of two or more fractions. 24 is a common denominator for $\frac{1}{3}$, $\frac{5}{8}$, and $\frac{3}{4}$ because 24 is the LCM of 3, 8, and 4.

común denominador   El múltiplo común de los denominadores de dos o más fracciones. 24 es un denominador común para $\frac{1}{3}$, $\frac{5}{8}$ y $\frac{3}{4}$ porque 24 es el mcm de 3, 8 y 4.

Commutative Property   The order in which two numbers are added or multiplied does not change their sum or product.

propiedad conmutativa   El orden en que se suman o multiplican dos números no altera el resultado.

complementary angles   Two angles are complementary if the sum of their measures is 90°.

∠1 and ∠2 are complementary angles.

complementary events   The events of one outcome happening and that outcome not happening. The sum of the probabilities of an event and its complement is 1 or 100%. In symbols, $P(A) + P(not\ A) = 1$.

complex fraction   A fraction $\frac{A}{B}$ where A or B are fractions and B does not equal zero.

composite figure   A figure that is made up of two or more three-dimensional figures.

compound event   An event consisting of two or more simple events.

cone   A three-dimensional figure with one circular base connected by a curved surface to a single vertex.

vertex

congruent   Having the same measure.

congruent angles   Angles that have the same measure.

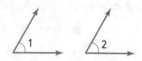

∠1 and ∠2 are congruent angles.

congruent figures   Figures that have the same size and same shape and corresponding sides and angles with equal measure.

congruent segments   Sides with the same length.

Side $\overline{AB}$ is congruent to side $\overline{BC}$.

ángulos complementarios   Dos ángulos son complementarios si la suma de sus medidas es 90°.

∠1 y ∠2 son complementarios.

eventos complementarios   Los eventos de un resultado que ocurre y ese resultado que no ocurre. La suma de las probabilidades de un evento y su complemento es 1 ó 100. En símbolos $P(A) + P(no\ A) = 1$.

fracción compleja   Una fracción $\frac{A}{B}$ en la cual A o B son fracciones y B no es igual a cero.

figura compuesta   Figura formada por dos o más figuras tridimensionales.

evento compuesto   Un evento que consiste en dos o más eventos simples.

cono   Una figura tridimensional con una base circular conectada por una superficie curva para un solo vértice.

vértice

congruente   Que tiene la misma medida.

ángulos congruentes   Ángulos que tienen la misma medida.

∠1 y ∠2 son congruentes.

figuras congruentes   Figuras que tienen el mismo tamaño y la misma forma y los lados y los ángulos correspondientes tienen igual medida.

segmentos congruentes   Lados con la misma longitud.

$\overline{AB}$ es congruente a $\overline{BC}$.

constant   A term that does not contain a variable.

constante   Término que no contiene ninguna variable.

constant of proportionality   A constant ratio or unit rate of two variable quantities. It is also called the constant of variation.

constante de proporcionalidad   Una razón constante o tasa por unidad de dos cantidades variables. También se llama constante de variación.

constant of variation   The constant ratio in a direct variation. It is also called the constant of proportionality.

constante de variación   Una razón constante o tasa por unidad de dos cantidades variables. También se llama constante de proporcionalidad.

constant rate of change   The rate of change in a linear relationship.

razón constante de cambio   Tasa de cambio en una relación lineal.

continuous data   Data that take on any real number value. It can be determined by considering what numbers are reasonable as part of the domain.

datos continuos   Datos que asumen cualquier valor numérico real. Se pueden determinar al considerar qué números son razonables como parte del dominio.

convenience sample   A sample which consists of members of a population that are easily accessed.

muestra de conveniencia   Muestra que incluye miembros de una población fácilmente accesibles.

coordinate plane   A plane in which a horizontal number line and a vertical number line intersect at their zero points. Also called a coordinate grid.

plano de coordenadas   Plano en el cual se han trazado dos rectas numéricas, una horizontal y una vertical, que se intersecan en sus puntos cero. También conocido como sistema de coordenadas.

coplanar   Lines or points that lie in the same plane.

coplanar   Líneas o puntos situados en el mismo plano.

corresponding angles   Angles in the same position on parallel lines in relation to a transversal.

ángulos correspondientes   Ángulos que están en la misma posición sobre rectas paralelas en relación con la transversal.

corresponding sides   The sides of similar figures that are in the same relative position.

lados correspondientes   Lados de figuras semejantes que estan en la misma posición.

counterexample   A specific case which proves a statement false.

contraejemplo   Caso específico que demuestra la falsedad de un enunciado.

cross product   The product of the numerator of one ratio and the denominator of the other ratio. The cross products of any proportion are equal.

producto cruzado   Producto del numerador de una razón por el denominador de la otra razón. Los productos cruzados de cualquier proporción son iguales.

cross section   The cross section of a solid and a plane.

sección transversal   Intersección de un sólido con un plano.

cube root One of three equal factors of a number. If $a^3 = b$, then a is the cube root of b. The cube root of 125 is 5 since $5^3 = 125$.

cubed The product in which a number is a factor three times. Two cubed is 8 because $2 \times 2 \times 2 = 8$.

cylinder A three-dimensional figure with two parallel congruent circular bases connected by a curved surface.

raíz cúbica Uno de tres factores iguales de un número. Si $a^3 = b$, entonces a es la raíz cúbica de b. La raíz cúbica de 125 es 5, dado que $5^3 = 125$.

al cubo El producto de un número por sí mismo, tres veces. Dos al cubo es 8 porque $2 \times 2 \times 2 = 8$.

cilindro Una figura tridimensional con dos paralelas congruentes circulares bases conectados por una superficie curva.

Dd

decagon A polygon having ten sides.

decágono Un polígono con diez lados.

defining a variable Choosing a variable and a quantity for the variable to represent in an expression or equation.

degrees The most common unit of measure for angles. If a circle were divided into 360 equal-sized parts, each part would have an angle measure of 1 degree.

dependent events Two or more events in which the outcome of one event affects the outcome of the other event(s).

dependent variable The variable in a relation with a value that depends on the value of the independent variable.

derived unit A unit that is derived from a measurement system base unit, such as length, mass, or time.

diagonal A line segment that connects two nonconsecutive vertices.

diameter The distance across a circle through its center.

definir una variable El elegir una variable y una cantidad que esté representada por la variable en una expresión o en una ecuacion.

grados La unidad más común para medir ángulos. Si un círculo se divide en 360 partes iguales, cada parte tiene una medida angular de 1 grado.

eventos dependientes Dos o más eventos en que el resultado de un evento afecta el resultado de otro u otros eventos.

variable dependiente La variable en una relación cuyo valor depende del valor de la variable independiente.

unidad derivada Unidad que se deriva de una unidad básica de un sistema de medidas, como la longitud, la masa o el tiempo.

diagonal Segmento de recta que une dos vértices no consecutivos de un polígono.

diámetro Segmento que pasa por el centro de un círculo y lo divide en dos partes iguales.

dimensional analysis The process of including units of measurement when you compute.

direct variation The relationship between two variable quantities that have a constant ratio.

discount The amount by which the regular price of an item is reduced.

discrete data When solutions of a function are only integer values. It can be determined by considering what numbers are reasonable as part of the domain.

disjoint events Events that cannot happen at the same time.

Distributive Property To multiply a sum by a number, multiply each addend of the sum by the number outside the parentheses. For any numbers a, b, and c, $a(b + c) = ab + ac$ and $a(b - c) = ab - ac$.

Example: $2(5 + 3) = (2 \times 5) + (2 \times 3)$ and $2(5 - 3) = (2 \times 5) - (2 \times 3)$

Division Property of Equality If you divide each side of an equation by the same nonzero number, the two sides remain equal.

Division Property of Inequality When you divide each side of an inequality by a negative number, the inequality symbol must be reversed for the inequality to remain true.

domain The set of input values for a function.

double box plot Two box plots graphed on the same number line.

double dot plot A method of visually displaying a distribution of two sets of data values where each value is shown as a dot above a number line.

análisis dimensional Proceso que incluye las unidades de medida al hacer cálculos.

variación directa Relación entre las cantidades de dos variables que tienen una tasa constante.

descuento Cantidad que se le rebaja al precio regular de un artículo.

datos discretos Cuando las soluciones de una función son solo valores enteros. Se pueden determinar considerando qué números son razonables como parte del dominio.

eventos disjuntos Eventos que no pueden ocurrir al mismo tiempo.

propiedad distributiva Para multiplicar una suma por un número, multiplíquese cada sumando de la suma por el número que está fuera del paréntesis. Sean cuales fuere los números a, b, y c, $a(b + c) = ab + ac$ y $a(b - c) = ab - ac$.

Ejemplo: $2(5 + 3) = (2 \cdot 5) + (2 \cdot 3)$ y $2(5 - 3) = (2 \cdot 5) - (2 \cdot 3)$

propiedad de igualdad de la división Si divides ambos lados de una ecuación entre el mismo número no nulo, los lados permanecen iguales.

propiedad de desigualdad en la división Cuando se divide cada lado de una desigualdad entre un número negativo, el símbolo de desigualdad debe invertirse para que la desigualdad siga siendo verdadera.

dominio El conjunto de valores de entrada de una función.

doble diagrama de caja Dos diagramas de caja sobre la misma recta numérica.

doble diagrama de puntos Un método de mostrar visualmente una distribución de dos conjuntos de valores donde cada valor se muestra como un punto arriba de una recta numérica.

Ee

edge The line segment where two faces of a polyhedron intersect.

enlargement An image larger than the original.

equation A mathematical sentence that contains an equals sign, =, stating that two quantities are equal.

borde El segmento de línea donde se cruzan dos caras de un poliedro.

ampliación Imagen más grande que la original.

ecuación Enunciado matemático que contiene el signo de igualdad = indicando que dos cantidades son iguales.

equiangular In a polygon, all of the angles are congruent.

equilateral In a polygon, all of the sides are congruent.

equilateral triangle A triangle having three congruent sides.

equivalent equations Two or more equations with the same solution.

equivalent expressions Expressions that have the same value.

equivalent ratios Two ratios that have the same value.

evaluate To find the value of an expression.

experimental probability An estimated probability based on the relative frequency of positive outcomes occurring during an experiment. It is based on what *actually* occurred during such an experiment.

exponent In a power, the number that tells how many times the base is used as a factor. In 5^3, the exponent is 3. That is, $5^3 = 5 \times 5 \times 5$.

exponential form Numbers written with exponents.

equiangular En un polígono, todos los ángulos son congruentes.

equilátero En un polígono, todos los lados son congruentes.

triángulo equilátero Triángulo con tres lados congruentes.

ecuaciones equivalentes Dos o más ecuaciones con la misma solución.

expresiones equivalentes Expresiones que tienen el mismo valor.

razones equivalentes Dos razones que tienen el mismo valor.

evaluar Calcular el valor de una expresión.

probabilidad experimental Probabilidad estimada que se basa en la frecuencia relativa de los resultados positivos que ocurren durante un experimento. Se basa en lo que *en realidad* ocurre durante dicho experimento.

exponente En una potencia, el número que indica las veces que la base se usa como factor. En 5^3, el exponente es 3. Es decir, $5^3 = 5 \times 5 \times 5$.

forma exponencial Números escritos usando exponentes.

Ff

face A flat surface of a polyhedron.

face

factor To write a number as a product of its factors.

factored form An expression expressed as the product of its factors.

factors Two or more numbers that are multiplied together to form a product.

cara Una superficie plana de un poliedro.

cara

factorizar Escribir un número como el producto de sus factores.

forma factorizada Una expresión expresada como el producto de sus factores.

factores Dos o más números que se multiplican entre sí para formar un producto.

fair game   A game where each player has an equally likely chance of winning.

juego justo   Juego donde cada jugador tiene igual posibilidad de ganar.

first quartile   For a data set with median M, the first quartile is the median of the data values less than M.

primer cuartil   Para un conjunto de datos con la mediana M, el primer cuartil es la mediana de los valores menores que M.

formula   An equation that shows the relationship among certain quantities.

fórmula   Ecuación que muestra la relación entre ciertas cantidades.

function   A relationship which assigns exactly one output value for each input value.

función   Relación que asigna exactamente un valor de salida a cada valor de entrada.

function rule   The operation performed on the input of a function.

regla de función   Operación que se efectúa en el valor de entrada.

function table   A table used to organize the input numbers, output numbers, and the function rule.

tabla de funciones   Tabla que organiza las entradas, la regla y las salidas de una función.

Fundamental Counting Principle   Uses multiplication of the number of ways each event in an experiment can occur to find the number of possible outcomes in a sample space.

Principio Fundamental de Contar   Este principio usa la multiplicación del número de veces que puede ocurrir cada evento en un experimento para calcular el número de posibles resultados en un espacio muestral.

Gg

gram   A unit of mass in the metric system equivalent to 0.001 kilogram. The amount of matter an object can hold.

gramo   Unidad de masa en el sistema métrico que equivale a 0.001 de kilogramo. La cantidad de materia que puede contener un objeto.

graph   The process of placing a point on a number line or on a coordinate plane at its proper location.

graficar   Proceso de dibujar o trazar un punto en una recta numérica o en un plano de coordenadas en su ubicación correcta.

gratuity   Also known as a tip. It is a small amount of money in return for a service.

gratificación   También conocida como propina. Es una cantidad pequeña de dinero en retribución por un servicio.

Hh

heptagon   A polygon having seven sides.

heptágono   Polígono con siete lados.

hexagon   A polygon having six sides.

hexágono   Polígono con seis lados.

histogram A type of bar graph used to display numerical data that have been organized into equal intervals.

histograma Tipo de gráfica de barras que se usa para exhibir datos que se han organizado en intervalos iguales.

Identity Property of Zero The sum of an addend and zero is the addend. Example: $5 + 0 = 5$

propiedad de identidad del cero La suma de un sumando y cero es igual al sumando. Ejemplo: $5 + 0 = 5$

independent events Two or more events in which the outcome of one event does not affect the outcome of the other event(s).

eventos independientes Dos o más eventos en los cuales el resultado de uno de ellos no afecta el resultado de los otros eventos.

independent variable The variable in a function with a value that is subject to choice.

variable independiente Variable en una función cuyo valor está sujeto a elección.

indirect measurement Finding a measurement using similar figures to find the length, width, or height of objects that are too difficult to measure directly.

medición indirecta Hallar una medición usando figuras semejantes para calcular el largo, ancho o altura de objetos que son difíciles de medir directamente.

inequality An open sentence that uses $<$, $>$, $\neq$, $\leq$, or $\geq$ to compare two quantities.

desigualdad Enunciado abierto que usa $<$, $>$, $\neq$, $\leq$ o $\geq$ para comparar dos cantidades.

integer Any number from the set $\{..., -4, -3, -2, -1, 0, 1, 2, 3, 4, ...\}$, where ... means continues without end.

entero Cualquier número del conjunto $\{..., -4, -3, -2, -1, 0, 1, 2, 3, 4, ...\}$, donde ... significa que continúa sin fin.

interquartile range A measure of variation in a set of numerical data. It is the distance between first and third quartiles of the data set.

rango intercuartil Una medida de la variación en un conjunto de datos numéricos. Es la distancia entre el primer y el tercer cuartiles del conjunto de datos.

inverse variation A relationship where the product of x and y is a constant k. As x increases in value, y decreases in value, or as y decreases in value, x increases in value.

variación inversa Relación en la cual el producto de x y y es una constante k. A medida que aumenta el valor de x, disminuye el valor de y o a medida que disminuye el valor de y, aumenta el valor de x.

irrational number A number that cannot be expressed as the ratio of two integers.

número irracional Número que no se puede expresar como el razón de dos enteros.

isosceles triangle A triangle having at least two congruent sides.

triángulo isósceles Triángulo que tiene por lo menos dos lados congruentes.

kilogram   The base unit of mass in the metric system. One kilogram equals 1,000 grams.

kilogramo   Unidad básica de masa del sistema métrico. Un kilogramo equivale a 1,000 gramos.

Ll

lateral face   In a polyhedron, a face that is not a base.

cara lateral   En un poliedro, las caras que no forman las bases.

lateral surface area   The sum of the areas of all of the lateral faces of a solid.

área de superficie lateral   Suma de las áreas de todas las caras de un sólido.

least common denominator (LCD)   The least common multiple of the denominators of two or more fractions. You can use the LCD to compare fractions.

mínimo común denominador (mcd)   El menor de los múltiplos de los denominadores de dos o más fracciones. Puedes usar el mínimo común denominador para comparar fracciones.

like fractions   Fractions that have the same denominators.

fracciones semejantes   Fracciones que tienen los mismos denominadores.

like terms   Terms that contain the same variables raised to the same power. Example: 5x and 6x are like terms.

términos semejante   Términos que contienen las mismas variables elevadas a la misma potencia. Ejemplo: 5x y 6x son *términos semejante*.

line graph   A type of statistical graph using lines to show how values change over a period of time.

gráfica lineal   Tipo de gráfica estadística que usa segmentos de recta para mostrar cómo cambian los valores durante un período de tiempo.

linear expression   An algebraic expression in which the variable is raised to the first power, and variables are not multiplied nor divided.

expresión lineal   Expresión algebraica en la cual la variable se eleva a la primera potencia.

linear function   A function for which the graph is a straight line.

función lineal   Función cuya gráfica es una recta.

linear relationship   A relationship for which the graph is a straight line.

relación lineal   Una relación para la cual la gráfica es una línea recta.

liter   The base unit of capacity in the metric system. The amount of dry or liquid material an object can hold.

litro   Unidad básica de capacidad del sistema métrico. La cantidad de materia líquida o sólida que puede contener un objeto.

Mm

markdown An amount by which the regular price of an item is reduced.

rebaja Una cantidad por la cual el precio regular de un artículo se reduce.

markup The amount the price of an item is increased above the price the store paid for the item.

margen de utilidad Cantidad de aumento en el precio de un artículo por encima del precio que paga la tienda por dicho artículo.

mean The sum of the data divided by the number of items in the data set.

media La suma de los datos dividida entre el número total de artículos en el conjunto de datos.

mean absolute deviation A measure of variation in a set of numerical data, computed by adding the distances between each data value and the mean, then dividing by the number of data values.

desviación media absoluta Una medida de variación en un conjunto de datos numéricos que se calcula sumando las distancias entre el valor de cada dato y la media, y luego dividiendo entre el número de valores.

measures of center Numbers that are used to describe the center of a set of data. These measures include the mean, median, and mode.

medidas del centro Números que se usan para describir el centro de un conjunto de datos. Estas medidas incluyen la media, la mediana y la moda.

measures of variation A measure used to describe the distribution of data.

medidas de variación Medida usada para describir la distribución de los datos.

median A measure of center in a set of numerical data. The median of a list of values is the value appearing at the center of a sorted version of the list—or the mean of the two central values, if the list contains an even number of values.

mediana Una medida del centro en un conjunto de dados númericos. La mediana de una lista de valores es el valor que aparace en el centro de una versíon ordenada de la lista, o la media de dos valores centrales si la lista contiene un número par de valores.

meter The base unit of length in the metric system.

metro Unidad fundamental de longitud del sistema métrico.

metric system A decimal system of measures. The prefixes commonly used in this system are kilo-, centi-, and milli-.

sistema métrico Sistema decimal de medidas. Los prefijos más comunes son kilo-, centi- y mili-.

mode The number or numbers that appear most often in a set of data. If there are two or more numbers that occur most often, all of them are modes.

moda El número o números que aparece con más frecuencia en un conjunto de datos. Si hay dos o más números que ocurren con más frecuencia, todosellos son modas.

monomial A number, variable, or product of a number and one or more variables.

monomio Número, variable o producto de un número y una o más variables.

Multiplication Property of Equality If you multiply each side of an equation by the same nonzero number, the two sides remain equal.

propiedad de multiplicación de la igualdad Si multiplicas ambos lados de una ecuación por el mismo número no nulo, lo lados permanecen iguales.

Multiplication Property of Inequality When you multiply each side of an inequality by a negative number, the inequality symbol must be reversed for the inequality to remain true.

propiedad de desigualdad en la multiplicación Cuando se multiplica cada lado de una desigualdad por un número negativo, el símbolo de desigualdad debe invertirse para que la desigualdad siga siendo verdadera.

Multiplicative Identity Property The product of any number and one is the number.

Multiplicative Property of Zero The product of any number and zero is zero.

multiplicative inverse Two numbers with a product of 1. For example, the multiplicative inverse of $\frac{2}{3}$ is $\frac{3}{2}$.

propiedad de identidad de la multiplicación El producto de cualquier número y uno es el mismo número.

propiedad del cero en la multiplicación El producto de cualquier número y cero es cero.

inverso multiplicativo Dos números cuyo producto es 1. Por ejemplo, el inverso multiplicativo de $\frac{2}{3}$ es $\frac{3}{2}$.

---

negative exponent Any nonzero number to the negative n power. It is the multiplicative inverse of its nth power.

negative integer An integer that is less than zero. Negative integers are written with a − sign.

net A two-dimensional figure that can be used to build a three-dimensional figure.

nonagon A polygon having nine sides.

nonlinear function A function for which the graph is *not* a straight line.

nonproportional The relationship between two ratios with a rate or ratio that is not constant.

numerical expression A combination of numbers and operations.

exponente negativo Cualquier número que no sea cero a la potencia negativa de n. Es el inverso multiplicativo de su $n$ésimo potencia.

entero negativo Número menor que cero. Se escriben con el signo −.

red Figura bidimensional que sirve para hacer una figura tridimensional.

enágono Polígono que tiene nueve lados.

nonlinear function Función cuya gráfica *no* es una línea recta.

no proporcional Relación entre dos razones cuya tasa o razón no es constante.

expresión numérica Combinación de números y operaciones.

---

obtuse angle Any angle that measures greater than 90° but less than 180°.

obtuse triangle A triangle having one obtuse angle.

ángulo obtuso Cualquier ángulo que mide más de 90° pero menos de 180°.

triángulo obtusángulo Triángulo que tiene un ángulo obtuso.

octagon A polygon having eight sides.

octágono Polígono que tiene ocho lados.

opposites Two integers are opposites if they are represented on the number line by points that are the same distance from zero, but on opposite sides of zero. The sum of two opposites is zero.

opuestos Dos enteros son opuestos si, en la recta numérica, están representados por puntos que equidistan de cero, pero en direcciones opuestas. La suma de dos opuestos es cero.

order of operations The rules to follow when more than one operation is used in a numerical expression.

1. Evaluate the expressions inside grouping symbols.
2. Evaluate all powers.
3. Multiply and divide in order from left to right.
4. Add and subtract in order from left to right.

orden de las operaciones Reglas a seguir cuando se usa más de una operación en una expresión numérica.

1. Primero, evalúa las expresiones dentro de los símbolos de agrupación.
2. Evalúa todas las potencias.
3. Multiplica y divide en orden de izquierda a derecha.
4. Suma y resta en orden de izquierda a derecha.

ordered pair A pair of numbers used to locate a point in the coordinate plane. An ordered pair is written in the form (x-coordinate, y-coordinate).

par ordenado Par de números que se utiliza para ubicar un punto en un plano de coordenadas. Se escribe de la siguiente forma: (coordenada x, coordenada y).

origin The point at which the x-axis and the y-axis intersect in a coordinate plane. The origin is at (0, 0).

origen Punto en que el eje x y el eje y se intersecan en un plano de coordenadas. El origen está ubicado en (0, 0).

outcome Any one of the possible results of an action. For example, 4 is an outcome when a number cube is rolled.

resultado Cualquiera de los resultados posibles de una acción. Por ejemplo, 4 puede ser un resultado al lanzar un cubo numerado.

outlier A data value that is either much *greater* or much *less* than the median.

valor atípico Valor de los datos que es mucho *mayor* o mucho *menor* que la mediana.

Pp

parallel lines Lines in a plane that never intersect.

rectas paralelas Rectas en un plano que nunca se intersecan.

parallelogram A quadrilateral with opposite sides parallel and opposite sides congruent.

paralelogramo Cuadrilátero cuyos lados opuestos son paralelos y congruentes.

pentagon   A polygon having five sides.

percent equation   An equation that describes the relationship between the part, whole, and percent.

$$\text{part} = \text{percent} \cdot \text{whole}$$

percent error   A ratio that compares the inaccuracy of an estimate (amount of error) to the actual amount.

percent of change   A ratio that compares the change in a quantity to the original amount.

$$\text{percent of change} = \frac{\text{amount of change}}{\text{original amount}}$$

percent of decrease   A negative percent of change.

percent of increase   A positive percent of change.

percent proportion   One ratio or fraction that compares part of a quantity to the whole quantity. The other ratio is the equivalent percent written as a fraction with a denominator of 100.

$$\frac{\text{part}}{\text{whole}} = \frac{\text{percent}}{100}$$

perfect cube   A rational number whose cube root is a whole number. 27 is a perfect cube because its cube root is 3.

perfect squares   Numbers with square roots that are whole numbers. 25 is a perfect square because the square root of 25 is 5.

permutation   An arrangement, or listing, of objects in which order is important.

perpendicular lines   Lines that meet or cross each other to form right angles.

pi   The ratio of the circumference of a circle to its diameter. The Greek letter π represents this number. The value of pi is 3.1415926. . . . Approximations for pi are 3.14 and $\frac{22}{7}$.

plane   A two-dimensional flat surface that extends in all directions.

pentágono   Polígono que tiene cinco lados.

ecuación porcentual   Ecuación que describe la relación entre la parte, el todo y el por ciento.

$$\text{parte} = \text{por ciento} \cdot \text{todo}$$

porcentaje de error   Una razón que compara la inexactitud de una estimación (cantidad del error) con la cantidad real.

porcentaje de cambio   Razón que compara el cambio en una cantidad a la cantidad original.

$$\text{porcentaje de cambio} = \frac{\text{cantidad del cambio}}{\text{cantidad original}}$$

porcentaje de disminución   Porcentaje de cambio negativo.

porcentaje de aumento   Porcentaje de cambio positivo.

proporción porcentual   Razón o fracción que compara parte de una cantidad a toda la cantidad. La otra razón es el porcentaje equivalente escrito como fracción con 100 de denominador.

$$\frac{\text{parte}}{\text{todo}} = \frac{\text{porcentaje}}{100}$$

cubo perfecto   Número racional cuya raíz cúbica es un número entero. 27 es un cubo perfecto porque su raíz cúbica es 3.

cuadrados perfectos   Números cuya raíz cuadrada es un número entero. 25 es un cuadrado perfecto porque la raíz cuadrada de 25 es 5.

permutación   Arreglo o lista de objetos en la cual el orden es importante.

rectas perpendiculares   Rectas que al encontrarse o cruzarse forman ángulos rectos.

pi   Relación entre la circunferencia de un círculo y su diámetro. La letra griega π representa este número. El valor de pi es 3.1415926. . . . Las aproximaciones de pi son 3.14 y $\frac{22}{7}$.

plano   Superficie bidimensional que se extiende en todas direcciones.

polygon   A simple closed figure formed by three or more straight line segments.

polyhedron   A three-dimensional figure with faces that are polygons.

population   The entire group of items or individuals from which the samples under consideration are taken.

positive integer   An integer that is greater than zero. They are written with or without a + sign.

powers   Numbers expressed using exponents. The power 3^2 is read *three to the second power,* or *three squared.*

precision   The ability of a measurement to be consistently reproduced.

principal   The amount of money deposited or borrowed.

prism   A polyhedron with two parallel congruent faces called bases.

probability   The chance that some event will happen. It is the ratio of the number of favorable outcomes to the number of possible outcomes.

probability model   A model used to assign probabilities to outcomes of a chance process by examining the nature of the process.

properties   Statements that are true for any number or variable.

proportion   An equation stating that two ratios or rates are equivalent.

proportional   The relationship between two ratios with a constant rate or ratio.

pyramid   A polyhedron with one base that is a polygon and three or more triangular faces that meet at a common vertex.

polígono   Figura cerrada simple formada por tres o más segmentos de recta.

poliedro   Una figura tridimensional con caras que son polígonos.

población   El grupo total de individuos o de artículos del cual se toman las muestras bajo estudio.

entero positivo   Entero que es mayor que cero; se escribe con o sin el signo +.

potencias   Números que se expresan usando exponentes. La potencia 3^2 se lee *tres a la segunda potencia o tres al cuadrado.*

precisión   Capacidad que tiene una medición de poder reproducirse consistentemente.

capital   Cantidad de dinero que se deposita o se toma prestada.

prisma   Un poliedro con dos caras congruentes paralelas llamadas bases.

probabilidad   La posibilidad de que suceda un evento. Es la razón del número de resultados favorables al número de resultados posibles.

modelo de probabilidad   Un modelo usado para asignar probabilidades a resultados de un proceso aleatorio examinando la naturaleza del proceso.

propiedades   Enunciados que son verdaderos para cualquier número o variable.

proporción   Ecuación que indica que dos razones o tasas son equivalentes.

proporcional   Relación entre dos razones con una tasa o razón constante.

pirámide   Un poliedro con una base que es un polígono y tres o más caras triangulares que se encuentran en un vértice común.

quadrant   One of the four regions into which the two perpendicular number lines of the coordinate plane separate the plane.

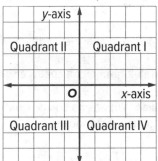

cuadrante   Una de las cuatro regiones en que dos rectas numéricas perpendiculares dividen el plano de coordenadas.

quadrilateral   A closed figure having four sides and four angles.

cuadrilátero   Figura cerrada que tiene cuatro lados y cuatro ángulos.

quartile   A value that divides the data set into four equal parts.

cuartil   Valor que divide el conjunto de datos en cuatro partes iguales.

radical sign   The symbol used to indicate a nonnegative square root, $\sqrt{\ }$.

signo radical   Símbolo que se usa para indicar una raíz cuadrada no negativa, $\sqrt{\ }$.

radius   The distance from the center of a circle to any point on the circle.

radio   Distancia desde el centro de un círculo hasta cualquiera de sus puntos.

random   Outcomes occur at random if each outcome occurs by chance. For example, rolling a number on a number cube occurs at random.

azar   Los resultados ocurren aleatoriamente si cada resultado ocurre por casualidad. Por ejemplo, sacar un número en un cubo numerado ocurre al azar.

range   The set of output values for a function.

rango   Conjunto de valores de salida para una función.

range   The difference between the greatest and least data value.

rango   La diferencia entre el número mayor y el menor en un conjunto de datos.

rate   A ratio that compares two quantities with different kinds of units.

tasa   Razón que compara dos cantidades que tienen distintas unidades de medida.

rate of change   A rate that describes how one quantity changes in relation to another. A rate of change is usually expressed as a unit rate.

tasa de cambio   Tasa que describe cómo cambia una cantidad con respecto a otra. Por lo general, se expresa como tasa unitaria.

rational numbers   The set of numbers that can be written in the form $\frac{a}{b}$, where a and b are integers and $b \neq 0$.

Examples: $1 = \frac{1}{1}, \frac{2}{9}, -2.3 = -2\frac{3}{10}$

números racionales   Conjunto de números que puede escribirse en la forma $\frac{a}{b}$ donde a y b son números enteros y $b \neq 0$.

Ejemplos: $1 = \frac{1}{1}, \frac{2}{9}, -2.3 = -2\frac{3}{10}$

real numbers   A set made up of rational and irrational numbers.

números reales   Conjunto de números racionales e irracionales.

reciprocal   The multiplicative inverse of a number.

recíproco   El inverso multiplicativo de un número.

rectangle   A parallelogram having four right angles.

rectángulo   Paralelogramo con cuatro ángulos rectos.

rectangular prism   A prism that has two parallel congruent bases that are rectangles.

prisma rectangular   Un prisma con dos bases paralelas congruentes que son rectángulos.

reduction   An image smaller than the original.

reducción   Imagen más pequeña que la original.

regular polygon   A polygon that has all sides congruent and all angles congruent.

polígono regular   Polígono con todos los lados y todos los ángulos congruentes.

regular pyramid   A pyramid whose base is a regular polygon and in which the segment from the vertex to the center of the base is the altitude.

pirámide regular   Pirámide cuya base es un polígono regular y en la cual el segmento desde el vértice hasta el centro de la base es la altura.

relation   Any set of ordered pairs.

relación   Cualquier conjunto de pares ordenados.

relative frequency   A ratio that compares the frequency of each category to the total.

frecuencia relativa   Razón que compara la frecuencia de cada categoría al total.

repeating decimal   The decimal form of a rational number.

decimal periódico   La forma decimal de un número racional.

rhombus   A parallelogram having four congruent sides.

rombo   Paralelogramo que tiene cuatro lados congruentes.

right angle   An angle that measures exactly 90°.

ángulo recto   Ángulo que mide exactamente 90°.

right triangle   A triangle having one right angle.

triángulo rectángulo   Triángulo que tiene un ángulo recto.

Ss

sales tax   An additional amount of money charged on items that people buy.

impuesto sobre las ventas   Cantidad de dinero adicional que se cobra por los artículos que se compran.

sample   A randomly selected group chosen for the purpose of collecting data.

muestra   Grupo escogido al azar o aleatoriamente que se usa con el propósito de recoger datos.

sample space   The set of all possible outcomes of a probability experiment.

espacio muestral   Conjunto de todos los resultados posibles de un experimento probabilístico.

scale   The scale that gives the ratio that compares the measurements of a drawing or model to the measurements of the real object.

escala   Razón que compara las medidas de un dibujo o modelo a las medidas del objeto real.

scale drawing   A drawing that is used to represent objects that are too large or too small to be drawn at actual size.

dibujo a escala   Dibujo que se usa para representar objetos que son demasiado grandes o demasiado pequeños como para dibujarlos de tamaño natural.

scale factor   A scale written as a ratio without units in simplest form.

factor de escala   Escala escrita como una razón sin unidades en forma simplificada.

scale model   A model used to represent objects that are too large or too small to be built at actual size.

modelo a escala   Réplica de un objeto real, el cual es demasiado grande o demasiado pequeño como para construirlo de tamaño natural.

scalene triangle   A triangle having no congruent sides.

triángulo escaleno   Triángulo sin lados congruentes.

scatter plot   In a scatter plot, two sets of related data are plotted as ordered pairs on the same graph.

diagrama de dispersión   Diagrama en que dos conjuntos de datos relacionados aparecen graficados como pares ordenados en la misma gráfica.

School Commute

Tiempo para llegar a la escuela

selling price   The amount the customer pays for an item.

precio de venta   Cantidad de dinero que paga un consumidor por un artículo.

semicircle   Half of a circle. The formula for the area of a semicircle is $A = \frac{1}{2}\pi r^2$.

semicírculo   Medio círculo La fórmula para el área de un semicírculo es $A = \frac{1}{2}\pi r^2$.

sequence   An ordered list of numbers, such as 0, 1, 2, 3 or 2, 4, 6, 8.

sucesión   Lista ordenada de números, como 0, 1, 2, 3 ó 2, 4, 6, 8.

similar figures   Figures that have the same shape but not necessarily the same size.

figuras semejantes   Figuras que tienen la misma forma, pero no necesariamente el mismo tamaño.

similar solids   Solids with the same shape. Their corresponding linear measures are proportional.

sólidos semejantes   Sólidos con la misma forma. Sus medidas lineales correspondientes son proporcionales.

simple event   One outcome or a collection of outcomes.

eventos simples   Un resultado o una colección de resultados.

simple interest   The amount paid or earned for the use of money. The formula for simple interest is $I = prt$.

interés simple   Cantidad que se paga o que se gana por el uso del dinero. La fórmula para calcular el interés simple es $I = prt$.

simple random sample   An unbiased sample where each item or person in the population is as likely to be chosen as any other.

muestra aleatoria simple   Muestra de una población que tiene la misma probabilidad de escogerse que cualquier otra.

simplest form   An expression is in simplest form when it is replaced by an equivalent expression having no like terms or parentheses.

expresión mínima   Expresión en su forma más simple cuando es reemplazada por una expresión equivalente que no tiene términos similares ni paréntesis.

simplify   Write an expression in simplest form.

simplificar   Escribir una expresión en su forma más simple.

simulation   An experiment that is designed to model the action in a given situation.

simulación   Un experimento diseñado para modelar la acción en una situación dada.

skew lines   Lines that do not intersect and are not coplanar.

rectas alabeadas   Rectas que no se intersecan y que no son coplanares.

slant height   The height of each lateral face.

altura oblicua   Altura de cada cara lateral.

slope   The rate of change between any two points on a line. It is the ratio of vertical change to horizontal change. The slope tells how steep the line is.

pendiente   Razón de cambio entre cualquier par de puntos en una recta. Es la razón del cambio vertical al cambio horizontal. La pendiente indica el grado de inclinación de la recta.

solution   A replacement value for the variable in an open sentence. A value for the variable that makes an equation true. Example: The *solution* of $12 = x + 7$ is 5.

solución   Valor de reemplazo de la variable en un enunciado abierto. Valor de la variable que hace que una ecuación sea verdadera. Ejemplo: La *solución* de $12 = x + 7$ es 5.

square   The product of a number and itself. 36 is the square of 6.

cuadrado   Producto de un número por sí mismo. 36 es el cuadrado de 6.

square   A parallelogram having four right angles and four congruent sides.

cuadrado   Paralelogramo con cuatro ángulos rectos y cuatro lados congruentes.

square root   The factors multiplied to form perfect squares.

al cuadrado   Factores multiplicados para formar cuadrados perfectos.

squared   The product of a number and itself. 36 is the square of 6.

raíz cuadrada   El producto de un número por sí mismo. 36 es el cuadrado de 6.

standard form   Numbers written without exponents.

forma estándar   Números escritos sin exponentes.

statistics   The study of collecting, organizing, and interpreting data.

estadística   Estudio que consiste en recopilar, organizar e interpretar datos.

straight angle   An angle that measures exactly 180°.

ángulo llano   Ángulo que mide exactamente 180°.

Subtraction Property of Equality   If you subtract the same number from each side of an equation, the two sides remain equal.

propiedad de sustracción de la igualdad   Si restas el mismo número de ambos lados de una ecuación, los dos lados permanecen iguales.

Subtraction Property of Inequality   If you subtract the same number from each side of an inequality, the inequality remains true.

propiedad de desigualdad en la resta   Si se resta el mismo número a cada lado de una desigualdad, la desigualdad sigue siendo verdadera.

supplementary angles   Two angles are supplementary if the sum of their measures is 180°.

ángulos suplementarios   Dos ángulos son suplementarios si la suma de sus medidas es 180°.

∠1 and ∠2 are supplementary angles.

∠1 y ∠2 son suplementarios.

surface area   The sum of the areas of all the surfaces (faces) of a three-dimensional figure.

área de superficie   La suma de las áreas de todas las superficies (caras) de una figura tridimensional.

survey   A question or set of questions designed to collect data about a specific group of people, or population.

encuesta   Pregunta o conjunto de preguntas diseñadas para recoger datos sobre un grupo específico de personas o población.

systematic random sample   A sample where the items or people are selected according to a specific time or item interval.

muestra aleatoria sistemática   Muestra en que los elementos o personas se eligen según un intervalo de tiempo o elemento específico.

Tt

term   Each number in a sequence.

término   Cada número en una sucesión.

term   A number, a variable, or a product or quotient of numbers and variables.

término   Número, variable, producto o cociente de números y de variables.

terminating decimal   A repeating decimal which has a repeating digit of 0.

decimal finito   Un decimal periódico que tiene un dígito que se repite que es 0.

theoretical probability   The ratio of the number of ways an event can occur to the number of possible outcomes. It is based on what *should* happen when conducting a probability experiment.

probabilidad teórica   Razón del número de maneras en que puede ocurrir un evento al número de resultados posibles. Se basa en lo que *debería* pasar cuando se conduce un experimento probabilístico.

three-dimensional figure   A figure with length, width, and height.

figura tridimensional   Figura que tiene largo, ancho y alto.

third quartile   For a data set with median *M*, the third quartile is the median of the data values greater than *M*.

tercer cuartil   Para un conjunto de datos con la mediana *M*, el tercer cuartil es la mediana de los valores mayores que *M*.

tip   Also known as a gratuity, it is a small amount of money in return for a service.

propina   También conocida como gratificación; es una cantidad pequeña de dinero en recompensa por un servicio.

total surface area   The sum of the areas of the surfaces of a solid.

área de superficie total   La suma del área de las superficies de un sólido.

transversal   The third line formed when two parallel lines are intersected.

transversal   Tercera recta que se forma cuando se intersecan dos rectas paralelas.

transversal

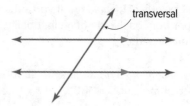

transversal

trapezoid   A quadrilateral with one pair of parallel sides.

trapecio   Cuadrilátero con un único par de lados paralelos.

tree diagram   A diagram used to show the sample space.

diagrama de árbol   Diagrama que se usa para mostrar el espacio muestral.

triangle   A figure with three sides and three angles.

triángulo   Figura con tres lados y tres ángulos.

triangular prism   A prism that has two parallel congruent bases that are triangles.

prisma triangular   Un prisma que tiene dos bases congruentes paralelas que triángulos.

two-step equation   An equation having two different operations.

ecuación de dos pasos   Ecuación que contiene dos operaciones distintas.

two-step inequality   An inequality than contains two operations.

desigualdad de dos pasos   Desigualdad que contiene dos operaciones.

Uu

unbiased sample A sample representative of the entire population.

unfair game A game where there is not a chance of each player being equally likely to win.

uniform probability model A probability model which assigns equal probability to all outcomes.

unit rate A rate that is simplified so that it has a denominator of 1 unit.

unit ratio A unit rate where the denominator is one unit.

unlike fractions Fractions with different denominators.

muestra no sesgada Muestra que se selecciona de modo que se representativa de la población entera.

juego injusto Juego donde cada jugador no tiene la misma posibilidad de ganar.

modelo de probabilidad uniforme Un modelo de probabilidad que asigna igual probabilidad a todos los resultados.

tasa unitaria Tasa simplificada para que tenga un denominador igual a 1.

razón unitaria Tasa unitaria en que el denominador es la unidad.

fracciones con distinto denominador Fracciones cuyos denominadores son diferentes.

Vv

variable A symbol, usually a letter, used to represent a number in mathematical expressions or sentences.

vertex A vertex of an angle is the common endpoint of the rays forming the angle.

vertex The point where three or more faces of a polyhedron intersect.

vertex The point at the tip of a cone.

vertical angles Opposite angles formed by the intersection of two lines. Vertical angles are congruent.

∠1 and ∠2 are vertical angles.

visual overlap A visual demonstration that compares the centers of two distributions with their variation, or spread.

variable Símbolo, por lo general una letra, que se usa para representar un número en expresiones o enunciados matemáticos.

vértice El vértice de un ángulo es el extremo común de los rayos que lo forman.

vértice El punto donde tres o más caras de un poliedro se cruzan.

vértice El punto en la punta de un cono.

ángulos opuestos por el vértice Ángulos opuestos formados por la intersección de dos rectas. Los ángulos opuestos por el vértice son congruentes.

∠1 y ∠2 son ángulos opuestos por el vértice.

superposición visual Una demostración visual que compara los centros de dos distribuciones con su variación, o magnitud.

volume   The number of cubic units needed to fill the space occupied by a solid.

volumen   Número de unidades cúbicas que se requieren para llenar el espacio que ocupa un sólido.

voluntary response sample   A sample which involves only those who want to participate in the sampling.

muestra de respuesta voluntaria   Muestra que involucra sólo aquellos que quieren participar en el muestreo.

x-axis   The horizontal number line in a coordinate plane.

eje x   La recta numérica horizontal en el plano de coordenadas.

x-coordinate   The first number of an ordered pair. It corresponds to a number on the x-axis.

coordenada x   El primer número de un par ordenado. Corresponde a un número en el eje x.

y-axis   The vertical number line in a coordinate plane.

eje y   La recta numérica vertical en el plano de coordenadas.

y-coordinate   The second number of an ordered pair. It corresponds to a number on the y-axis.

coordenada y   El segundo número de un par ordenado. Corresponde a un número en el eje y.

zero pair   The result when one positive counter is paired with one negative counter. The value of a zero pair is 0.

par nulo   Resultado de hacer coordinar una ficha positiva con una negativa. El valor de un par nulo es 0.

Chapter 1 Ratios and Proportional Reasoning

Page 6 Chapter 1 Are You Ready?

1. $\frac{2}{15}$ **3.** $\frac{1}{51}$ **5.** No; $\frac{12}{20} = \frac{3}{5}$, $\frac{15}{30} = \frac{1}{2}$

Pages 13–14 Lesson 1-1 Independent Practice

1. 60 mi/h **3** 3.5 m/s **5.** Sample answer: about $0.50 per pair **7.** 510 words **9** **a.** 20.04 mi/h **b.** about 1.5 h **13.** Sometimes; a ratio that compares two measurements with different units is a rate, such as $\frac{2 \text{ miles}}{10 \text{ minutes}}$. **15.** $6.40; Sample answer: The unit rate for the 96-oz container is $0.05 per ounce. So, 128 ounces would cost $0.05 × 128 or $6.40.

Pages 15–16 Lesson 1-1 Extra Practice

17. 203.75 Calories per serving **19.** 32 mi/gal
21. $108.75 ÷ 15 = $7.25, $7.25 × 18 = $130.50

23.

	Hours Worked	Amount Earned ($)	Earnings per hour ($)	Highest Hourly Rate?
Caleb	5	36.25	7.25	
Jeremy	7.5	65.25	8.70	✔
Rosa	8	54.00	6.75	
Maria	4.25	34.00	8.00	

25. $\frac{2}{7}$ **27.** $\frac{2}{3}$

Pages 21–22 Lesson 1-2 Independent Practice

1. $1\frac{1}{2}$ **3** $\frac{4}{27}$ **5.** $\frac{2}{25}$ **7** $6 per yard **9.** $\frac{5}{6}$ page per minute **11.** $\frac{39}{250}$ **13.** $\frac{11}{200}$ **15.** Sample answer: If one of the numbers in the ratio is a fraction, then the ratio can be a complex fraction. **17.** $\frac{1}{2}$ **19.** $12\frac{1}{2}$ mph

Pages 23–24 Lesson 1-2 Extra Practice

21. 20 **23.** 2 **25.** $\frac{3}{2}$ or $1\frac{1}{2}$ **27.** 3,000 square feet per hour **29.** $\frac{31}{400}$ **31.** Sample answer: Set $1\frac{1}{4}$ over 100. Write $1\frac{1}{4}$ as an improper fraction. Then divide the numerator by the denominator.

33.

	Rider	Speed (mph)
Slowest	Julio	$8\frac{1}{6}$
	Elena	$9\frac{1}{9}$
	Kevin	$12\frac{2}{5}$
Fastest	Lorena	$14\frac{1}{4}$

35. 10,000 **37.** 100 **39.** 1,000

Pages 29–30 Lesson 1-3 Independent Practice

1 115 mi/h **3** 322,000 m/h **5.** 6.1 mi/h
7. 7,200 Mb/h **9.** 500 ft/min; Sample answer: All of the other rates are equal to 60 miles per hour. **11.** 461.5 yd/h

Pages 31–32 Lesson 1-3 Extra Practice

13. 1,760 **15.** 66 **17.** 35.2 **19a.** 6.45 ft/s
19b. 2,280 times **19c.** 0.11 mi **19d.** 900,000 times
21.

Animal	Top Speed (mph)
Cheetah	70
Elk	45
Lion	50
Quarter Horse	55

cheetah
23. yes; Since the unit rates are the same, $\frac{1 \text{ poster}}{3 \text{ students}}$, the rates are equivalent.

Pages 37–38 Lesson 1-4 Independent Practice

1

Time (days)	1	2	3	4
Water (L)	225	450	675	900

Yes; the time to water ratios are all equal to $\frac{1}{225}$.
3. The table for Desmond's Time shows a proportional relationship. The ratio between the time and the number of laps is always 73.

5 **a.** yes; Sample answer:

Side Length (units)	1	2	3	4
Perimeter (units)	4	8	12	16

The side length to perimeter ratio for side lengths of 1, 2, 3, and 4 units is $\frac{1}{4}$, $\frac{2}{8}$ or $\frac{1}{4}$, $\frac{3}{12}$ or $\frac{1}{4}$, $\frac{4}{16}$ or $\frac{1}{4}$. Since these ratios are all equal to $\frac{1}{4}$, the measure of the side length of a square is proportional to the square's perimeter.

b. no; Sample answer:

Side Length (units)	1	2	3	4
Area (units^2)	1	4	9	16

The side length to area ratio for side lengths of 1, 2, 3, and 4 units is $\frac{1}{1}$ or 1, $\frac{2}{4}$ or $\frac{1}{2}$, $\frac{3}{9}$ or $\frac{1}{3}$, $\frac{4}{16}$ or $\frac{1}{4}$. Since these ratios are not equal, the measure of the side length of a square is not proportional to the square's area. **7.** It is not proportional because the ratio of laps to time is not consistent; $\frac{4}{1} \neq \frac{6}{2} \neq \frac{8}{3} \neq \frac{10}{4}$. **9.** Sample answer: At Beautiful Bouquet, there are always 2 red flowers for every 8 pink flowers in a bouquet. At All Occasions Flowers, there are always 3 more pink flowers than red flowers in a bouquet. The bouquet for Beautiful Bouquet is a proportional relationship, while the bouquet for All Occasions Flowers is nonproportional.

Pages 39–40 Lesson 1-4 Extra Practice

11.

Degrees Celsius	0	10	20	30
Degrees Fahrenheit	32	50	68	86

No; the degrees Celsius to degrees Fahrenheit ratios are not all equal. **13a.** No; the fee to ride tickets ratios are not equal. **13b.** no; Sample answer: The fee increase is inconsistent. The table shows an increase of $4.50 from 5 to 10 tickets, an increase of $4 from 10 to 15 tickets, and an increase of $2.50 from 15 to 20 tickets. **15a.** yes **15b.** no **15c.** no **17.** 20 **19.** 12 **21.** 3

Page 43 Problem-Solving Investigation The Four-Step Plan

Case 3. $360 **Case 5.** Add 2 to the first term, 3 to the second, 4 to the third, and so on; 15, 21, 28.

Pages 49–50 Lesson 1-5 Independent Practice

not proportional; The graph does not pass through the origin.
3 Plant B; The graph is a straight line through the origin.
5. proportional; Sample answer: The ordered pairs would be (0, 0), (1, 35), (2, 70). This would be a straight line through the origin.

7.

not proportional; The graph does not pass through the origin.

Pages 51–52 Lesson 1-5 Extra Practice

9.

not proportional; The graph does not pass through the origin.

11.

not proportional; The graph does not pass through the origin. **13a.** Yes **13b.** No **13c.** Yes **15.** $\frac{2}{3}$ **17.** $\frac{1}{3}$

Pages 59–60 Lesson 1-6 Independent Practice

1 40 **3.** 3.5 **5.** $\frac{2}{5} = \frac{x}{20}$; 8 ounces **7** $c = 0.50p$; $4.00
9. $\frac{360}{3} = \frac{n}{7}$; 840 visitors **11.** 256 c; Sample answer: The ratio of cups of mix to cups of water is 1:8, which means that the proportion $\frac{1}{8} = \frac{32}{x}$ is true and can be solved. **13.** 18
15. Sample answer: The product of the length and width is constant. The length is not proportional to the width. The proportions are not equal.

Pages 61–62 Lesson 1-6 Extra Practice

17. 7.2 **19.** $\frac{6}{7} = \frac{c}{40}$; about 34 patients **21.** $s = 45w$; $360
23. 11.25 c **25.** No; sample answer: $\frac{12.50}{1} \neq \frac{20}{2} \neq \frac{27.50}{3} \neq \frac{35}{4}$
27. 20 mi/gal

Pages 69–70 Lesson 1-7 Independent Practice

1 6 m per s **3** $9 per shirt; Sample answer: The point (0, 0) represents 0 T-shirts purchased and 0 dollars spent. The point (1, 9) represents 9 dollars spent for 1 T-shirt.
5. 10 inches per hour
7. Sample answer:

Feet	Inches
3	18
6	36
9	54
12	72

9. $x = 8$, $y = 16$, $z = 24$

Pages 71–72 Lesson 1-7 Extra Practice

11. $0.03 per minute **13.** Josh; sample answer: The unit rate for Ramona is $9 per hour. The unit rate for Josh is $10 per hour. **15.** 195 mi

17.

Input	Add 4	Output
1	1 + 4	5
2	2 + 4	6
3	3 + 4	7
4	4 + 4	8

19.

Input	Multiply by 2	Output
1	1 × 2	2
2	2 × 2	4
3	3 × 2	6
4	4 × 2	8

Pages 77–78 Lesson 1-8 Independent Practice

1

$\frac{50}{1}$ or 50; Adriano read 50 pages every hour.

3 a. It shows that car A travels 120 miles in 2 hours.
b. It shows that car B travels 67.5 miles in 1.5 hours. **c.** the speed of each car at that point **d.** the average speed of the car **e.** Car A; the slope is steeper. **5.** Marisol found $\frac{\text{run}}{\text{rise}}$. Her answer should be $\frac{3}{2}$. **7.** no; Sample answer: the slope of $\overline{AB}$ is $\frac{0-1}{1-5}$ or $\frac{1}{4}$ and the slope of $\overline{BC}$ is $\frac{3-0}{3-1}$ or $\frac{3}{2}$. If the points were on the same line, the slopes would be equal.

Pages 79–80 Lesson 1-8 Extra Practice

9.

$\frac{8}{1}$; So, there are 8 markers in every box.

11.

13.

15. 12 **17.** No; sample answer: $\frac{3.50}{1} \neq \frac{4.50}{2}$ **19.** Yes; sample answer: $\frac{7.50}{1} = \frac{15}{2} = \frac{22.5}{3} = \frac{30}{4}$

Pages 85–86   Lesson 1-9   Independent Practice

1 30 lb per bag

3.

Time (h)	1	2	3	4
Charge ($)	75	100	125	150

No; sample answer: $\frac{75}{1} \neq \frac{100}{2}$; Because there is no constant ratio and the line does not go through the origin, there is no direct variation.   **5** no   **7.** no   **9.** $y = \frac{7}{4}x$; 21   **11.** $y = \frac{1}{4}x$; 28
13. Sample answer: 9; $5\frac{1}{2}$; 36; 22
15.

3.5 cm

6.3 cm

19.6 cm

Pages 87–88   Lesson 1-9   Extra Practice

17. 7 c   **19.** yes; 0.2   **21a.** No   **21b.** Yes   **21c.** Yes
21d. No
23.

Page 91   Chapter Review   Vocabulary Check

1. rate   **3.** ordered   **5.** complex   **7.** slope   **9.** proportion
11. Dimensional

Page 92   Chapter Review   Key Concept Check

1. denominator   **3.** vertical change to horizontal change

Chapter 2 Percents

Page 98   Chapter 2   Are You Ready?

1. 48   **3.** $70   **5.** 72.5%   **7.** 92%

Pages 107–108   Lesson 2-1   Independent Practice

1. 120.9   **3.** $147.20   **5** 17.5   **7.** 1.3   **9.** 30.1   **11.** $7.19 at Pirate Bay, $4.46 at Funtopia, $9.62 at Zoomland   **13.** 4
15 0.61   **17.** 520   **19.** 158   **21.** 0.14   **23.** Sample answer: It is easiest to use a fraction when the denominator of the fraction is a factor of the number. If this is not the case, a decimal may be easier to use.

Pages 109–110   Lesson 2-1   Extra Practice

25. 45.9   **27.** 14.7   **29.** $54   **31.** 0.3   **33.** 2.3   **35.** $19.95
37. 92 customers   **39.** 91.8   **41.** 133.92

Pages 115–116   Lesson 2-2   Independent Practice

1. Sample answer: 35
$$\frac{1}{2} \cdot 70 = 35$$
$$0.1 \cdot 70 = 7 \text{ and}$$
$$5 \cdot 7 = 35$$
3 Sample answer: 18
$$\frac{1}{5} \cdot 90 = 18$$
$$0.1 \cdot 90 = 9 \text{ and}$$
$$2 \cdot 9 = 18$$
5. Sample answer: 168
$$\frac{7}{10} \cdot 240 = 168$$
$$0.1 \cdot 240 = 24 \text{ and}$$
$$7 \cdot 24 = 168$$
7. Sample answer: 720
$$(2 \cdot 320) + \left(\frac{1}{4} \cdot 320\right) = 720$$
9. Sample answer: 2
$$0.01 \cdot 500 = 5 \text{ and}$$
$$\frac{2}{5} \cdot 5 = 2$$
11 Sample answer: about 96 mi; $0.01 \cdot 12{,}000 = 120$ and
$$\frac{4}{5} \cdot 120 = 96$$
13. Sample answer: 6
$$\frac{2}{3} \cdot 9 = 6$$
15. Sample answer: 24
$$\frac{1}{10} \cdot 240 = 24$$
17a. Sample answer: about 260 canned foods;
$200 + 0.3 \cdot 200$ **17b.** Sample answer: about 780 canned foods; $600 + 0.3 \cdot 600$ **19.** sometimes; Sample answer: one estimate for 37% of 60 is $\frac{2}{5} \cdot 60 = 24$.

Pages 117–118   Lesson 2-2   Extra Practice

21. Sample answer: 135

23. Sample answer: 90

$$\frac{9}{10} \cdot 100 = 90$$

$$0.1 \cdot 100 = 10 \text{ and}$$

$$9 \cdot 10 = 90$$

25. Sample answer: 0.7

$$0.01 \cdot 70 = 0.7$$

27. Sample answer: about 12 muscles; $\frac{3}{10} \cdot 40 = 12$

29a. Sample answer: 420; $\frac{7}{10} \cdot 600 = 420$ **29b.** Greater;
both the number of passes and the percent were rounded up.
29c. Tony Romo; sample answer: 64% of 520 must be greater
than 64% of 325.   **31a.** Yes   **31b.** Yes   **31c.** No   **33.** 300

35. $\frac{1}{4}$

Pages 125–126   Lesson 2-3   Independent Practice

1. 25%   **3** 75   **5.** 36%   **7.** $68   **9.** 80   **11** 0.2%
13a. about 3.41%   **13b.** about 24,795.62 km   **13c.** about
6,378.16 km   **15.** 20% of 500, 20% of 100, 5% of 100; If the
percent is the same but the base is greater, then the part is
greater. If the base is the same but the percent is greater, then
the part is greater.

Pages 127–128   Lesson 2-3   Extra Practice

17. 45   **19.** 20   **21.** 20%   **23.** 8 pencils; $\frac{2}{b} = \frac{25}{100}$
25. 120%   **27.** 60%   **29.** $\frac{1}{3}$ **31.** $\frac{1}{21}$ **33.** $\frac{2}{5}$

Pages 133–134   Lesson 2-4   Independent Practice

1 75 = $n \cdot$ 150; 50%   **3.** $p = 0.65 \cdot 98$; 63.7   **5.** $p = 0.24 \cdot$
25; 6   **7.** 50 books   **9** a. 37%   **b.** 31%   **11.** $p = 0.004 \cdot 82.1$;
0.3   **13.** 230 = $n \cdot$ 200; 115%   **15.** Sample answer: If the
percent is less than 100%, then the part is less than the whole; if
the percent equals 100%, then the part equals the whole; if the
percent is greater than 100%, then the part is greater than the
whole.   **17.** Sample answer: It may be easier if the percent and
the base are known because after writing the percent as a
decimal or fraction, the only step is to multiply. When using the
percent proportion, you must first find the cross products and
then divide.

Pages 135–136   Lesson 2-4   Extra Practice

19. 26 = $n \times$ 96; 27.1%   **21.** 30 = $n \cdot$ 64; 46.9%
23. 84 = 0.75 $\cdot$ w; 112   **25.** 64 = 0.8 $\cdot$ w; 80
27. $p = 0.0002 \cdot 5{,}000$; 1   **29.** $14.80   **31.** <   **33.** <

*Page 139   Problem-Solving Investigation   Determine Reasonable
Answers*

Case 3. no; Sample answer: 48% − 24% = 24% and 24% of 140
is about 35   **Case 5.** 15 + b = 0.5(36 + b); 6 boys; 42 students

Pages 147–148   Lesson 2-5   Independent Practice

1. 20%; increase   **3** 25%; decrease   **5.** 41%; decrease
7 28%   **9.** 38%; decrease   **11a.** 100%   **11b.** 300%
13. about 4.2%   **15.** He did not write a ratio comparing the
change to the original amount. It should have had a
denominator of $52 and the percent of change would be
about 140%.

Pages 149–150   Lesson 2-5   Extra Practice

17. 50%; decrease   **19.** 33%; increase   **21a.** about 3.8%;
increase   **21b.** about 2.9%; decrease   **23.** 25%
25. Monica; 2%   **27.** 3.75   **29.** $75.14

Pages 155–156   Lesson 2-6   Independent Practice

1. $69.60   **3** $1,605   **5** $35.79   **7.** $334.80   **9.** $10.29
11. 7%   **13.** $54, $64.80; The percent of gratuity is 20%. All of
the other pairs have a gratuity of 15%.   **15.** false; Sample
answer: An item costs $25 and you want to mark it up 125%.
Multiply $25 by 125% or 1.25. The new price is $25 + $31.25
or $56.25

Pages 157–158   Lesson 2-6   Extra Practice

17. $14.95   **19.** $44.85   **21.** $14.88   **23.** He should have
added the markup to the cost. $40 + $12 = $52   **25.** printer
paper, file cabinet   **27.** 57.85   **29.** $50

Pages 163–164   Lesson 2-7   Independent Practice

1. $51.20   **3** $6.35   **5** $4.50   **7a.** $28.76, $25.29,
$28.87   **7b.** Funtopia   **9.** $9.00
11. Sample answers are given.

Tax   Discount

You pay   Percent   You pay
more   of the   less
money.   regular   money.
            price.

13. $25

Pages 165–166   Lesson 2-7   Extra Practice

15. $102.29   **17.** $169.15   **19.** Mr. Chang; $22.50 < $23.99
21. washing machine, dryer, chest freezer   **23.** 29%; increase
25. 35%; decrease

Pages 171–172   Lesson 2-8   Independent Practice

1. $38.40   **3.** $5.80   **5** $1,417.50   **7.** $75.78   **9** a. 5%
b. Yes; he would have $5,208.   **11.** Sample answer: If the rate
is increased by 1%, then the interest earned is $60 more. If the
time is increased by 1 year, then the interest earned is $36
more.   **13.** Investment A; Sample answer: Investment A has a
balance of $2,850 after 30 years and Investment B has a
balance of $2,512.50 after 15 years.

Pages 173–174   Lesson 2-8   Extra Practice

15. $6.25   **17.** $123.75   **19.** $45.31   **21.** $14.06   **23a.** True
23b. False   **23c.** True

25–27.

Page 179   Chapter Review   Vocabulary Check

Down

1. increase   **3.** markdown   **5.** selling   **7.** discount
9. sales tax

Across

11. interest

Page 180   Chapter Review   Key Concept Check

1. 300   **3.** 18   **5.** 12

Chapter 3 Integers

Page 190   Chapter 3   Are You Ready?

1. 6   **3.** 24

5–9.

Pages 195–196   Lesson 3-1   Independent Practice

1. 9   **3.** −53

5.

7. 10   **9.** 8   **11.** −7   **13.** $299.97; |−200| + |−40| + |−60|
= 200 + 40 + 60 = 300   **15.** always; It is true if A and B are
both positive or if A or B is negative, and if both A and B are
negative.   **17a.** Always; the absolute value of a number and
its opposite are equal.   **17b.** Sometimes; the expressions are
equal when x = 0.   **17c.** Sometimes; the expressions are
equal when x = 0.

Pages 197–198   Lesson 3-1   Extra Practice

19. 12

21.

23. 11   **25.** 25   **27.** 5   **29a.** True   **29b.** True   **29c.** True
29d. False   **31.** (−2, 4); II   **33.** (−3, −1); III

35–37.

Pages 207–208   Lesson 3-2   Independent Practice

1. −38   **3.** 16   **5.** 0   **7.** 9   **9.** −4   **11.** green: profit of $1;
white: profit of $3; black: profit of $3   **13.** Sample answer: In
science, atoms may contain 2 positive charges and 2 negative
charges. In business, a stock's value may fall 0.75 one day and
rise 0.75 the next day.   **15.** a   **17.** m + (−15)

Pages 209–210   Lesson 3-2   Extra Practice

19. 13   **21.** −6   **23.** 15   **25.** 22   **27.** −19   **29.** −5 + (−15)
+ 12; The team has lost a total of 8 yards.   **31a.** Yes   **31b.** No
31c. Yes   **33.** 75   **35.** −13   **37.** −12

Pages 219–220   Lesson 3-3   Independent Practice

1. −10   **3.** −12   **5.** −30   **7.** 23   **9.** 104   **11.** 0
13. a. 2,415 ft   b. 3,124 ft   c. 627 ft   d. 8 ft   **15.** 16
17. Sample answer: −5 − 11 = −5 + (−11) = −16; Add 5 and 11
and keep the negative sign.   **19.** He did not find the additive
inverse of −18. −15 − (−18) = −15 + 18 or 3. The correct
answer is 3.   **21.** Sample answer: The temperature of a deep
freezer was −15°F. When the lid was opened, it lost −7°F.
What was the resulting temperature after the lid was opened?
−15 − (−7) = −8; −8°F

Pages 221–222   Lesson 3-3   Extra Practice

23. 35   **25.** −14   **27.** 6   **29.** 15   **31.** 11   **33.** 1
35a. Sometimes True   **35b.** Always True   **35c.** Always
True   **35d.** Sometimes True   **37.** 180   **39.** 360   **41.** 8

Page 227   Problem-Solving Investigation   Look for a Pattern

Case 3. Add the previous 2 terms; 89, 144
Case 5. 13 toothpicks

Pages 237–238   Lesson 3-4   Independent Practice

1. −96   **3.** 36   **5.** −64   **7.** 5(−650); −3,250; Ethan
burns 3,250 Calories each week.   **9.** 5 black T-shirts
11.

×	+	−
+	+	−
−	−	+

Sample answer: When you multiply a negative and a positive
integer, the product is negative. When you multiply two
negative integers the product is positive.   **13.** Sample
answer: Evaluate −7 + 7 first. Since −7 + 7 = 0, and any
number times 0 is 0, the value of the expression is 0.
15. −3 and 7

Pages 239–240 Lesson 3-4 Extra Practice

17. 160 **19.** −64 **21.** −45 **23.** 12(−4); −48; Lily's gift card has $48 less than its starting amount. **25.** 16 **27.** −12
29. 648 **31.** −243 **33.** Sample answer: The answer should be −24. A negative multiplied by a negative will be positive. Then, if it is multiplied by a negative it will be negative. **35.** 612 ft
37. < **39.** >
41.

$$-4\ -3\ -2\ -1\ \ 0\ \ 1\ \ 2\ \ 3$$

Pages 247–248 Lesson 3-5 Independent Practice

1. −10 **3** 5 **5.** −11 **7.** −2 **9.** −3 **11.** −6
13 −$60 miles per hour **15.** 4 **17.** 16 **19.** no; Sample answer: 9 ÷ 3 ≠ 3 ÷ 9 **21.** −2 **23.** no; Sample answer: When two integers are divided, the quotient is sometimes an integer. Other times it is a decimal. For example, −5 ÷ (−10) = 0.5.

Pages 249–250 Lesson 3-5 Extra Practice

25. 9 **27.** 4 **29.** 9 **31.** −12 **33.** 2 **35.** −10°F; The boiling point decreases 10°F at an altitude of 5,000 ft.
37. −200 ft per min **39.** −8 **41.** 7 **43.** 9 rows

Page 253 Chapter Review Vocabulary Check

1. additive **3.** integers **5.** opposites

Page 254 Chapter Review Key Concept Check

1. not correct; |−5| + |2| = 5 + 2 or 7 **3.** not correct; −24 ÷ |−2| = −24 ÷ 2 = −12

Chapter 4 Rational Numbers

Page 260 Chapter 4 Are You Ready?

1. $\frac{2}{3}$ **3.** $\frac{8}{11}$
5–7.

$$0\ \ \frac{1}{2}\ \frac{3}{4}\ \ 1\ \ 1\frac{1}{4}\ \ \ \ 2\ \ \ \ 2\frac{1}{2}\ \ \ 3$$

Pages 267–268 Lesson 4-1 Independent Practice

1. 0.5 **3** 0.125 **5.** −0.66 **7.** 5.875 **9.** −0.$\overline{8}$ **11.** −0.$\overline{72}$
13. −$\frac{1}{5}$ **15.** 5$\frac{24}{25}$ **17** 10$\frac{1}{2}$ cm **19.** Sample answer: $\frac{3}{5}$
21. Sample answer: $3\frac{1}{7} \approx 3.14286$ and $3\frac{10}{71} \approx 3.14085$; Since 3.1415926... is between $3\frac{1}{7}$ and $3\frac{10}{71}$, Archimedes was correct.
23. Sample answer: Jason was building a cabin. He cut a board to the length of $8\frac{7}{16}$ feet long.

Pages 269–270 Lesson 4-1 Extra Practice

25. −7.05 **27.** 5.$\overline{3}$ **29.** −$\frac{9}{10}$ **31.** 2$\frac{33}{50}$ **33.** $\frac{22}{3}$
35. 2.3 hours **37.** 12$\frac{1}{20}$; $\frac{241}{20}$; 12$\frac{5}{100}$ **39.** 0.1
41–43.

$$0\ \ \ \ \ \ \ \ \ \ \frac{1}{2}\ \ \frac{2}{3}\ \frac{3}{4}\ \ \ \ \ 1$$

Pages 275–276 Lesson 4-2 Independent Practice

1. >

$$-1\ \ \ -\frac{4}{5}\ \ -\frac{3}{5}\ \ \ \ \ \ \ \ \ \ 0$$

3. > **5** first quiz **7.** −$\frac{5}{8}$, −0.62, −0.615 **9** <
11. Yes; 69$\frac{1}{8}$ < 69$\frac{6}{8}$. **13.** Sample answer: $\frac{63}{32}$ is closest to 2 because the difference of $\frac{63}{32}$ and 2 is the least. **15.** Sample answer: The lengths of four birds are 0.375 foot, $\frac{5}{8}$ foot, 0.4 foot, and $\frac{2}{3}$ feet. List the lengths from least to greatest.; 0.375, 0.4, $\frac{5}{8}$, $\frac{2}{3}$

Pages 277–278 Lesson 4-2 Extra Practice

17. =

$$-4\ \ \ \ \ -3\frac{4}{6}\ \ \ \ \ -3\frac{2}{6}\ \ \ \ \ -3$$

19. > **21.** 7.5%, 7.49, 7$\frac{49}{50}$ **23a.** Masked Shrew
23b. Eastern Chipmunk **23c.** European Mole, Eastern Chipmunk, Spiny Pocket Mouse, Masked Shrew **25a.** True
25b. False **25c.** True **27.** > **29.** > **31.** >

Pages 287–288 Lesson 4-3 Independent Practice

1. 1$\frac{4}{7}$ **3.** −$\frac{2}{3}$ **5** −1$\frac{1}{2}$ **7** $\frac{3}{14}$ **9a.** $\frac{33}{100}$ **9b.** $\frac{67}{100}$
9c. $\frac{41}{100}$ **11.** Sample answer: $\frac{11}{18}$ and $\frac{5}{18}$; $\frac{11}{18}$ − $\frac{5}{18}$ = $\frac{6}{18}$, which simplifies to $\frac{1}{3}$. **13.** always; Sample answer: $\frac{5}{12}$ − $\left(-\frac{1}{12}\right) = \frac{5}{12} + \frac{1}{12}$ or $\frac{6}{12}$ **15.** 17 ft; Sample answer: $3\frac{9}{12} + 3\frac{9}{12} + 4\frac{9}{12} + 4\frac{9}{12} = 14\frac{36}{12}$ or 17 ft

Pages 289–290 Lesson 4-3 Extra Practice

17. −1$\frac{2}{3}$ **19.** $\frac{1}{4}$ **21.** $\frac{1}{9}$ **23.** 1$\frac{47}{100}$ **25.** $\frac{1}{2}$ c **27.** 1$\frac{3}{8}$ or 1.375 pizzas **29.** > **31.** < **33.** 6 **35.** 30 **37.** pizza

Pages 295–296 Lesson 4-4 Independent Practice

1 $\frac{13}{24}$ **3.** 1$\frac{2}{5}$ **5.** $\frac{4}{9}$ **7.** −$\frac{26}{45}$ **9.** 1$\frac{11}{18}$
11 subtraction; Sample answer: To find how much time remained, subtract $\left(\frac{1}{6} + \frac{1}{4}\right)$ from $\frac{2}{3}$; $\frac{1}{4}$ h

13.

Homework	Fraction of Time	
	Pepita	Francisco
Math	$\frac{1}{6}$	$\frac{1}{2}$
English	$\frac{2}{3}$	$\frac{1}{8}$
Science	$\frac{1}{6}$	$\frac{3}{8}$

15. Sample answer: Let $\frac{1}{a}$ and $\frac{1}{b}$ represent the unit fractions, where a and b are not zero. Multiply the first numerator by b and the second numerator by a. Write the product over the denominator ab. Write in simplest form. **17.** $\frac{5}{12}$; Sample answer: $\frac{1}{6}$ of the bucket will be filled with one faucet, while another $\frac{1}{4}$ of the bucket will be filled by the other faucet. Add these fractions to find the sum.

Pages 297–298 Lesson 4-4 Extra Practice

19. $\frac{19}{30}$ **21.** $\frac{11}{20}$ **23.** $-\frac{13}{24}$ **25.** subtraction; Sample answer: To find how much more turkey Makalaya bought, subtract $\frac{1}{4}$ from $\frac{5}{8}$; $\frac{3}{8}$ lb **27.** Theresa did not rename the fractions using the LCD. $\frac{5}{20} + \frac{12}{20} = \frac{17}{20}$ **29a.** False **29b.** True **29c.** True **31.** $4\frac{2}{3}$ **33.** $2\frac{4}{9}$ **35.** $2\frac{7}{8}$

Pages 303–304 Lesson 4-5 Independent Practice

1. $9\frac{5}{9}$ **3.** $8\frac{3}{5}$ **5** $7\frac{5}{12}$ **7.** $4\frac{14}{15}$ **9.** $4\frac{1}{3}$

11 Subtraction; the width is shorter than the length; $1\frac{3}{4}$ ft

13. -5 **15.** $13\frac{5}{9}$ **17.** Sample answer: A board with a length of $3\frac{7}{8}$ ft needs to be cut from a $5\frac{1}{2}$-foot existing board. How much wood will be left after the cut is made?; $1\frac{5}{8}$ ft

19. Sample answer:

$2\frac{3}{4}$ ft $2\frac{3}{4}$ ft

$2\frac{3}{4}$ ft

Pages 305–306 Lesson 4-5 Extra Practice

21. $18\frac{17}{24}$ **23.** $7\frac{5}{7}$ **25.** $5\frac{7}{8}$ **27.** Subtraction twice; the amount of flour is less than the original amount; $2\frac{2}{3}$ c

29. $7\frac{1}{8}$ yd **31.** $3\frac{1}{12}$; $7\frac{5}{6}$ **33.** 5; 8; 40 **35.** 14 mi; Sample answer: $6\frac{4}{5} \approx 7$ and $1\frac{3}{4} \approx 2$; $7 \times 2 = 14$

Page 309 Problem-Solving Investigation Draw a Diagram

Case 3. $\frac{3}{8}$ **Case 5.** $\frac{3}{5}$ mi

Pages 315–316 Lesson 4-6 Independent Practice

1. $\frac{3}{32}$ **3.** $-4\frac{1}{2}$ **5.** $\frac{1}{6}$ **7** $\frac{3}{8}$ **9.** -1 **11** $\frac{1}{16}$

13. $\frac{1}{3} \times \left(\frac{11}{16}\right) = \frac{11}{48}$ **15.** Sample answer: Three fourths of the students at Walnut Middle School were on the honor roll. Of that group, only $\frac{1}{8}$ of them received all As. What fraction of the students received all As? **17a.** Sample answer: $\frac{1}{2} \times \frac{2}{3} = \frac{2}{6}$ or $\frac{1}{3}$ **17b.** Sample answer: $\frac{3}{4} \times \frac{4}{5} = \frac{12}{20}$ or $\frac{3}{5}$

Pages 317–318 Lesson 4-6 Extra Practice

19. $\frac{1}{9}$ **21.** $\frac{1}{4}$ **23.** $2\frac{1}{6}$ **25.** $\frac{3}{16}$ **27.** $-\frac{8}{27}$ **29.** broccoli: $1\frac{7}{8}$ c, pasta: $5\frac{5}{8}$ c, salad dressing: 1 c, cheese: 2 c; Multiply each amount by $1\frac{1}{2}$. **31a.** True **31b.** True **31c.** False **33.** $12 \div 4 = 3$; $12 \div 3 = 4$ **35.** $10\frac{4}{5} \div 4\frac{1}{2} = 2\frac{2}{5}$; $10\frac{4}{5} \div 2\frac{2}{5} = 4\frac{1}{2}$

Pages 323–324 Lesson 4-7 Independent Practice

1. 12.7 **3** 128.17 **5.** 0.04 **7.** 15.75 **9.** 1.5 **11.** 887.21 mL **13** 1.5 lb **15.** 1,000 mL or 1 L **17.** 0.031 m, 0.1 ft, 0.6 in., 1.2 cm **19.** 0.7 gal, 950 mL, 0.4 L, $1\frac{1}{4}$ c **21.** 5.4 cm; 6.7 cm

Pages 325–326 Lesson 4-7 Extra Practice

23. 158.76 **25.** 121.28 **27.** 41.89 **29.** 2 L **31.** 3 gal **33.** 4 mi **35.** 15.2 cm; 0.152 m **37.** 5.7 **39.** 15,840

Pages 331–332 Lesson 4-8 Independent Practice

1. $\frac{7}{16}$ **3** $\frac{1}{15}$ **5.** $\frac{2}{9}$ **7** 84 movies **9.** $1\frac{1}{4}$

Sample answer: The model on the left shows that one half of a rectangle with ten sections is five sections. Two fifths of ten sections is four sections. The model on the right shows the five sections divided into $1\frac{1}{4}$ groups of four sections

11. $\frac{1}{6}$ of a dozen; 2 folders **13.** $\frac{10}{3}$

Pages 333–334 Lesson 4-8 Extra Practice

15. $\frac{2}{3}$ **17.** $-7\frac{4}{5}$ **19.** 11 servings **21.** $\frac{1}{2}$ **23.** 13 bracelets **25.** $\frac{9}{20}$ **27.** $\frac{46}{63}$ **29.** $\frac{3}{4}$ ft

Pages IN5–IN6 Indiana Lesson Independent Practice

1. 3^3 **3.** 4^6 **5.** 3×7^2 **7.** $2^3 \times 11$ **9.** 3×11^2 **11.** $2^3 \times 3^3$ **13.** $28 = 2^2 \times 7$; $42 = 2 \times 3 \times 7$ **15.** about 2,200 mi **17.** Siberian Husky **19.** German Shepherd and Boxer **21.** 3^5; $3^5 = 343$ and $5^3 = 125$, because the base in 3^5 is used as a factor more times than the base in 5^3 **23.** Sample answer: $2^3 \times 5 \times 11$

Pages IN7–IN8 Indiana Lesson Extra Practice

25. 13^3 **27.** $8^3 \times 9^2$ **29.** $11^4 \times 2^2$ **31.** $2^3 \times 11$ **33.** $2^4 \times 3^3$
35. 7×9^2 **37.** mouse; 67 **39.** $2^6 \times 5^6$; $2^9 \times 5^9$; $2^{12} \times 5^{12}$;
41. $1\frac{1}{10}$ **43.** $1\frac{1}{9}$ **45.** -19

Pages IN13–IN14 Indiana Lesson Independent Practice

1. 4 **3.** no real solution **5.** -1.6 **7.** ± 9 **9.** ± 0.13
11. -0.5 **13.** 13 students **15.** 44 in. **17.** 24 m
19. $\frac{25}{81}$ **21.** x **23.** Sample answer: There are no two equal
numbers that have a product of -4, but $(-2)(-2)(-2) = -8$.

Pages IN15–IN16 Indiana Lesson Extra Practice

25. -9 **27.** $-\frac{4}{5}$ **29.** -6 **31.** -10 **33.** ± 10 **35.** ± 1.1
37. 1.1 **39.** 25 **41.** 110.25 **43.** 156,816 ft^2, 174,724 ft^2
45. 2,197 **47.** 3,375 **49.** 55 **51.** 20 **53.** $64r^9s^3$ units^3

Pages IN21–IN22 Indiana Lesson Independent Practice

1. rational **3.** rational **5.** $<$ **7.** $<$
9. $\sqrt{5}, \frac{7}{3}, \sqrt{6}, 2.5, 2.55$

11. about 1.9 m^2 **13.** $>$ **15.** $<$ **17.** always **19.** always

Pages IN23–IN24 Indiana Lesson Extra Practice

21. irrational **23.** natural, whole, integer, rational
25. irrational **27.** $>$ **29.** 18.52 m **31.** $<$ **33.** $>$
35. real, rational, whole, integer, natural **37.** 5 or -5
39. 0.8 or -0.8 **41.** 5.736×10^5

Page 337 Chapter Review Vocabulary Check

1. bar notation **3.** common denominator **5.** terminating

Page 338 Chapter Review Key Concept Check

1. $\frac{3}{5}$ **3.** denominator **5.** multiply

Index

Ss

Zz

Index

Name _____

$$=$$

Work Mats

0
1
2
3
4
5
6
7
8
9

−11
−10
−9
−8
−7
−6
−5
−4
−3
−2
−1
0
1
2
3
4
5
6
7
8
9
10
11

What Are Foldables and How Do I Create Them?

Foldables are three-dimensional graphic organizers that help you create study guides for each chapter in your book.

Step 1 Go to the back of your book to find the Foldable for the chapter you are currently studying. Follow the cutting and assembly instructions at the top of the page.

Step 2 Go to the Key Concept Check at the end of the chapter you are currently studying. Match up the tabs and attach your Foldable to this page. Dotted tabs show where to place your Foldable. Striped tabs indicate where to tape the Foldable.

How Will I Know When to Use My Foldable?

When it's time to work on your Foldable, you will see a Foldables logo at the bottom of the **Rate Yourself!** box on the Guided Practice pages. This lets you know that it is time to update it with concepts from that lesson. Once you've completed your Foldable, use it to study for the chapter test.

How Do I Complete My Foldable?

No two Foldables in your book will look alike. However, some will ask you to fill in similar information. Below are some of the instructions you'll see as you complete your Foldable. **HAVE FUN** learning math using Foldables!

Instructions and what they mean

Best Used to...	Complete the sentence explaining when the concept should be used.
Definition	Write a definition in your own words.
Description	Describe the concept using words.
Equation	Write an equation that uses the concept. You may use one already in the text or you can make up your own.
Example	Write an example about the concept. You may use one already in the text or you can make up your own.
Formulas	Write a formula that uses the concept. You may use one already in the text.
How do I ...?	Explain the steps involved in the concept.
Models	Draw a model to illustrate the concept.
Picture	Draw a picture to illustrate the concept.
Solve Algebraically	Write and solve an equation that uses the concept.
Symbols	Write or use the symbols that pertain to the concept.
Write About It	Write a definition or description in your own words.
Words	Write the words that pertain to the concept.

Meet Foldables Author Dinah Zike

Dinah Zike is known for designing hands-on manipulatives that are used nationally and internationally by teachers and parents. Dinah is an explosion of energy and ideas. Her excitement and joy for learning inspires everyone she touches.

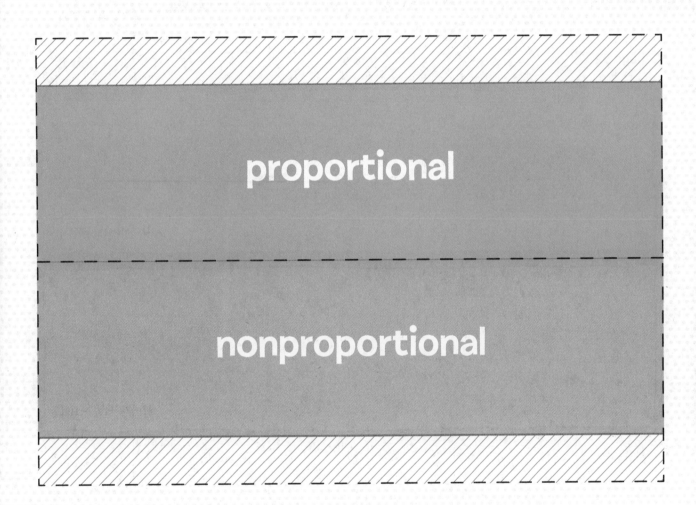

proportional

nonproportional

✂ cut on all dashed lines ⌐ fold on all solid lines ⬚ tape to page 92 **FOLDABLES**®

page 92   Tab 1

Write About It

Write About It

page 92   Tab 2

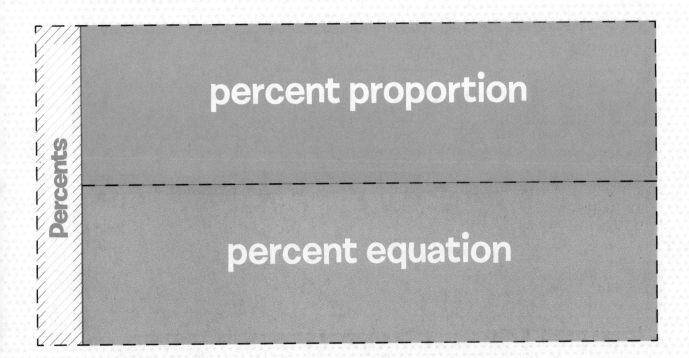

Percents

percent proportion

percent equation

Definition

Definition

page 180

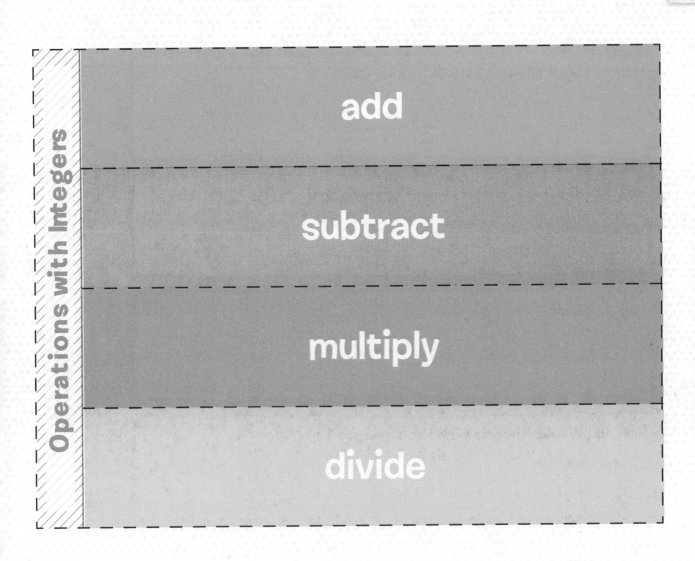

Operations with Integers

add

subtract

multiply

divide

✂ cut on all dashed lines   📄 fold on all solid lines   📑 tape to page 254   **FOLDABLES**

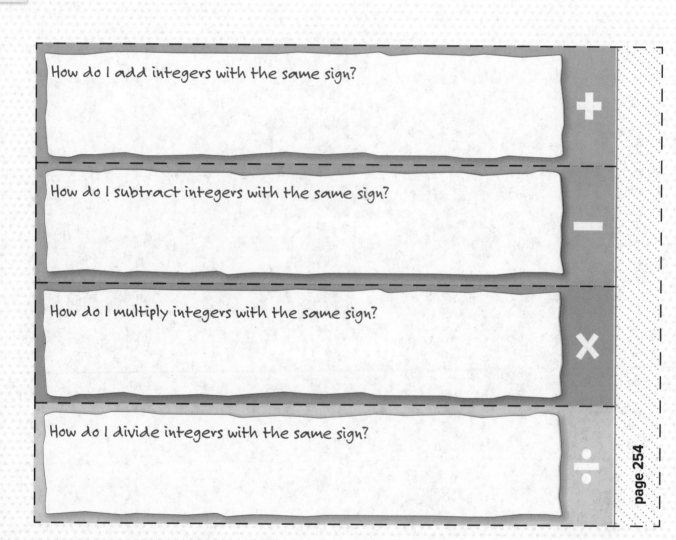

How do I add integers with the same sign?

+

How do I subtract integers with the same sign?

−

How do I multiply integers with the same sign?

✕

How do I divide integers with the same sign?

÷

page 254

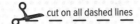
Operations with Fractions

+ or −
like fractions

÷
fractions

✕
fractions

+ or −
unlike fractions

Foldables

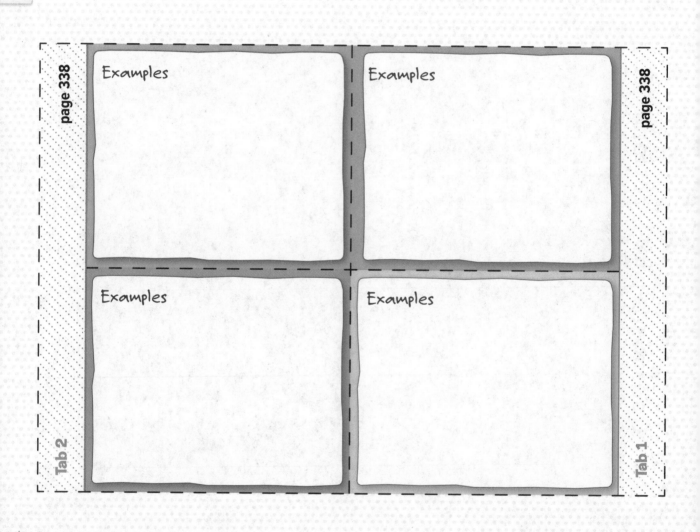

page 338

Examples

Examples

Tab 2

Examples

Examples

page 338

Tab 1

Mathematics Reference Sheet

Formulas

Area

▭	Rectangle	$A = \ell w$
▱	Parallelogram	$A = bh$
△	Triangle	$A = \frac{1}{2}bh$
◺	Trapezoid	$A = \frac{1}{2}h(b_1 + b_2)$
⊙	Circle	$A = \pi r^2$

Circumference

⊙	Circle	$C = \pi d$ or $C = 2\pi r$

Volume

▱	Rectangular Prism	$V = \ell wh$
⬭	Right Circular Cylinder	$V = \pi r^2 h$

Measurement

Conversions within a System of Measure	Conversions between Systems of Measure
1 yard = 3 feet	1 inch ≈ 2.54 centimeters
1 mile = 1760 yards = 5280 feet	1 foot ≈ 0.305 meter
1 acre = 43,560 square feet	1 mile ≈ 1.61 kilometers
1 minute = 60 seconds	1 cup ≈ 0.24 liter
1 hour = 60 minutes	1 gallon ≈ 3.785 liters
1 year = 52 weeks = 365 days	1 ounce ≈ 28.35 grams
	1 pound ≈ 0.454 kilograms
1 liter = 1000 milliliters = 1000 cubic centimeters	
1 meter = 100 centimeters = 1000 millimeters	1 centimeter ≈ 0.39 inch
1 kilometer = 1000 meters	1 meter ≈ 3.28 feet
1 gram = 1000 milligrams	1 kilometer ≈ 0.62 mile
1 kilogram = 1000 grams	1 liter ≈ 4.23 cups
	1 liter ≈ 0.26 gallon
1 cup = 8 fluid ounces	1 gram ≈ 0.035 ounce
1 pint = 2 cups	1 kilogram ≈ 2.21 pounds
1 quart = 2 pints	
1 gallon = 4 quarts	

Conversions between Systems of Measure

1 pound = 16 ounces	$C = (F - 32) \div 1.8$
1 ton = 2000 pounds	$F = (C \times 1.8) + 32$